WORLD® AIR POWER
J O U R N A L

Aerospace Publishing Ltd
AIRtime Publishing Inc.

Published quarterly by
Aerospace Publishing Ltd
179 Dalling Road
London W6 0ES
UK

ISSN 0959-7050
Aerospace ISBN   1 86184 004 7
                 (softback)
                 1 86184 005 5
                 (hardback)
Airtime ISBN   1-880588-07-2
                 (hardback)

Published under licence in USA and
Canada by AIRtime Publishing Inc.,
USA

Editorial Offices:
WORLD AIR POWER JOURNAL
Aerospace Publishing Ltd
3A Brackenbury Road
London   W6 0BE   UK
E-mail: info@aerospacepbl.co.uk

Publisher: Stan Morse
Managing Editor: David Donald

Editors: Robert Hewson
         E-mail: rob@aerospacepbl.co.uk

         David Donald
         E-mail: dave@aerospacepbl.co.uk

Sub Editor: Karen Leverington

Editorial Assistant: Tim Senior

Origination by Chroma Graphics
Printed in Italy by Officine Grafiche
      de Agostini

Correspondents:
General military: Jon Lake
USA Washington: Robert F. Dorr
USA Southwest: Randy Jolly
Europe: John Fricker
Russia/CIS: Yefim Gordon
Asia: Pushpindar Singh
Canada: Jeff Rankin-Lowe
Argentina: Jorge Nunez Padin
Chile: Patrick Laureau

The editorial team at World Air Power
Journal can now be contacted, via E-mail, on
the individual addresses opposite. General queries
should be addressed to info@aerospacepbl.co.uk

The publishers gratefully acknowledge the
assistance given by the following people:

The author extends his thanks to the following
EA-6B Pilot: Bret C. Carroll. EA-6B ECMOs:
Tom Burke, William Engvall, G. Allen Epps, Rick
Morgan, Dave 'Tone' Overton. EA-6B
maintenance and support personnel: John C.
Eubanks, Jon Hubbard, Scott Combs.
Grumman's Dave Stafford and John Vosilla.
Thanks also to: Ian C. Anderson, Mike Benolkin,
John Binford, Brad Elward, Alec Fushi, John
Gresham, Paul Hart, Craig Kaston, Tom Mariner,
Matt Olafsen, Warren Thompson and
Roberta Walker.

The author would like to express his sincere
thanks to Mr Vladimir Babak, Deputy Designer
General at Sukhoi Shturmoviki, and to Mikhail
Simonov and Vladimir Antonov of the Sukhoi
OKB for their invaluable assistance in the
preparation of the Su-25 feature. Thanks are also
due to Katsuhiko Tokunaga for his timely
assistance.

Thanks for help, advice and corrections with the
Tornado variants feature go out to Andy Ward,
David Ireland and Max Waldron. The author also
extends his special thanks to Brian Hardman,
at British Aerospace, Warton.

The Editors, and author, also wish to express their
sincere gratitude to all the personnel of the Iceland
Defence Force. Without their extensive assistance,
and great goodwill, the article featured in an earlier
issue of World Air Power Journal
(Volume 28) could not have been completed.

This issue of World Air Power Journal is
dedicated to Marine Corps aviators Lieutenant
Colonel Joe Connell, Major Jack Bacheller,
Captain Greg Glaeser and Captain Brian Hussey
– a VMAQ-1 Prowler crew who made a major
contribution to the EA-6B Prowler feature,
but who were tragically killed in a subsequent

World Air Power Journal is a
registered trademark in the
United States of America of
AIRtime Publishing Inc.

World Air Power Journal is
published quarterly and is
available by subscription and
from many fine book and hobby
stores.

SUBSCRIPTION AND BACK
NUMBERS:

UK and World (except USA and
Canada) write to:
Aerospace Publishing Ltd
FREEPOST
PO Box 2822
London
W6 0BR
UK

(No stamp required if posted in
the UK)

USA and Canada, write to:
AIRtime Publishing Inc.
Subscription Dept
10 Bay Street
Westport
CT 06880, USA
(203) 838-7979
Toll-free order number in USA:
1 800 359-3003

Prevailing subscription rates are
as follows:
Softbound edition for 1 year:
      $59.95
Softbound edition for 2 years:
      $112.00
Softbound back numbers
(subject to availability) are
$16.00 each, plus shipping and
handling. All rates are for
delivery within mainland USA,
Alaska and Hawaii. Canadian
and overseas prices available
upon request. American Express,
Discover Card, MasterCard and
Visa accepted. When ordering
please include card number,
expiration date and signature.

U.S. Publisher:
   Mel Williams
Subscriptions Director:
   Linda DeAngelis
Charter Member Services
Managers:
   Geetha Shirol
   Zoë Williams
Retail Sales Director: Jill Brooks
Shipping Manager: E. Rex Anku

WORLD AIR POWER ®

JOURNAL

CONTENTS

Military Aviation Review

International

UK FLA doubts resurface

The Ministry of Defence was exploring possible alternatives to the RAF's original requirement for 45 Future Large Aircraft as replacements for its 30 or so remaining Lockheed C-130Ks from about 2004, including the lease of six MDC C-17 turbofan transports. C-17s are seen as the optimum choice for UK strategic airlift requirements, currently undertaken by nine Lockheed TriStars and 27 BAe VC10 transport/tankers with limited cargo capabilities. They would also allow RAF FLA procurement to be reduced to about 25, according to the MoD, to provide what many UK officials consider a more cost-effective and operationally capable airlift package to be acquired in a shorter overall timescale.

Proposals and pricing data for a 10-year lease of C-17s, possibly to be operated jointly with commercial carriers, were supplied on request by MDC (now being taken over by Boeing). In the light of French and German government refusals to allocate R&D funding for the FLA in current defence budgets, plus similar omissions by the other European partners, the RAF has been pessimistic over its future prospects and proposed in-service dates. The MoD also has reservations concerning the turboprop FLA's speed capability to fulfil RAF air tanker requirements for refuelling high-performance combat aircraft, but went on record in March as rejecting as 'nonsense' claims that the UK was delaying progress.

While France, Italy and Turkey were then prepared to issue FLA requests for proposals, this move was apparently vetoed by the UK and Germany as being premature. The MoD

A major upgrade, adding a completely new ESM fit, is underway for the NATO E-3A force. The first modified aircraft are now returning to service.

said that it was important for the FLA's next stage to go ahead only when it was clear that the programme was on a sound footing. "Britain does not wish to encourage industry to invest considerable sums in developing firm proposals," added the MoD, "unless all the nations are able to demonstrate their commitment, including funding."

Meanwhile, Aérospatiale was reported to have found French bank backing for its Fr7 billion ($1.23 billion) share of FLA R&D, given firm French government guarantees of buying the 52 aircraft required by the French air force. Apart from the UK, other FLA requirements were then quoted by Aérospatiale as 12 for Belgium; Germany, 75; Italy, 44; Portugal, nine; Spain, 36; and Turkey, 20.

RAF air transport replacement plans have been complicated by notification of delays of about a year in deliveries of its initial batch of 25 C-130Js, including 15 or more stretched -30 Hercules C.Mk 4s. The first of them now are not expected before November 1997, because of software integration problems.

Eurofighter progress – on some fronts

Although all four Eurofighter partners reaffirmed their 'full commitment' to the programme in London in December 1996, firm budget appropriations for the production investment and support phase had been allocated only by the UK and Spain by spring 1996. Germany again had proved to be the main stumbling block, due to continued disagreement between the Defence and Finance Ministers over programme funding authorisations. This had precluded further progress towards intergovernmental MoUs for finalisation of contracts with Eurofighter and Eurojet, as prime contractors.

On 14 March 1997 EF 2000 DA.4 (ZH590) made its maiden flight from Warton – the same day that the last surviving de Havilland Comet (flown by MoD(PE)) made its final flight.

Eurofighter production investment approval from the Bundestag was hoped to follow agreement with DASA early in 1997 on a 28 per cent reduction in overall weapons system costs for the required 180 German aircraft, to a revised total of DM22.57 billion ($13.23 billion). This compares with original estimates of DM26 billion ($15.24 billion), although even the lower figure represents a system unit price of DM125.38 million ($73.52 million), probably including support and operating costs over a 10-year period. These totals, however, appear to exclude Germany's DM6.5 billion ($3.81 billion) share of Eurofighter R&D, which would bring its overall programme costs to DM29.07 billion ($17.04 billion), or some DM161.5 billion ($94.7 million) for each German EF 2000.

This compares with the last officially-quoted figures for the UK share of the Eurofighter programme for 232 higher-specification EF 2000s of £15.4 billion ($24.64 billion), including £4.13 billion ($6.6 billion) in R&D costs, or £66.38 million ($106.2 million) each. Spanish Eurofighter costs of Pts980 billion ($6.77 billion) for 87 production EF 2000s, plus Pts180 billion ($1.243 billion) for R&D, indicate an overall programme unit cost of some $92.1 million.

The first flight in Italy on 27 January 1997 of Alenia's second Eurofighter development aircraft (DA.7), following Spain's two-seat DA.6 which started flying in August 1996, brought the number of EF 2000s in the flight-test programme to five, from the seven planned. Alenia's first Eurofighter, DA.3, which first flew in June 1996, was also the first with the definitive Eurojet EJ200 turbofans, after initial development with DASA's DA.1 and BAe's DA.2 using interim RB.199 engines. By late 1996, most were flying with upgraded Phase 2A flight-control software, allowing considerable expansion of the flight envelope in terms of performance and agility.

Although last-numbered, DA.7 was not the last development aircraft to fly.

After delays attributed to prolonged bad winter weather, DASA's second EF 2000, DA.5 – the first to incorporate the new ECR-90 fire-control radar and associated avionics – eventually made its initial flight at Manching on 24 February in the hands of DASA chief test pilot Wolfgang Schirdewahn. And on 14 March, BAe CTP Derek Reeh followed suit with an 80-minute initial flight in DA.4, the first two-seat EF 2000, which was rolled out last year. They are now being used for avionics, weapons and radar integration trials.

Franco/German helicopter programme accord

A summit meeting at Nuremberg in December 1996 between the French and German heads of state and their staffs resolved most of the problems arising with joint military procurement programmes from defence budget economies. Particularly affected were the Tiger and NH 90 attack and utility helicopter programmes, the latter including both TTH 90 and NFH 90 tactical and frigate-based versions, in which major cut-backs had been proposed. In both projects, originally planned totals have now been largely restored. France agreed to continue procurement of its full requirement of 215 Tigers, and Germany, its original 212. Initial orders were planned for spring 1997 for 80 each, with deliveries from multi-year procurement to start in 2003 and 2001, respectively. NH 90 plans will now involve 647 helicopters, comprising, with former total requirements in brackets: France, 133 TTH 90, 27 NFH 90 (220); Germany, 205 TTH 90, 38 NFH 90 (272); Italy, 160 TTH 90, 64 NFH 90 (214); Netherlands (lead customer), 20 NFH 90s (20) by 2003.

Agreement was still awaited on assembly line numbers and locations. France was proposing a single Tiger final assembly line in Germany, in return for a similar French NH 90 facility. Germany and Italy were both seeking their own NH 90 assembly lines, but this will not be viable if French demands for a 10 per cent reduction in programme costs are to be achieved.

Western Europe

BELGIUM:

F-16 upgrades authorised

Europe's $1.26 billion mid-life upgrade (MLU) programme for the F-16A/B was recently expanded to include another 24 aircraft from Belgium. The programme originally involved around 300 upgrade kits for four NATO countries, with additional participation and funding by the US. Following Belgian parliamentary approval for another BFr3.5 billion ($100 million), these kits are now being installed in 72

Belgian, 61 Danish, 136 Dutch and 56 Norwegian Block 10/15 F-16A/Bs at two European factories by SABCA at Gosselies and Fokker at Woensdrecht, plus the air force depots of Aalborg (Denmark) and Kjeller (Norway).

Prototype installations in the US are now being followed by operational testing with seven upgraded F-16s from Leeuwarden, in Holland, for planned programme completion by 1999. In 1998, the FAeB hopes to fund another 18 upgrades of F-16s currently in storage, to increase its overall in-service total to 90 aircraft.

Above: Seen at its home base of Prerov (33 Helicopter Base), this Czech Mi-17 was one of two attached to the Canadian 5 CAMB Brigade for IFOR duties until September 1996.

This Polish air force Yak-40, seen at Bydgoscz, is wearing a new red VIP scheme. Yak-40s attached to 36 SPLT (the PWL's VIP unit) have hitherto worn a blue and white scheme.

CROATIA:

More PC-9s delivered

Another 17 Pilatus PC-9s have recently been delivered to the Croatian Military Air Force and Air Defence. They supplement three ex-US Army PC-9s at the main CMAF/AD training base at Zemunik-Zadar.

CYPRUS:

SA-10 controversy

US mediation between Greece and Turkey was required earlier in 1997 over the Greek Cypriot government's contentious $600 million purchase of Russian Patriot-class Antey SA-10 'Grumble' (S-300V) advanced SAMs for the air defence of southern Cyprus. Their acquisition was aimed at deterring frequent overflights by Turkish aircraft over southern Cyprus, and led to the Ankara government threatening possible military action against the SA-10 battery from its northern enclave. Turkey also said it would build air and naval bases there, if Greece continues similar activities in the south. Both countries rejected US proposals to ban all military flights over Cyprus, but the Greek Cypriot government promised to defer S-300 deployment for 16 months, pending further negotiations.

The Greek Cypriot government officially denied Moscow reports that it had also threatened to supplement its SA-10 purchase by acquiring the equally potent but shorter-range Antey/Fakel SM-330 Tor (SA-15 'Gauntlet') mobile SAM system, in response to Turkish warnings of possible retaliation. With a claimed reaction time of only five to six seconds, the SA-15 can intercept targets flying at up to Mach 2 and 20,000 ft (6096 m).

At least eight SA-10 batteries, including 32 launchers and 128 missiles, were bought by the Bosnian Serbs in 1995. Other known SA-10 customers have included Bulgaria, China, Croatia, Czech Republic, Iran, Slovakia, Russian Federation, Ukraine and the USA.

CZECH REPUBLIC:

Free US fighters

A no-cost five-year lease contract offered in January 1997 by the US to the Czech government for six surplus F/A-18s and a two-seat F/A-18B, with 18-month delivery, was described by Lockheed Martin as being similar to its 1996 proposal to supply ex-USAF F-16s to some ex-WarPac countries. So far, this has found no takers in Eastern Europe, although Jordan has accepted a similar offer. Although the free lease has an optional one-year extension, the recipients, which could also include Hungary and Poland as other NATO aspirants, must pay for setting up the necessary support infrastructure, pilot and technician training, and spares.

FINLAND:

New Russian SAMs

Replacement was recently completed of Finland's S-125 Pechora (SA-3B 'Goa') SAMs, delivered in 1979 for the defence of Helsinki, with three batteries of Novator/Altair 9K37M1 Buk-1/Gang (SA-11 'Gadfly') SAM/ABMs. Each battery comprises a 9S470 command post, 9S18M 'Snow Drift' acquisition radar, 'Flap Lid' guidance radar, and six 9A310 self-propelled tracked launch units, each with four 9M38/39 Mach 3 missiles. They have a slant range of 1.6-16nm (1.8-18.4 miles; 3-30 km) against aircraft, helicopters or missiles flying up to 72,178 ft (22000 m). Their $200 million cost is being offset from Russia's FMk5.5 billion ($1.12 billion) trade debt to Finland.

FRANCE:

Rafale production decision

Negotiations were being finalised early in 1997 between Dassault Aviation chairman Serge Dassault and the French Defence Ministry for a multi-year Rafale production contract. French industry was also seeking to add 10 Rafales (for potential export customers) to the 15 naval M versions, and 33 planned for the French air force (21 two-seat Bs and 12 single-seat Cs). Provision for full-scale Rafale production was included in the severely curtailed five-year long-term defence plan for 1997-2002, but was conditional on a 10 per cent price cut in the FFr17 billion ($3.24 billion) programme demanded by the French government.

Dassault had originally insisted that such economies were not possible, and offered reductions of only 2.5 per cent. Recent budget cuts, however, saw overall requirements reduced from the original 234 Rafale B/Cs for the French air force and 86 Rafale Ms for the navy to 212 and 60, respectively. Delivery schedules were also stretched by several years through budget economies. French naval aviation will now have its first six Rafale Ms at sea on the Charles de Gaulle in 2001, three years after the ship is commissioned, and the first air force Rafales will enter service a year later.

Apart from two prototypes for each of the two French services, including a two-seat Rafale B combat trainer for the air force, only 15 initial production aircraft had previously been ordered (two AA Bs and 13 navalised Ms), plus 42 production SNECMA M88-2 turbofans. The navy is particularly anxious to avoid further programme delays, since its ageing Vought F-8P Crusader shipboard interceptors are already overdue for replacement.

IRELAND:

Police air support unit

The Irish Air Corps inventory was expanded from June 1997 after delivery to Casement Aerodrome, Baldonnel of a Pilatus Britten-Norman PBN2T-4S Defender 4000 (c/n C-4008) transport. The aircraft is actually owned by and operated for the national police force (Garda Siochana), under the Department of Justice. This is the first Defender 4000 sold, and is equipped with infra-red, TV and photographic systems, in addition to special police and military communications equipment. The Defender 4000 will be joined by a Eurocopter AS 355N Twin Squirrel as part of the newly-established Garda Air Support Unit, which received governmental go-ahead on 23 April 1997. The airborne unit is intended to give 24-hour support to Garda operations, which already enjoy considerable assistance from existing Air Corps resources. The two aircraft were acquired through international tenders and are valued at IR£5.5 million. The aircraft will be piloted by Air Corps crews, with Garda 'observers', and wear Irish military serials (254/AS 355N and 255/Defender 4000).

ITALY:

C-130J approved

Further progress with Italian air force (AMI) plans to acquire 18 Lockheed Martin C-130Js was achieved early in 1997 following parliamentary authorisation of L2,000 billion ($1.18 billion) for this programme. Funding was also sought for four more C-130Js equipped with surveillance radar, processing and data-transfer systems for airborne early warning, although the AMI was prepared to complete the last four of its initial 18 in AEW configuration if this was not forthcoming. The C-130Js will supplement the 12 recently refurbished C-130Hs and Alenia G222s of 46ª Brigata Aerea at Pisa, scheduled for eventual replacement by 44 Future Large Aircraft if this European project goes ahead. The AMI would become the fourth C-130J customer, after the UK, USAF and RAAF.

Last Tornado F.Mk 3s delivered

The second batch of 12 leased RAF Tornado F.Mk 3s delivered to the AMI early in 1997 has replaced the F-104ASAs of 21° Gruppo, 53° Stormo at Cameri. They will supplement the first 12 F.Mk 3s operated by 156° Gruppo, 36° Stormo at Gioia del Colle.

NETHERLANDS:

Apache training begins

Formerly operated by the US Army's 11th Aviation Brigade at Illesheim, Germany, 12 AH-64As arrived late in 1996 to equip No. 301 Sqn of the RNAF at Gilze-Rijen. They are being leased by the KLu for training purposes until 1999, pending deliveries of the 30 AH-64D Longbow-equipped Apaches on order and due from 1998. They will equip Nos 301 and 302 Sqns, as part of the KLu's Tactical Helicopter Group formed in 1995 to support the Dutch 11 Air Mobile Brigade. This also includes 17 AS 532U2 Cougar Mk 2 troop transports of 300 Sqn and the seven heavy-lift tandem-rotor ex-CAF CH-47Ds of 298 Sqn, now being delivered to Soesterburg.

Arms disposal offers

Offers have been made to several Eastern European countries, including Poland and Slovenia, of surplus Dutch military equipment at very low prices. This includes 20 GD F-16A/Bs withdrawn from KLu service prior to the current European Falcon mid-life upgrade programme, and therefore offered for only DFl10 million ($3.58 million) each. Among other surplus Dutch military equipment on offer are eight upgraded Raytheon Hawk PIP-II SAM units.

NORWAY:

Eurofighter export prospects

The first prospective Eurofighter export customer could be the Royal Norwegian air force, which has short-listed the EF 2000 and the Block 50N F-16C/D with Northrop Grumman AN/APG-78 radar for its KFA-96 new combat aircraft requirement. This is for up to 48 aircraft to replace Norway's

On show at IDEX '97, held in Dubai in March 1997, was a pair of Kamov Ka-50 'Black Sharks', one of which participated in the flying display.

F-5s, for which the Rafale, F/A-18C and JAS 39 Gripen were rejected by the RNoAF, after extensive evaluation. Deliveries of the selected type are required from 2003, which might prove marginal for the EF 2000.

RUSSIA:

New fighter plans

Although Russia's F-22 equivalent (the prototype MiG 1.42) now has been relegated strictly to technology demonstrator status, Sukhoi reportedly is continuing development of a radical fifth-generation fighter known as the S-32. The main feature of the new project, under development since at least 1990 and apparently similar in size to the Su-27, is unique forward-swept mainplanes. It also has Su-35-type aft-swept canards and leading-edge strakes, plus similarly swept stabilator surfaces, and twin vectored-thrust turbofans. Funding is being sought to complete its development, together with that of the Su-27M (Su-35) and Su-27IB (Su-34 or Su-32FN for export), for the VVS.

While doubts have emerged concerning the future of the Su-35 for the VVS unless export orders are forthcoming, the Su-27IB has completed its 'scheduled state flight programme' which began in April 1990, according to a recent Russian air force announcement in Moscow. Two pre-production Su-27IBs (T.10Vs) built at Russia's Novosibirsk Chkalov plant, where four more are nearing completion, have begun flight development of their Leninetz primary phased-array attack radars at St Petersburg, and a third example joined the programme in December 1996.

Advanced trainer orders

Reports from Moscow of Russian air force plans to order an initial production batch of 10 MiG-AT advanced trainers in 1997 followed within a few weeks of confirmation by SNECMA/Turboméca of a reorder from MIG MAPO for 10 3,200-lb (14.3-kN) Larzac 04-R20 turbofans, as used in this type. Although five Larzacs were

Above: The Ka-50 in the IDEX '97 static display had a new nose-mounted day/night sensor turret and a small mast-mounted radome, in the style of the Longbow Apache.

This 1 Regiment, Army Air Corps Lynx AH.Mk 7 is seen at Saarbrücken in January 1997 before leaving to join NATO's SFOR continuation force in Bosnia.

supplied from the French group under the original joint development and marketing agreement, two more flight prototypes of the MiG-AT are nearing completion, and the follow-up Larzac order was obviously inadequate for these and another 10 aircraft.

Negotiations have also been reported from Russia, however, for another 20 Larzacs for initial production MiG-ATs, which indicates VVS acceptance of Western powerplants, at least for the first of its advanced trainers. They are planned for delivery from late 1998, and if their order is confirmed it will be the first for any Russian military aircraft since 1995. As partner with Yakovlev in joint development and marketing of the competing Yak/AEM-130, Aermacchi claimed receipt in early 1996 of Russian government R&D funding for this programme, together with an official pledge to buy 150-200 of this type for the VVS. Yakovlev also alleges that the VVS placed a recent evaluation order for 10 Yak-130s.

SWEDEN:

More Gripen orders funded

Although funding for a third batch of JAS 39 Gripens recently received Swedish parliamentary approval, the numbers involved have again been reduced, to between 40 and 60, including some two-seaters, compared with the 60-70 requested, and original requirements for up to 160. This

follows a further scaling-down of proposed SAF strength in the recent five-year defence plan by planned disbandments by 2000 of another two wings to only 13 squadrons, from the current 16. These will comprise 12 with Gripens, plus one Viggen unit.

The last of the initial 30 JAS 39A order was delivered on 13 December 1996, followed six days later by the first of the second batch of 110, which includes 14 two-seat JAS 39Bs. Flight-tests of the first production JAS 39B started in late 1996, for initial service from April 1998. Final totals of third-batch Gripens, possibly with new Eurojet EJ200 or SNECMA M88 powerplants as JAS 39Cs, will be determined from industry negotiations later in 1997, for deliveries from 2003 to 2006.

SAF upgrade programmes

Following completion of the AJS Viggen upgrade programme, Saab is now involved in mid-life upgrades of some 60 of the SAF's 125 JA 37 'fighter' Viggens. In addition to an upgraded PS-46/A radar for AIM-120 AMRAAM operation, plus new cockpit displays, GPS and data transfer unit, the JA 37s are receiving the digital 1553B weapons interface of the JAS 39, with its Ericsson Saab Avionics stores management computer. The prototype upgraded JA 37 Mod D made its first flight on 4 June 1996, and four SAF squadrons will re-equip with this new version from 1998, for service until replaced by third-batch Gripens in 2010 or beyond.

The same service life is planned for 96 SAF Saab Sk 60W jet trainers, now being re-engined with two 1,900-lb (8.48-kN) Williams/Roll-Royce FJ-44-1C turbofans replacing their original Turboméca Aubisque engines. The first Sk 60W was redelivered last September to the Defence Materiel Administration for the Flight Academy (F5 Wing), Ljungbyhed, after service trials. With 134 Sk 60s operated for basic and tactical training, plus light ground-attack roles since 1965, the SAF originally planned to upgrade 115, prior to recent budget economies. Re-engining, intake modifications and some airframe reinforcement are being undertaken jointly by Saab Military Aircraft and the SAF's Flight Academy, for completion by 1998.

SWITZERLAND:

Hornet deliveries begin

The retitled Swiss air force, or Schweizerische Luftwaffe (prior to 1 January 1996 it was known as the Corps of Aviation and Air Defence Troops), took formal delivery on 23 January 1997 of the first of 34 Hornets ordered through a SwsFr.3.49 billion ($2.45 billion) contract in 1993. Swiss air force C-in-C Lieutenant General Fernand Carrel accepted the aircraft concerned (J-5232), which was the first F-18D combat trainer to be assembled by Schweizer Flugzeuge und Systeme (formerly F+W) at Emmen. Another six Swiss F-18Ds are being assembled by SFS, plus 25 single-seat F-18Cs, following MDC completion of single examples of each (J-5231 and J-5201), which are now employed on trials and training.

Intended initially as replacements for ageing Swiss Mirage IIIS interceptors, the Hornets are optimised for air defence roles, armed with AIM-120B and AIM-9P/5s. 17 Sqn, currently operating 10 Mirage IIISs from Payerne alongside 16 Sqn, will be the first to re-equip, from the end of 1997. It will be followed in 1998 by 18 Sqn, now flying F-5E/Fs at the same base, and by 11 Sqn, with Tigers at Alpnach, by November 1999.

Funding is planned for a second similar batch of Swiss Hornets, equipped to F/A-18C/D standards for multi-role operation. They would replace both 18 Mirage IIIRSs for tactical reconnaissance from about 2006, and the remaining F-5s for ground attack from 2010. Swiss air force combat strength will decrease by more than 50 per cent after that time, from about 180 aircraft to around 80.

TURKEY:

F-4 upgrade finalised

After prolonged negotiations and a $457 million Israeli bank loan towards the $630 million programme cost, a contract was finally signed by the Turkish air force (THK) with IAI in

Right: The Project Anneka Nimrod R.Mk 1 (a newly converted MR.Mk 2P) made its first flight from Waddington, on 2 April 1997, in its revised (Elint) configuration.

Below: This Bulldog T.Mk 1 is flown by Southampton UAS (2 AEF) and has now been repainted in a yellow and black training scheme.

Bottom: This is one of eight No. 41 Sqn Jaguar GR.Mk 1As that made a courtesy visit to Cairo West in December 1996 in support of a UK/Egyptian defence agreement.

December 1996 for the upgrade of 54 F-4E Phantoms. New avionics include Elta EL/M 2032 radar, Kaiser/El Op HUD and Elisra EW systems, and will allow Turkish F-4s to operate with 150 Rafael Popeye heavy attack missiles recently ordered, and other PGMs. IAI Lahav is modifying the first 32 THK F-4s, which began arriving in Israel in February 1997, and will supply component kits for the remaining 22 to be upgraded at Eskisehir, in Turkey.

IAI and Elbit are also teamed with Singapore Technologies Aerospace as one of five contenders to respond to the THK's request for proposals (RFPs) for its $100 million Avionics Modernisation Programme, covering 20 F-5As and eight F-5Bs, plus 14 NF-5As and six NF-5Bs. They are to be upgraded as lead-in fighter trainers for THK F-16s, with new cockpit layout including HUD and MFDs, INS/GPS, mission/air data computers and HOTAS. Eidetics, Northrop Grumman, Sierra Technologies and SOGERMA are also competing to supply upgrade and integration kits for installation at Eskisehir.

Helicopter requirements and orders

Longer-term funding is now being sought for large-scale THK re-equipment, including planned procurement over the next 30 years of 640 combat aircraft, several AEW aircraft, and 750 helicopters. Immediate requirements are being finalised for some 145 attack helicopters and up to 100 advanced trainers. The army's attack helicopter requirement has become more urgent following Turkey's recent cancellation of its $150 million follow-up order for another 10 Bell AH-1W Super Cobras, because of US restrictions to prevent their use against Kurdish rebel forces. Only 10 AH-1Ws are therefore being operated by the TKK, following earlier receipts of 32 AH-1Ps. The Turkish army is nevertheless evaluating the CH-47D and CH-53D against Russian offers of the Mil Mi-26 for its $120 million programme to acquire four new heavy-lift cargo helicopters.

A FFr2.5 billion ($430 million) Turkish government order for 30 more

Eurocopter Cougar Mk 1s, including component manufacture and final assembly, has followed recent deliveries of an initial batch of 20 for the Turkish army. That service will receive 10 second-batch AS 532UL Cougars, while 20 new AS 532ALs with provision for cannon and rocket armament will be air force-operated on SAR and armed combat rescue roles. Eurocopter will deliver the first two new Cougars in 1999, the rest following from Turkish assembly by 2002, via a new EUROTAI consortium formed by Eurocopter and TUSAS Aerospace Industries.

This contract could mark the end of previous $1 billion Turkish plans for licensed production of at least 50 S-70A Black Hawks, suspended since 1992 because of US Congressional opposition to Turkey's Kurdish policies. A Turkish navy order for four SH-60 Seahawks costing $113 million was finally approved in February 1997.

UNITED KINGDOM:

UAVs in Tornado replacement studies

The RAF's long-standing Future Offensive Aircraft (FOA) programme (Staff Requirement Air 425) to replace its 142 Tornado GR.Mk 4/4As from 2015 has been redesignated the Future Offensive Air System by the MoD, to cover other possible technical solutions. In addition to Eurofighter variants (possibly with a bigger wing), and other new-design and off-the-shelf combat aircraft, the MoD is looking at unmanned or uninhabited air vehicles (UAVs), and also at very long-range stand-off air-to-surface missiles launched from large transport aircraft. Some MoD officials, however, appear to regard UAVs as operationally inflexible and employing technologies insufficiently advanced to meet the required service date.

A £35 million feasibility study announced by the MoD's Equipment Approvals Committee in December 1996 will examine a full range of future air strike technologies over the next few years. It aims to provide comprehensive data on feasibility, cost and operational effectiveness of designs incorporating fly-by-light as well as fly-by-wire, stealth, virtual reality cockpits and integrated modular avionics. The MoD is also seeking stringent design-to-cost disciplines, plus collaborative options in Europe and further afield.

Study contracts are now being placed with several contractors, and with the Defence Evaluation and Research Agency, under the management of the MoD Procurement Executive in Bristol. The study will benefit from a £6 million joint Anglo-French technology demonstration programme to allow computer modelling of various weapons systems.

So far, the MoD has shown little apparent interest in the US Joint Strike Fighter programme for SR(A) 425, beyond its $200 million investment in STOVL development to meet a Royal Navy requirement for up to 67 Sea Harrier FA.2 replacements. Most FOA studies to date appear to have concentrated on two-crew twin-turbofan designs, although the new study will undoubtedly assess JSF suitability for Tornado GR.Mk 4 replacement.

ASTOR contenders

Rival teams led by Lockheed Martin and Raytheon E-Systems were shortlisted by the Defence Ministry in March 1997 to submit best and final offers for development, production and in-service support of the RAF's long-standing SR(Land/Air) 925 requirement for an Airborne Stand-Off Radar (ASTOR) battlefield surveillance system. This followed costed proposals from a project definition phase submitted in September 1996, which also included the U-2 and E-8 J-STARS, now eliminated by MoD.

Defence Procurement Minister James Arbuthnot said that ASTOR would use highly capable new airborne radars to provide a wide area of coverage and high resolution. Award of the contract worth about £750 million is expected in 1998, about a year later than recently planned. Both teams are aiming at a high UK content to fulfil the contract, which will include five long-range transport aircraft platforms to operate at 50,000 ft (15240 m) or more with associated surveillance equipment and datalinks, plus nine ground data-processing stations.

TeamASTOR, led by Lockheed Martin UK Government Systems (formerly Loral) as prime contractor and systems integrator, includes CAE, GEC-Marconi Defence Systems, Logica, Marshall Aerospace, MSI and Racal-Thorn Defence. Another key member is Gulfstream Aerospace, which will provide the Gulfstream GV, modified by Marshall to accommodate Racal's Searchwater 2000 radar below the forward fuselage. This is a developed version of the radar already selected by the MoD for the Nimrod 2000 and upgraded AEW Sea King, optimised for dual-mode overland operation with moving target indication (MTI) and synthetic aperture imagery using a single antenna. Over 65 per cent direct UK workshare is claimed for this weapon system, which includes real-time intelligence-gathering and distribution systems, designed and integrated in Britain.

Raytheon E-Systems is handling its ASTOR bid through a new UK sub-

sidiary (RESL), in conjunction with Bombardier's Short Brothers to supply the Global Express airborne platform. This would carry Hughes U-2-derived ASARS-2 dual-mode SAR/MTI radar, developed for ASTOR roles in conjunction with GEC-Marconi Avionics and Thomson-CSF. Other team members include Cubic Defense Systems (datalink system), Cossor, Marshall and Motorola.

Nimrod 2000 progress

BAe's £2 billion contract to rebuild 21 RAF Nimrod MR.Mk 2 maritime-patrol aircraft to Nimrod 2000 standard now utilises only about 20 per cent of the original airframe, comprising the fuselage pressure hull (with new bulkheads and floors), keel structure, weapons bay, tailcone, tailplane and fin. BAe is building a completely new and bigger centre-fuselage box and inner wing sections at Chadderton, to accommodate the larger 15,000-lb (66.73-kN) BMW Rolls-Royce BR710 turbofans replacing the original Speys, and the new upgraded landing gear. This is required to cope with the 20 per cent higher maximum take-off weight of 232,800 lb (105600 kg). New outer wing panels have now also been specified.

The first three Nimrod fuselages were individually airlifted in January 1997 by a Heavy Lift/Volga 'Dnepr An-124 from storage at RAF Kinloss in Scotland to Bournemouth (Hurn) Airport, where Flight Refuelling Aviation will build new fuselage components and undertake final assembly in batches of six in 15-month cycles. BAe will then install and integrate the Boeing-supplied mission system avionics at Warton, for redelivery of the aircraft to the RAF between 2001-2007.

RAF unit moves

Extensive relocation plans for RAF units over the next few years were announced in February 1997 by Armed Forces Minister Nicholas Soames. After some 20 years of operation at Cottesmore since 1980, for operational conversion of British, German and Italian pilots, the Tri-National Tornado Training Establishment is being disbanded by joint agreement on 31 March 1999. Its 33 early production pooled Tornados from the three squadrons of the integral OCU will then revert to their original owners. Ten RAF GR.Mk 1s will be transferred to form the basis of a new national OCU within the Tornado maritime strike wing at Lossiemouth from 1 April 1999. This will supplement the weapons training roles already undertaken at the same base by No. 15 Reserve Squadron. Germany and Italy will undertake their own

The Royal Jordanian Air Force took delivery of 18 surplus Bell UH-1Hs from the United States in 1995. These aircraft are now in service with No. 8 Squadron, based at Amman/Marka.

Tornado operational conversion on an individual basis.

Cottesmore will then be available for the Harrier GR.Mk 7s of Nos 3 and 4 Sqns, which will transfer from Laarbruch by 1 December 1999 following the planned closure of their German base. At the same time, No. 1 Sqn will move its GR.Mk 7s from Wittering to Cottesmore, which will become the main UK Harrier base; it will have about 50 aircraft, and principal engineering support facilities transferred from both Wittering and Laarbruch. No. 20(R) Sqn, the Harrier OCU, will continue operating its T.Mk 10s and GR.Mk 7s from Wittering as a twinned V/STOL base.

Laarbruch's helicopter wing has already started moving back to the UK, with the five SA 330 Puma HC.Mk 1s of No. 18 Sqn transferred to No. 72 Sqn at Aldergrove in April 1997, and its six Chinook HC.Mk 2s to Odiham in July, displacing the 12 Pumas of No. 33 Sqn to Benson. At the latter base, No. 60 Sqn retired its last two Westland Wessex HC.Mk 2 utility helicopters and disbanded on 31 March, although it immediately reformed as No. 60(R) Sqn with Bell 412EP Griffin HT.Mk 1s as part of the

newly-formed Defence Helicopter Flying School at Shawbury. Benson will also receive the Puma contingent from No. 27(R) Sqn at Odiham in 1998, and the first operational RAF EH101 Merlins in 2001.

Storm Shadow contract

A contract worth over £700 million was signed by the MoD in February 1997 with MATRA BAe Dynamics for the Storm Shadow weapon system, to meet the RAF's SR(A) 1236 requirement for a conventionally-armed stand-off missile (CASOM). Powered by a Microturbo (UK) turbojet, Storm Shadow will be launched from RAF Harrier GR.Mk 7s, Tornado GR.Mk 4s and EF 2000s to deliver a 1,080-lb (490-kg) BAe Royal Ordnance BROACH kinetic energy penetration unitary warhead with GEC-Marconi Sensors IIR seeker guidance against hardened pinpoint targets at ranges of up to 300 nm (345 miles; 556 km) or more. Following Luftwaffe rejection of the APACHE for its Tornado force, Storm Shadow is being offered to Germany as an alternative to the proposed LFK Taurus.

Central Asia

AZERBAIJAN:

Air force expansion?

In early 1997, Azerbaijan was accused by neighbouring Armenia of covertly acquiring 12 MiG-21s, four Su-15s, eight Su-24s and Su-25s, plus Kh-25ML 'Kegler' and Kh-29L 'Kedge' anti-radar missiles, and KAB-500L LGBs from CIS sources. They supplemented original Azerbaijani air strength of about 50 combat aircraft and a few Mi-24 attack helicopters, and were claimed to be additional to notified procurement of 10 combat aircraft and other arms from Ukraine in 1993-95. Azerbaijan's agreed CFE treaty limits by August 1995 were 100 combat aircraft and 50 armed helicopters.

GEORGIA:

New 'Frogfoot' order?

With no production contracts from Russia since the collapse of Commu-

nism, and several years of inactivity, the Sukhoi Su-25 production facility at Tbilisi in Georgia claimed orders in February 1997 for up to 50 new 'Frogfoots' from the national government, for delivery by 2004. All single-seat Su-25s were originally built in Tbilisi, where around 800 had been completed when production tapered off in 1992. Among the last were a dozen upgraded Su-25Ts, although most of their planned advanced avionics and new nav/attack systems for all-weather operations with precision-guided weapons did not materialise after the Soviet break-up. They and about 20 other partly-completed Su-25Ks were thought to be the basis of the reported order, about which doubts have been expressed by the Sukhoi design bureau. Development of the still later Su-25TM, equipped with Phazotron Kopyo radar in a ventral pod, has been continued in conjunction with the Russian air force and the Sukhoi production plant at Ulan Ude, in Siberia.

Above: HAL HPT-32 Deepaks are in service with the Indian Air Force Academy, at Allahabad.

Above right: The Indian Navy has three Westland Sea King Mk 42 squadrons (INAS 330, 336 and 339).

Right: In 1996 the IAF established the 'Surya Kirans' display team, equipped with Kiran Mk IIs.

Below: HAL Chetaks are in service with the Indian Air Force, Army, Navy and Coast Guard.

Middle East

ISRAEL:

Air tanker reinforcement

Israel's Defence Force/Air Force gained its seventh tanker/transport in January from IAI's Bedek Aviation Group, which delivered an upgraded Boeing 707-300B. Modified for quick-change passenger transport/refuelling roles, an improved capability is claimed for this aircraft, from its integrated boom system, with remote electro-optical scanning. This includes a 3-D IR facility for the boom operator, to facilitate night operations.

IDF/AF helicopter plans

Flight development recently started in Israel of an IDF/AF Bell AH-1S Cobra attack helicopter with a modified 1,890-shp (1410-kW) GE T700-701C turboshaft. It replaces the original 1,800-shp (1340-kW) AlliedSignal/ Lycoming T53-703 powerplant, and follows a 1996 collaboration agreement between General Electric Aircraft Engines and IAI's MATA helicopter division. Apart from being more fuel-efficient, the T700 is expected to increase the Cobra's load capabilities and reduce maintenance requirements. Engine commonality would also be achieved with AH-64A Apaches and UH-60 Black Hawks. If flight trials are successful, Israel's entire 40 or so Cobras could be similarly upgraded.

Israel is seeking $300 million in US government loans to buy up to 14 more UH-60s to supersede Bell 212s. They would supplement 10 surplus US UH-60s donated to Israel after the Gulf War. Israel's annual $1.8 billion in US grant aid is currently fully committed to cover F-15I procurement.

Hawkeyes withdrawn

In a surprise decision, Israel's four Grumman E-2C AEW aircraft have been withdrawn from IDF/AF service, for possible disposal. Their retirement was attributed to high maintenance costs, plus their replacement by several IAI/Boeing 707 Phalcons.

JORDAN:

US equipment supplied

Equipment worth some $100 million delivered to the Jordanian armed forces late in 1996 under US aid programmes included 18 Bell UH-1H helicopters, as well as 50 M60A3 tanks. They were followed in March 1997 by a C-130H.

QATAR:

Cuts in UK orders?

The UK MoD denied reports from the Gulf states in February 1997 that Qatar was scaling down plans to buy equipment from the MoU (worth £500 million), signed in November 1996 with the UK. The package reportedly included BAe Hawks, as well as two Vosper Thorneycroft fast attack vessels, 90 GKN Piranha APCs, and 15 Shorts Starburst air-defence missile systems.

Qatar has made a down-payment to the UK as a commitment to some or all of this package, and a BAe spokesman said that the company had no reason to suppose that there had been any changes from the original MoU agreement. Strong competition is expected from French manufacturers, however, which are receiving official support from their government in continuing strenuous sales efforts in Qatar. Delivery of nine Mirage 2000-5EDAs and three two-seat 2000-5DDAs from earlier orders began to Qatar in 1997.

SAUDI ARABIA:

F-16 procurement interest

Saudi interest in acquiring up to 180 new F-16C/Ds was renewed in January 1997, having begun in 1995 when discussions were also taking place with Northrop Grumman and others concerning possible upgrades of 70 or so RSAF F-5s as an alternative. Seventy-eight F-5Es, 41 F-5B/Fs and 10 RF-5Es have been received since 1971, some 80 of which still equip five squadrons, and the RSAF regards their replacement or upgrade as quite urgent. However, priority has been given to follow-up deliveries of 72 F-15Ss and 48 Tornados.

Falling oil prices have made it difficult for the Saudis to meet their payment schedules, and F-5 replacement has been deferred because of other priorities. They include up to 10 more tankers with HDU pods, to supplement the RSAF's existing eight (boom-only equipped) Boeing KE-6As.

As possible F-5 replacements, BAe and Saab have offered the JAS 39X Export Gripen, plus the Hawk 200 from BAe alone. Although confirming that pricing information on the F-16 had been requested by Saudi Arabia, the Pentagon said no formal approach had then been made for its procurement. Lockheed Martin was reportedly quoting prices for 80-180 F-16C/Ds. Publicity for the F-16 negotiations in the press had also reportedly blunted Saudi interest in the (previously unsuspected) deal.

UAE:

Eurofighter back in contention

Having been dropped from the 1996 short-list of the Rafale and Block 60 F-16C/D after evaluation for the UAE's $5 billion requirement for up to 80 new strike aircraft, the EF 2000 was formally restored as a third contender in March 1997. This followed a new defence co-operation agreement signed by the UK and the UAE, and renewed marketing efforts in the Gulf by British Aerospace. Further evaluations were planned in the following months of all three contenders, with new proposals made for Rafale offsets through a joint programme office established in Abu Dhabi by Dassault, SNECMA and Thomson-CSF. A decision on the UAE programme was considered possible before the end of 1997.

Southern Asia

INDIA:

More fighter delays

TD-1, the first of two Hindustan Light Combat Aircraft demonstrators, was rolled out in November 1995 and had been due to fly in June 1996; flight development now is not expected to start before November 1997. The second GE F404-F2J3-powered example, TD-2, is scheduled for completion on the same date. Most of the delays in the LCA programme, which started in 1983, are attributed to funding shortages relating to severe cost escalation that now totals more than $730 million, and to extended ground-testing, particularly of the fly-by-wire control system. Five pre-series prototypes are due to follow the two demonstrators with initial flights from mid-1998, and will include the first two-seat combat trainer and a fully-navalised version for carrier operation. They will also be fitted with the definitive LCA's GTX-35VS Kaveri turbofan, which is under long-term development by India's Gas Turbine Research Establishment, and will be followed by up to 210 production LCAs to start replacing 120 IAF MiG-27s from 2002.

Military Aviation Review

Malaysia took delivery of the first of eight F/A-18Ds on 19 March 1997. The first aircraft for Malaysia made its maiden flight on 1 February.

Below: The first of six Sikorsky S-70B Seahawks for the Royal Thai Navy was handed over on 6 March 1997.

Another indigenous Indian fighter programme has also been promised by Dr Abdul Kalam, scientific director of India's Defence Research and Development Organisation. He said that a $1.5 billion follow-on R&D programme would start in 2010 for a Medium Combat Aircraft (MCA), possibly with twin Kaveri turbofans, to replace the the IAF's Mirage 2000H/THs, and Jaguars.

IAF Sukhoi Su-30 plans

The IAF's No. 24 Squadron will be the first IAF unit to re-equip with Sukhoi Su-30 multi-role fighters. On 30 November 1996, in Russia, a contract worth Rs70 billion ($1.95 billion) was signed for 40 aircraft, with options on another 20, resulting in a programme unit cost of $48.75 million. Fifty IAF pilots and technicians have been undergoing three months of training on the first Su-30s in Russian service, in preparation for initial deliveries to India of eight similar aircraft from the Irkutsk Aircraft Production Association (IAPO) from May. Known as the 'Hunting Hawks', India's No. 24 Sqn currently flies the MiG-21bis from Ambala. Initial Su-30KI (for India) operation is planned from Pune (formerly Poona), south of Bombay.

Retaining most of the standard Su-27 radar/avionics, plus AL-31F turbofans, the first eight Su-30KIs delivered later in 1997 will be generally similar to current Russian air force versions in being optimised for air superiority roles, with limited air-to-ground capabilities. Those capabilities will be expanded in subsequent aircraft from incorporation of some Western avionics, for which contractors – notably Sextant Avionique, with cockpit MFDs, VEH 3000 HUD and Totem INS/GPS – are still being finalised.

Some avionics improvements, including Ryazan rear-facing radar, are planned in the next batch of eight in 1998. After imminent flight trials in Russia with the first canard-equipped Su-30MK, the next 12 IAF deliveries in 1999 will conform to this standard. Only the last 12, in the following year, will incorporate uprated AL-37FU turbofans with thrust-vectoring nozzles, although all Indian Su-30s will be retrofitted with MKI modifications. After initial component production, licensed production is then planned by Hindustan Aeronautics at a new factory site at Ozhar, near HAL's Nasik MiG facility.

Radar upgrade for Jaguars

A unique upgrade is being made by HAL, with Israeli assistance, to eight Jaguar Ms operated by No. 6 Sqn of the Indian Air Force for maritime strike roles, armed with BAe Sea Eagle anti-ship missiles. The original Thomson-CSF Agave radar system is being replaced by IAI's Elta EL/M 2032 pulse-Doppler radars and associated equipment. Selected after strong competition from Russia's Phazotron Moskit, a prototype EL/M 2032 installation is now being completed by HAL and Israeli technicians in an IAF Jaguar, which is planned to begin flight development in mid-1998.

Indian Navy changes

Retirement on 31 January 1997 of the aircraft-carrier INS *Vikrant* halved India's sea-going fighter and ASW capability, leaving in current service only the 24,000-ton *Viraat* (formerly HMS *Hermes*). A major refit due in 1998 will withdraw this vessel from service until at least 1999, and will extend its useful life only to about 2004. Evaluations of future replacements, probably along the lines of current Spanish and Thai V/STOL carriers, are now being made for inclusion in the proposed $42.8 billion long-term defence plan for 1997-2000, although the required funding may be difficult to find.

A possible production order for Kamov Ka-31 naval AEW helicopters, which have been flying in Ka-29RLD prototype form for several years, is implied by a recent Indian Defence Ministry indication of interest in the purchase of three examples. The co-axial Ka-31 carries under its fuselage a large 360° NNIIRT planar-array radar which folds flush to its underside for take-off and landing.

PAKISTAN:

Orions arrive

The Pakistani navy's maritime patrol fleet of four Breguet Atlantics was finally reinforced on 6 December 1996 with delivery of the first of three P-3C-II.5 Orions built by Lockheed from a 1990 order. This was vetoed by Congress because of Pakistan's nuclear weapons programmes, until lifted last year by the release of $368 million worth of previously-paid defensive US military equipment. The Orions were withdrawn from long-term storage at AMARC for Pakistani navy crew training in the US, and subsequent delivery to Drigh Rd, near Karachi.

Far East

BRUNEI:

Air Wing expansion plans

The mainly helicopter-equipped Air Wing of the Royal Brunei Armed Forces was expected to expand its inventory further by finalising its long-promised $300 million order for 10 BAe Hawks. Early in 1997, four Pilatus PC-7s and the first of three Airtech CN.235M transports and maritime patrol aircraft were delivered. The Hawk order forms part of a major UK arms package, which also includes three patrol vessels from GEC's Yarrow shipyard, and was expected to comprise four two-seat Hawk 100 lead-in fighter trainers, and six single-seat radar-equipped Hawk 200 light strike/interceptors. Options were also expected for another six Hawk 200s by 1999, to equip a full squadron at a new air base to be built in southwestern Brunei.

CHINA:

New combat aircraft

A completely new twin-jet delta-winged multi-role fighter with long leading-edge strakes is undergoing preliminary design studies in China, according to an annual review from the US Office of Naval Intelligence. Referred to by the ONI as the XXJ, the aircraft is described as a long-term single- and two-seat project, with a low radar cross-section, in the MiG-29 class, for service entry around 2015. Armament may include a new AMR-1 medium-range AAM with an active radar seeker. The ONI estimates that the aircraft will supplement the Lavi-based J-10 which will begin entering large-scale AF/PLA service from about 2005. Only about 100 of China's 4,000 or so current fighters are thought to be of modern design, but are scheduled for additional replacement by Chengdu FC-1 light combat aircraft and at least 200 licence-built Sukhoi Su-27s.

INDONESIA:

New naval patrol and transport aircraft

IPTN is licence-building six CN.212 Aviocars for Indonesian naval aviation (TNI-AL), equipped for maritime patrol and surveillance operations with Thomson-CSF AMASCOS (Airborne Maritime Situation Control System) avionics. In addition to Ocean Master surveillance radar, T-CSF/DASA's $50 million avionics contract includes the group's CHLIO FLIR, and Sextant Avionique systems. Three newly-built IPTN/MBB BO 105s are being fitted with similar equipment, less the CHLIO system, for the TNI-AL. That service already flies eight CN.212s in general transport and support roles.

TNI-AL negotiations in 1996 with Australia to acquire 20 surplus army AsTA Nomads resulted in their delivery to Indonesia by June. Six of the Nomads are stretched N-24 versions and the remainder are standard N-22s, supplementing nine N-22s and six N-24s already in TNI-AL service.

JAPAN:

FY97 procurement plans

Parliamentary approval was expected by late March 1997 of Japan's Yen4,940 billion ($43.3 billion) 1997 defence budget, starting 1 April. It represents a 1.98 per cent increase over the previous year and includes Yen841 billion ($7.37 billion) for equipment procurement. Some $2.54 billion of this is allocated for tri-service purchases of 56 aircraft, from 65 originally requested. Approved procurement, with original requests in brackets where different, and unit prices, comprised: JASDF: Mitsubishi F-2, eight (nine), $99.68 million; T-4, 13, $25.32 million; Gulfstream GIV (U-4), one (three), $36.57 million; Raytheon Hawker 125-800 (U-125), four, $30.94 million; UH-60J, three, $28.34

million. JGSDF: Beech 350 King Air, two (three), $10.69 million; AH-1S, one, $31.52 million; UH-1J, three, $12 million; CH-47J, two, $48.93 million; Kawasaki OH-1 (OH-X), three (five), $15.8 million; UH-60J, four (six), $29.85 million. JMSDF: ShinMaywa US-1A, one (two), $66.23 million; UH-60J, two, $31.18 million; SH-60J Seahawk, seven, $42.99 million; OH-6DA, two, $2.25 million. F-15J, P-3D and T-5 procurement has ended.

Although the JMSDF is still taking delivery of 90 licence-built SH-60J ASW helicopters, the 60 or more already delivered are being upgraded by the manufacturers to SH-60J Kai standards at a cost of Yen40 billion ($350 million). Improved ASW and anti-surface warfare capabilities are planned from new synthetic-aperture radar, FLIR, active sonar, tactical information processing and display systems, enhanced ECM, an automatic approach and ship-landing system, and anti-ship missiles. Performance increases and reduced maintenance are planned from a new main-rotor head and composite blades.

SOUTH KOREA:

AEW bids short-listed

The Boeing 767 is the preferred airframe choice of submissions short-listed for the RoKAF's requirement for four AEW&C aircraft, the other being the Saab/Ericsson 340B with a PS-890A Erieye dorsal phased-array radar. Boeing's own 767AEW submission features the standard Northrop Grumman APY-2A dorsal radome, while IAI's Elta division is proposing its conformal side-mounted Phalcon phased-arrays on a Boeing 767. They would be supplemented by nose- and tail-mounted radars to give 360° coverage. Final selection is expected in 1998.

MALAYSIA:

First Hornets delivered

Delivery took place in March 1997 to the RMAF of the first batch of four F/A-18Ds. Powered by F404-GE-402 enhanced-performance turbofans, and equipped with APG-73 radar, the Hornets are operated by No. 18 Sqn at Butterworth, which received its second batch of F/A-18Ds in June.

Army Air Corps formed

Formal inauguration of the Malaysian Army Air Corps took place at its Keluang base in Johore on 13 March, although army pilots and ground crew had been training on 10 former RMAF Aérospatiale Alouette IIIs since 1995. These aircraft equip No. 881 Squadron

as the first MAAC flying unit, to be followed by Nos 882 and 883 Squadrons which will form an aviation regiment to undertake airlift, tactical support and reconnaissance for Malaysia's Rapid Deployment Force. Procurement of up to 300 new attack and transport helicopters is planned by Malaysia over the next 15 years.

South Africa's CSH-2 Rooivalk is well placed for the MAAC attack helicopter order, following completion of a defence and industrial co-operation agreement between the two countries in March. MAAC procurement is planned of six to eight attack helicopters, and Denel is able to offer the Rooivalk on attractive terms since the SAAF's scheduled receipt of 12 from 1998 is reportedly contingent on Denel achieving an export order.

SINGAPORE:

F-5 upgrade progress

Now well advanced with the installation of FIAR Grifo radar and other upgrades to 49 F-E/Fs of the RepSAF, Singapore Technologies Aerospace (STAe) has also started conversion at Paya Lebar of eight Taiwanese F-5Es to RF-4E Tigereye standards. This involves installation of a new nose section with camera and IR linescan sensors, which STAe had undertaken from 1990 to convert six RepSAF F-5Es to Tigereye configuration.

KC-135 upgrades extended

Further upgrades are planned of four ex-USAF Boeing KC-135A tankers now being re-engined for the Singapore air force with CFM56-2B turbofans. They are also being fitted with underwing Flight Refuelling Mk 32B hose-reel pods, and modified to KC-135R standard by Boeing Wichita from a $500 million contract. After delivery in 1999, they will undergo an avionics refit in Singapore based on the USAF's own Pacer Craig KC-135 cockpit upgrade programme. This involves multi-function colour display screens, GPS/INS and other changes, to achieve two-crew operation.

More helicopters sought

Malaysian interest in attack helicopter procurement is being matched by Singapore, which is also evaluating the leading international types in this category. They continue to be led by the AH-64D, but RepSAF teams are examining the Rooivalk, Tiger, Ka-50/52 and Mi-28. RepSAF negotiations have also been reported with Boeing for a $150 million lease-to-buy contract for a second batch of six CH-47Ds. They would replace Singapore's first six CH-47Ds, now operated on extended mission training from the Dallas Army Aviation Support Facility at Grand Prairie, TX, which would then be transferred to Singapore.

TAIWAN:

French arms sales veto after Mirage deliveries

In February 1997, several weeks ahead of schedule, Taiwan formally accepted in France the first five of 60 Dassault Mirage 2000-5 advanced air superiority fighters ordered in 1992. Further deliveries of the 48 single-seat Mirage 2000-5Es and 12 two-seat 2000-5D combat trainers are continuing as planned, but the French government has vetoed additional arms sales to Taipei. This is in belated deference to Chinese objections to any military supplies to the Taiwanese government, which is regarded as illegal by Beijing, and is intended to smooth the way for President Chirac's state visit to the PRC in May 1997.

Above left: On 24 October 1996 seven ex-Spanish AV-8Ss and two TAV-8Ss were transferred to 301 Sqn, Royal Thai Navy.

Above and left: This No. 1 Sqn, RAAF, F-111C is wearing a new low-vis grey scheme and carrying AGM-84 Harpoon and a GBU-12 LGB. The No. 11 Sqn P-3C is armed with Harpoon and a Mk 35 Destructor mine.

Below: Ex-No. 42 Sqn, RNZAF, Andovers have found a new life with Zaïre's Eureka Aviation.

Negotiations between France and Taiwan for now-vetoed sales of many other military items have reportedly included armoured vehicles, radar, MATRA BAe Mistral infantry SAMs, and anti-tank missiles. Its veto is not expected to affect deliveries of military equipment for which contracts have already been signed. The first Mirages were shipped into Keelung port in February, instead of April or May as originally planned, following conversion training of RoCAF pilots and technicians in France.

Taiwan's Mirage 2000-5 weapons include 400 MATRA Magic close-combat infra-red homing air-to-air missiles, and 960 medium-range active radar-guided MICA AAMs. The RoCAF was reported to have received its first MICAs several months ago, although they were only just beginning to enter service with the French air force.

THAILAND:

New aircraft deliveries

Six Sikorsky S-70B Seahawk shipborne utility helicopters recently delivered to the Royal Thai navy have provision for ASW and ASV equipment, although initially they will be restricted to SAR, maritime patrol and surveillance roles. The Seahawks will operate from the RTN's new V/STOL carrier Chakri Naruebet after it is commissioned in August.

Thai army aviation has also now received both CASA C.212-300 light turboprop transports it had on order.

The air force of Burkina Faso (Force Aérienne de Burkina Faso) was established in 1964 with French assistance (following its independence from France, as Upper Volta, in 1960). Combat aircraft were delivered only during the mid-1980s, from the USSR, comprising a squadron of MiG-21s. Contrary to most reports, at least one MiG-21bis still survives and is reportedly airworthy (left). However, the status of the MiG-17 (above) is unknown. Note the wreckage of an SF-260 (10 acquired in 1984/86) and Mil Mi-4 (another hitherto unreported type in Burkina Faso) in the background.

Australasia

AUSTRALIA:

Hawks to stay with Adour

Selection by the RAAF of the Rolls-Royce/Turboméca Adour as the preferred powerplant for its planned $A2 billion ($1.59 billion) purchase of BAe Hawk 100s followed an independent evaluation requested from BAe Australia, assessing the merits of the Adour and the newer AlliedSignal F124-GA-100. The latter has a potentially lower fuel consumption, and made a single flight in a T-45 Goshawk in 1996, before being ruled out by the RAAF.

The results of the final evaluation were understood to have been close, but, apart from development costs, a deciding factor was the RAAF's firm requirement for deliveries of its first 12 Hawks from mid-1999. They will be from an initial contract which is expected to increase to 32-40 Hawks, and will be powered by 5,990-lb (26.64-kN) Adour Mk 871s direct from Rolls-Royce in the UK. Engines for subsequent RAAF Hawks will be assembled by QANTAS Airways.

SH-2G selected for RAN

In January the Royal Australian Navy selected the Kaman SH-2G Super Seasprite in preference to the Westland Super Lynx to meet its $A500 million ($396.4 million) Project 1411 requirement for 14 multi-mission helicopters for its new ANZAC frigates. This effectively imposed a similar decision on the Royal New Zealand Navy, in view of the proposed joint procurement programme. Although the RNZN had favoured the Super Lynx, its requirements were for only six frigate-based ASW helicopters, so the RAN is also planning options for up to 18 more helicopters to equip its proposed offshore patrol combatant ships.

Initial Australian funding was nevertheless allocated for only 11 SH-2Gs, with new, digitised mission avionics, including an ASN-150 tactical management system, for delivery from about 2001. The RAN already operates 16 Sikorsky S-70B-2s in ASW roles, but its SH-2Gs will also be armed with Kongsberg Penguin Mk 2s for ASV missions. Although the SH-2G is on the upper limit for OPC operation, its Penguin compatibility was apparently a key factor in its selection.

Six RAN Sea King Mk 50As have recently been returned to service with HS 817 Squadron at Nowra, after completion of a $45 million 27-month upgrade. This also converted them from ASW to maritime utility/support roles while retaining a quick-change dunking-sonar capability, and extending their planned operating lives to at least 2008. The modifications have been done by BAe Australia, and subcontracted by Westland Helicopters, with other Australian companies.

Upgrades included new Racal and Rockwell Collins mission systems avionics and other changes, such as particle separation intake filters, heavy-duty flooring and cabin extensions to accommodate up to 25 troops for assault and trooping roles. A seventh RAN Sea King (HAS.Mk 5 XZ918 acquired from the UK in 1996 to replace an Australian example which crashed) is still being upgraded.

P-3 upgrade launched

Following the award of a $470 million contract to a consortium led by Raytheon E-Systems for modernisation of 18 RAAF P-3C Orions to meet Project Air 5275 requirements, the Australian Defence Department is backing a joint project for the international marketing of the planned AP-3C upgrade. This includes installation of Elta EL-2022A(V)3 high-resolution radar, Lockheed Martin DDC-060 data management systems, Canadian Computing Devices UYS-503 acoustic processors, Honeywell H-764G RLG/INS/GPS enhanced navigation and Boeing Australia (ex-AsTA) communications equipment. These last two companies, and BAe Australia, are also involved in the RAAF's Project Sea Sentinel upgrade consortium, which will complete the programme locally following delivery of the first modified AP-3C from Raytheon in the US in September 1998.

Caribou replacements

The RAAF was evaluating responses to its Project Air 5190 invitations to tender issued in September 1996 for 14 (DHC-4) STOL transport replacements. CASA in Spain and IPTN in Indonesia are competing for this contract with individual versions of the CN.235M. IPTN has a co-operation agreement with Aerospace Technical Services (ATS) as its Canberra-based agent, and with Hawker de Havilland and Honeywell Australia for the promotion and licensed production of the Indonesian company's proposed upgraded CN.235-330 Phoenix.

Apart from replacing the RAAF's 21 remaining Caribou, the IPTN consortium sees the five C-47s and 10 BAe 748s, plus two operating with the RAN, as additional sales prospects. CASA has teamed with Air New Zealand Engineering Services to offer its CN.235M-9 version. The third mainstream contender is the projected C-27J version of the G222 offered by Alenia and Lockheed Martin.

More army Chinooks

Government approval was announced in January 1997 for Army Aviation Corps plans to acquire another two CH-47Ds from Boeing, for about $40 million. They will supplement four CH-47Ds operating with the AAAC's 5th Army Aviation Regiment since 1995, when they were among 11 grounded RAAF CH-47Cs that underwent a major upgrade by Boeing. The remaining seven were retained by Boeing as payment.

NEW ZEALAND:

SH-2 for RNZN ASW

Although the Royal New Zealand Navy originally picked the Westland Super Lynx as its next frigate-based helicopter, it finally agreed in March to Australia's earlier choice of the Kaman SH-2G, in order to economise from joint procurement, operation, maintenance, technical support and training. Four upgraded SH-2Gs are being ordered by the New Zealand Defence Ministry within a NZ$274 million ($190 million) budget, to replace the current RNZN Westland Wasps, although six were originally sought. RNZN requirements are urgent, since delivery of its first ANZAC frigate was in March 1997, and an SH-2F is being loaned for training pending SH-2G deliveries from 2000. Armament will include Maverick ASMs for ASV roles, Mk 46 torpedoes and depth charges.

C-130 defensive aids

Raytheon's Sea Sentinel upgrades for RAAF AP-3C Orions are also being offered for New Zealand's six P-3Ks, following recent receipt by the US group of another $8.3 million RNZAF contract. Project Delphi will involve installing new defensive aids, including RWR/MAWS, chaff/flare dispensers and flight-deck armour, in the RNZAF's five C-130Hs. Raytheon will deliver the first modified C-130H from Greenville in March 1998, the remaining four being completed locally from US kits by Air New Zealand from mid-1998.

Africa

ETHIOPIA:

Modernisation plans

After years of chaos, with most of its Soviet-supplied combat aircraft and armed helicopters grounded, the Ethiopian air force is now being reorganised, with some US military aid. Following Eritrea's March 1996 order for six Aermacchi MB.339FD armed trainers, the EthAF is discussing the possible upgrade of up to 18 of its MiG-21MFs to MiG-21-2000 standard with IAI. Some involvement is also being discussed with Ukraine.

SOUTH AFRICA:

C-130 upgrade programme

The South African government has awarded a joint contract to its Denel group and Marshall Aerospace in the UK for avionics, structural and mechanical upgrades of SAAF C-130s, to extend their useful lives to about 2015. In addition to seven C-130Bs operated since new in 1962-63, this includes two recently-delivered surplus USAF C-130Bs and three ex-USN C-130Fs. Completion will be in 2002, and the SAAF's Transall C.160s are now being retired.

TUNISIA:

American aid transfers

Recent US military aid has included five surplus USAF C-130B Hercules from AMARC storage. They have supplemented two C-130Hs delivered new from Lockheed in March 1985, and were accompanied by 10 SAR helicopters of unspecified type.

South America

ARGENTINA:

Navy to receive P-3s

During a ceremony held at Punta Indio NAS, the commander of the Argentine navy, Admiral C. Marron, announced that the Aviación Naval Argentina will receive Lockheed P-3 Orions. The aircraft selected from the AMARC facility by Argentine officers are six P-3Bs from middle production batches. They will be transferred from the US Navy at no cost, although the Argentine Navy must come up with $7 million to cover reactivation costs.

Since 1976 the Aviación Naval has attempted to purchase P-3s – without success – and following the withdrawal of its last SP-2H Neptune in 1982 it lost its maritime patrol capabilities. As a stop-gap measure, the service operated a fleet of locally modified Lockheed L-188 Electras (named Electrón) but these aircraft lacked the capability to carry any kind of weapons.

The first two P-3Bs will be delivered to the Escuadrilla Aeronaval de Exploración during the second half of 1997, and the remaining four during 1998. The P-3Bs will replace the L-188s, although it is possible that the Elint Electrónes will remain in service.

Beechcraft 200 conversions

On 6 March 1997 the first Beechcraft 200 Super King Air modified for maritime patrol was delivered to the newly activated Escuadrilla Aeronaval de Vigilancia Maritima. The aircraft (6-G-48) is the first of a total of three converted to Cormoran standard, the major feature of which is the installation of Bendix RDR-I500 search radar. Conversion work is undertaken at Arsenal Aeronaval Nº 1 (Punta Indio NAS). The Escuadrilla Aeronaval de Vigilancia Maritima is located at Base Aeronaval Almirante Zar, at Trelew, and operates a fleet of Super King Airs transferred from the Escuadrilla Aeronaval de Propositos Generales. At the end of Project Cormoran, the strength of this unit will include three aircraft converted for maritime/coastal patrol, two – already converted – for photographic reconnaissance, and two for transport/liaison tasks.

BRAZIL:

AEW aircraft changes

The Brazilian air force (FAB) had planned to equip EMB-120 Brasilias with Ericsson Erieye phased-array radar for AEW and control roles for its Raytheon SIVAM Amazonian surveillance system. This plan has changed, and the FAB now will use twin-turbofan EMB-145s. With uprated Allison AE3001 engines and take-off weight increased to 45,415 lb (20600 kg) from extra fuel, these aircraft will offer more cabin space plus better range, speed and altitude. Five EMB-145 AEWs with Erieye radar will be supplemented by three EMB-145RS (remote-sensing) versions with a so far unspecified synthetic aperture radar, plus Raytheon E-Systems electronic intelligence and communications equipment.

One hundred new EMBRAER A-29 (AL-X) ground-attack/advanced trainer versions of the EMB-312H, for which Israel's Elbit group has recently been chosen to supply the mission system avionics, will be used mainly for SIVAM enforcement.

CHILE:

Upgraded Halcons in service

Delivery started in late 1996 of the first Chilean air force ENAER-built CASA C.101 (A-36) Halcon 2 close-support aircraft and lead-in fighter trainer to be upgraded with the SAGEM MAESTRO nav/attack system. Also installed in Chile's Mirage Elkans, MAESTRO integrates in a single LRU, autonomous ULISS 92 INS/GPS, multiplexed 1553B bus control, an improved GMAv HUD, analog interfaces, and new navigation, weapons management and fire control computer systems. About 20 A-36s from the FACh's Grupo 1 at Iquique will be upgraded jointly by SAGEM and ENAER.

COLOMBIA:

UH-60s reordered

Sikorsky received a firm contract early in 1997, following 1996 FMS notification to Congress of the proposed supply to Colombia of 12 more Black Hawk helicopters. The new contract, however, was for only seven UH-60Ls, due for delivery by 30 June 1997, to supplement 14 delivered by 1994.

ECUADOR:

More Kfirs considered

The Ecuadorian air force is seeking to buy more upgraded Mirage IIIs, following 1982 deliveries from Israel of 10 IAI Kfir C.2s and two TC.2 combat trainers, plus another four C.2s in 1996. The FAE still has options for four more Kfirs from the previous contract, and is considering acquiring another complete squadron to replace some 30 Lockheed AT-33s withdrawn in 1996 from Escuadrón de Combate 2312. Apart from funding considerations, US approval is still needed for Kfir transfers, because of its J79 powerplant.

PERU:

Ex-Belarus arms vetoed

According to some reports, Peru encountered problems with its late 1996 plans to buy several batches of Russian combat aircraft from stocks held by Belarus. Planned deliveries of

The current operational component of Burkina Faso's air arm consists of a small number of Cessna and Beech lightplanes and twin-turboprop transports, formed into a transport squadron (Escadrille de Transport), based at Ougadougou, the national capital. Also based there is an Escadrille d'Hélicoptères equipped with a mix of Mil Mi-8s and Mi-17s. The aircraft above is an Mi-17 'Hip-H' (some of which fly without PZU engine filters). The example below is an Mi-8S Salon ('Hip-C') VIP transport.

at least a dozen MiG-29s to Peru reportedly stopped after only the fourth aircraft, after Russia's MIG MAPO refused any technical support for customers using aircraft which they had not supplied. Belarus was also expected to supply up to 14 Su-25s to Peru, together with Antey SM-330 Tor (SA-15 'Gauntlet') mobile SAMs and 26S Tunguska 30-mm (SA-19 'Grisom') self-propelled air defence systems. Similar aircraft and equipment have also been offered from Belarus to Ecuador, Peru's recent border adversary, according to General Wesley Clark, commander of US Southern Command

URUGUAY:

RAF Wessex transfers

Six RAF Wessex HC.Mk 2s have been sold to Uruguay for military use, complete with spares and support equipment. The helicopters were withdrawn from service with No. 28 Sqn at Sek Kong in June 1996.

North America

CANADA:

Labrador replacements

Requests for proposals were issued late in 1996 by the Canadian Defence Department for its $C600 million ($449 million) programme for 15 new and off-the-shelf SAR helicopters. They are required to replace 13 CH-113 Labradors of the Canadian Air Command, in service since 1964 and scheduled for retirement between 1999 and 2001. Main contenders are the Bell 412, Boeing CH-47D, Eurocopter AS 532 Cougar Mk 2, Sikorsky UH-60, and Westland/Agusta, which is entering its lower-cost Cormorant version of the EH101. Ironically, at one stage Canada had ordered the EH101 to fill this requirement. The selected type could also be favourably placed for the later and associated $C1.5 billion CAC requirement for 35 CH-124 ASW replacements, for which the EH101 Merlin was also originally ordered.

UNITED STATES:

Special Operations changes

Air Force Special Operations Command (AFSOC) implemented minor changes to its structure during late

The EMBRAER EMB-145 has been chosen as the airframe for Brazil's SIVAM airborne radar project, replacing the turboprop-powered EMB-120.

On 21 February 1997 F/A-18E prototype E1 (above) flew with a full weapons and fuel load-out for the first time, thus making the heaviest flight by any of the F/A-18E/F test fleet to date. In January 1997 the number 1 F/A-18F conducted the type's initial carrier compatibility trials aboard the USS John C. Stennis. In April 1997 Under-Secretary for Defense Acquisition Paul Kaminski approved the E/F for initial low-rate production. In a three-phase programme 62 aircraft will be built, for first delivery in 1999. This move may shield the F/A-18 from cancellation – though that still remains a threat.

1996 and early 1997 with the formation of two additional squadrons at Hurlburt Field, FL dedicated to aircrew training. The 6th SOS had been formed by February 1997 with two UH-1Ns assigned, both of which were previously operated by the 1st Helicopter Squadron, 89th Airlift Wing at Andrews AFB, MD. The squadron has the primary role of training overseas air forces personnel involved in internal defence to fly and maintain helicopters. The two UH-1Ns are also employed to help squadron personnel remain current and proficient in basic rotary-winged operations without the need to deploy elsewhere to achieve this. The squadron had been formed by 11 October 1996 when the two helicopters were received. The second new unit to form is the 19th SOS, which had also been activated at Hurlburt by February, with an inventory of two AC-130Us and a single AC-130H. The squadron has no complement of its own, and aircraft are drawn from the 4th and 16th SOS as required.

The majority of aircrew training for AFSOC is performed by 58th SOW, which is part of Air Education and Training Command (AETC) stationed at Kirtland AFB, NM. This includes training personnel for the MH-53J and MC-130E/H/P. However, the small number of MH-60Gs and AC-130H/Us in the inventory, combined with intensive tasking for AFSOC generally, does not permit either the MH-60G or the AC-130H/U to be permanently assigned directly to training. The two new squadrons were formed under AFSOC for convenience, rather than with AETC.

Prior to the recent additions, the 16th SOW was one of the largest units in the Air Force, composed of seven squadrons that between them operated a total of 83 aircraft and helicopters,

including those receiving major overhaul, deployed overseas for UN duties, or on loan to other units. The addition of the two new squadrons ensures that the 16th SOW is the largest wing in the Air Force, since its nearest rival for the title is the 56th FW at Luke AFB, AZ with eight F-16C/D squadrons.

The 4th SOS received the 13th and final AC-130U when 87-0128 was delivered to the squadron in January 1997. The aircraft had spent all of its career to date on evaluation with the Air Force Flight Test Center at Edwards AFB, CA and with Rockwell International, the primary contractor, at Palmdale, CA.

AFSOC is to transfer four of its 10 MH-60Gs to Air Combat Command between April and September 1997, although the gaining unit is not yet known. The 55th SOS maintains a three-aircraft detachment at Incirlik AB, Turkey for Operation Provide Comfort, which will continue with aircraft drawn from AFSOC as well as the ACC unit. The USAF operates only 13 MH-60G versions of the Pave Hawk, with 10 assigned to AFSOC and the remaining three officially with the Ogden Air Logistics Center at Hill AFB, UT. Despite having been assigned to the Ogden ALC since late in 1993, they have not been seen at the base, and may reside at one of the secret Air Force facilities in Nevada.

The 8th SOS reduced its complement of MC-130Es during the winter of 1996/97 with two of its eight Combat Talon Is being transferred to the 711th SOS, 919th SOW at Duke Field, FL which is part of the Air Force Reserve. The 711th SOS now has eight MC-130Es, although both units have a single aircraft receiving major overhaul with the Warner Robins Air Logistics Center at Robins AFB, GA at any one time. The programme to pro-

vide all 14 MC-130Es with underwing air refuelling pods to house hose-and-drogue units for special forces helicopter operations was completed in 1996. The Talon Is have also completed a major modification programme (Mod 90) which included the installation of forward- and rear-facing RWR, a retractable FLIR sensor mounted aft of the nosecone, a new EW suite with the AN/ALQ-117 Pave Mint radar jammer, together with AN/ALE-40 chaff/flare dispensers. The aircraft have also been fitted with a fully integrated navigation capability including dual precision INS, a new dual-mission computer and GPS. Nine of the 14 MC-130Es are capable of carrying the Fulton recovery system, though the system was not used extensively, and in recent years the Fulton yokes have been removed from most of the fleet. The use of the Fulton system was finally abandoned in 1996 and the last training sortie was carried out by MC-130E 64-0568 at Hurlburt Field on 14 September.

SR-71 operational again

On 1 January 1997 the US Air Force declared two of the three SR-71As mission-ready, enabling operational service to recommence seven years after the programme was hastily terminated. Detachment 1 of the 9th Reconnaissance Wing at Edwards AFB, CA operates the two aircraft, which are available to conduct operational sorties at the discretion of the Joint Chiefs of Staff. The aircraft have been fitted with the Advanced Synthetic Aperture Radar System (ASARS) which provides near real-time imagery during day or night and in all weathers. During the work-up period in 1996 a computer simulation of an SR-71 deployment to Europe was performed to determine the suitability and necessary level of backup support. Fairford was the destination. The Air Force expects to demonstrate its SR-71 mobility capability later this year, which will almost certainly involve an aircraft being flown to Europe to participate in a major exercise.

Theatre airlift transfer

Updating a previous report, Air Combat Command (ACC) is to transfer its theatre airlift capability to Air Mobility Command (AMC). The reassignment is due to take place in April 1997 involving Stateside-based C-130E/H versions of the Hercules. Most of the airlift squadrons involved are assigned to ACC units operating other types, with the Air Force being required to form several additional wings or groups as parent organisations for the Hercules. They will be formed at Dyess AFB, TX (7th Wing); Pope AFB, NC (23rd Wing); and Moody AFB, GA (347th Wing). One of the new units is believed to be the 43rd Airlift Group which will form at Pope AFB, although this has yet to be confirmed. The 314th AW at Little Rock AFB,

AR will join AETC, while retaining an operational airlift capability.

AMC will also gain the Stateside active-duty fleet of C-21A Learjets which is at present assigned to ACC, AETC, Air Force Space Command, and Air Force Materiel Command. The centralisation will involve the transfer of 41 aircraft which will join the 18 already operated by AMC. Several of the aircraft are assigned to airlift flights which will presumably be reassigned to a parent wing, possibly the 375th AW with headquarters at Scott AFB, IL. The C-21s and C-130s stationed in Europe and the Pacific are unaffected by the change.

Another First Lady retires

The first KC-135 to enter service, serial 55-3118, was retired from service on 15 October 1996 at McConnell AFB, KA after assignment to various flying units since 24 January 1957 when the aircraft was officially accepted. As the first KC-135A, 53118 was bailed back to Boeing for extensive flight test, and remained at Renton until 7 July 1960 when the aircraft was flown to Tinker AFB, OK for overhaul with the Oklahoma City Air Material Area. In early November 1960 the aircraft joined the Wright Air Development Center at Wright-Patterson AFB, OH where it received the designation JKC-135A, denoting temporary test duties.

55-3118 reverted to being a KC-135A on 12 January 1961 prior to being relocated to Seymour Johnson AFB, NC where it joined the 4th Tactical Fighter Wing as an airborne command post, probably for the commander of the 19th Air Force (Tactical Air Command). On 6 October 1964 the aircraft changed designation to become an EC-135A, but had been redesignated as an EC-135K by 31 May 1967. Throughout its 40 years of service the aircraft did not join Strategic Air Command as a tanker. For the majority of its career, 53118 was an airborne command post (ACP) and flew hundreds of missions to support the deployment of fighter cells on intercontinental flights. Apart from performing ACP duties, 53118 was also employed to transport the Commander in Chief and senior personnel of TAC and later Air Combat Command on official business.

Retirement to mcdonnell AFB, where the Boeing company has a large facility, will presumably see 53118 receiving an overhaul and repaint before being placed on display.

Holloman F-4Es retire

The last examples of the F-4E are to be retired from service by the 20th Fighter Squadron, which is part of the 49th FW at Holloman AFB, NM. Thirteen F-4Es from FY 1967 and 1968 were operated alongside seven F-4Es from FY 1975, which are the survivors of 10 which the German government purchased specifically for training duties in the USA. The primary

Luftwaffe F-4F Phantoms have replaced the USAF-operated F-4Es previously used to train German Phantom aircrews at Holloman AFB, New Mexico.

Above: The QF-106 had its last major operational outing during the William Tell '96 weapons meet, at Tyndall AFB. The Delta Dart has finally been replaced by the QF-4.

This 1965-vintage Boeing 720-060B (N7381/Enchantable Annie) is operated by the US DoD as a trials platform for sensors and potential weapons for anti-missile defence.

role of the 20th FS has been to train prospective F-4F pilots for the German air force. The 1st German Air Force Training Squadron was formed as the link between the USAF and Luftwaffe. The US contributed 20 instructor pilots and nine instructor weapons systems officers, while the Germans have three pilots and one WSO at Holloman to train students.

The F-4Es will be withdrawn during the first half of 1997, since 24 German F-4Fs are being flown to Holloman AFB as replacements. The first nine F-4Fs arrived at the base on 16 January 1997. Eight more are scheduled to arrive in April 1997, and the remaining seven a few months later. The F-4Fs are owned by Germany but come under the operational control of the USAF. Eight of the aircraft to be stationed at Holloman will have received the ICE upgrade, but the other 18 will have only a new navigation system.

The assignment of German F-4Fs in lieu of the F-4Es has taken place as part of a streamlining of the Luftwaffe training system. The Luftwaffe considers the F-4F to be far more capable than the F-4Es, which prevents a smooth transition and creates a steep learning curve for aircrew fresh from graduation on the Phantom in the USA.

The Taktische Ausbildungskommando has been formed at Holloman AFB to oversee training, with the organisation split between the Ausbildungsstaffel Phantom operating the 24 F-4Fs, and the Ausbildungsstaffel Tornado flying 48 Tornados. The first dozen Tornados had arrived at Holloman by the end of 1996, and the training programme is due to be fully operational by the end of the decade.

Unusual afterlife for the A-6

Ceremonies on opposite coasts on 28 February 1997 marked the disestablishment of VA-75 'Sunday Punchers' (on 31 March 1997) and VA-196 'Main Battery' (on 28 February 1997). VA-75 was located at NAS Oceana, VA; VA-196 at NAS Whidbey Island, WA. VA-75 flew the US Navy's last two operational Grumman A-6 Intruders to AMARC on 19 March 1997. The aircraft were A-6Es (164382/500; 162179/501). The retirement of the Intruder from service led to a unique new lease of life for some, which were cannibalised of useful parts before being sunk off the coast of northeast Florida to form artificial reefs.

Citation for the Army

In January 1997 the US Army began to receive the first of 35 Cessna 560 Citation V Ultras, to be designated UC-35A. The first aircraft, 95-0123, was flown on 10 January from the USA via Keflavik to Wiesbaden, Germany, where it will join the 207th Aviation Company. The unit is expected to operate three or four of the new aircraft on communications duties with US Army Europe. The Citations will be flown from Wiesbaden despite the remainder of the 207th Aviation Company fleet of C-12Fs, UH-1Hs and UH-60As being stationed at Heidelberg. The runway at Heidelberg is slightly over 1000 m (3,280 ft) long and is possibly too short for the Citation to be operated safely.

New York ANG supports Antarctic science foundation

The 109th Airlift Squadron at Schenectady Airport, NY began flights to Antarctica with its new LC-130Hs in December 1996 to provide logistical support to the National Science Foundation's US Antarctic Program. The role previously was performed by the LC-130F/Rs of the US Navy's VXE-6 based at NAS Point Mugu. The 1996/97 season is the first involving the LC-130s of the New York Air National Guard. Throughout their stay in the southern hemisphere, operations by the LC-130s will be centred at Christchurch, New Zealand, and will include resupply sorties to numerous sites on the Antarctic continent. The elderly LC-130Fs operated by the Navy for the last 30 years will be retired, and the four USN LC-130Rs possibly will revert to their USAF identities and join the 109th AS.

NSAWC established

The Navy consolidated three centres of learning under the Naval Strike and Air Warfare Center (NSAWC) which was formed at NAS Fallon, NV on 11 July 1996. The Naval Strike Warfare Center (NSWC) was already at NAS Fallon, and was joined by the Navy Fighter Weapons School (NFWS), and

the Carrier Airborne Early Warning Weapons School (CAEWWS). These three units are better known as the Strike U, Topgun and Topdome, respectively. The Center operates approximately 30 aircraft, consisting of F-14As, F/A-18A/Bs and a pair of SH-60Bs. No EA-6Bs or E-2Cs are assigned, so aircraft are borrowed from visiting air wings for courses. The eventual complement will be 45, including a number of early production E-2Cs and the exchange of older Hornets for the F/A-18C/D.

The role of the three sections is largely unchanged following centralisation at Fallon. The NFWS trains selected Navy and Marine Corps fighter pilots to be master tacticians of aerial combat. Strike U is the centre where entire carrier air wings assemble for final training prior to deployment for an operational cruise. CVWs deploy to Fallon *en masse* six months before they are due to begin their operational cruise.

The final element is the CAEWWS, which moved from NAS Miramar in January 1996. The School is primarily concerned with activities of airborne early warning, electronic warfare, and electronic intelligence. Topdome has no aircraft of its own yet, but anticipates being provided with two or three E-2Cs. They will probably be early production aircraft which can be upgraded to Group II status. The School also wishes to obtain an E-2C weapon system simulator to enable complex training scenarios to be reproduced. The NSAWC is also tasked with developing C-SAR, a duty performed by the SH-60s.

Some NSAWC aircraft carry the colour schemes of those assigned to operational squadrons, but many have been painted in 'threat' camouflage. This includes F/A-18s in desert schemes and F-14s repainted to resemble Su-27 'Flankers'. Even the SH-60s wear desert camouflage.

Surplus equipment transfers

KC-135: Two surplus KC-135As departed from the Aircraft Maintenance and Regeneration Center at Davis-Monthan AFB, AZ in October 1996 for the Boeing facility at Wichita, KA for preparation and the installation of F108-CF-100 turbofans. Once the work has been completed, the two aircraft will be delivered to the Turkish air force. Turkey borrowed two KC-135Rs from the US Air Force in 1996 pending delivery of its own aircraft in 1997. Additional surplus KC-135As are being transferred from AMARC to Wichita for conversion to KC-135R standard for both Turkey and France. Singapore is also to receive four surplus USAF KC-135As which are now being fitted with turbofans, as well as undergoing Flight Refuelling Ltd Mk 32B hose reel pods. The aircraft will be redesignated as KC-135Rs under a programme budget estimated at $500 million. After delivery in 1999 the aircraft will receive an avionics refit in Singapore, which will be similar to the USAF's Pacer Crag cockpit update.

C-130: The first two of five C-130B/Fs were delivered to the South African Air Force during mid-December 1996. Former VRC-50

Left: This Cessna 560 Citation V has been reported as a Lockheed Martin-owned aircraft used for airborne LO trials. However, the FLIR and radar (APG-65?) fit on the aircraft also resembles that carried by US Customs 'O-47' Citation anti-smuggling and drug interdiction aircraft.

Bearcat III (86-1678) is the first of two US Army CH-47Ds to undergo the ICH upgrade. Two airframes will serve as demonstrators for a programme that could extend the CH-47's operational life to 2040.

The successful ferry flight was the last milestone or exit criteria established by the Defense Acquisition Board for full funding release of Low Rate Initial Production.

C-130Fs 149787 and 149793 were flown to Waterkloof Air Base near Johannesburg for preparation and painting. The aircraft were officially handed over to 28 Squadron on 18 December. Another C-130F and two ex USAF C-130Bs will be acquired, with one due for delivery early in 1997 followed by the final pair during the summer of 1997. The seven existing C-130Bs operated by South Africa were upgraded to C-130H configuration early in their careers with the installation of the Allison T56-A-15 powerplants. The new aircraft will receive similar conversion by Denel, which has teamed with Marshall Aerospace, before they enter operational service. The programme also involves avionics, structural and mechanical improvements, including replacement brakes and electrical systems, with the work due to take place between 1997 and 2002. Three aircraft will be reworked in the UK and will serve as prototypes for the remainder.

C-12: The US Army received most of the former USAF fleet of C-12Fs during 1996, enabling its C-12Cs to be retired. Sixteen of the C-12Cs have been transferred to the US Customs Service Air Interdiction Division. They have been allocated civilian registrations. Other surplus C-12Cs have been assigned to local government and law enforcement agencies.

A-4: Brazil is negotiating with the US for the supply of 23 surplus A-4 Skyhawks for operations aboard the aircraft-carrier *Minais Gerais* – subject to the vessel undergoing a substantial refit. In the meantime, the Brazilian navy has sent helicopter pilots to Argentina and Uruguay for transition training to fixed-wing types. Ecuador is hoping to obtain up to 15 A-4Ms from the USA to replace its A-37Bs.

UH-1H: The first batch of 20 surplus US Army UH-1Hs for Mexico were finally delivered in a C-5 flight on 20 November 1996; the remaining 35 are due to follow soon after.

Unit news

The 47th FS at Barksdale AFB, LA has switched roles from combat to pilot training for AFRes personnel flying the OA/A-10A.

The Air Force has announced that the first unit scheduled to re-equip with the standard C-130J is the 135th AS at Baltimore State Airport, MD.

The 52nd FW at Spangdahlem AB, Germany will perform F-15C/D and

F-16C/D sorties from nearby Bitburg AB between June and September 1997 while the former base undergoes runway work. The A-10s of the 81st FS will continue to fly from Spangdahlem, utilising a taxiway as a temporary runway. The activation of Bitburg for flight operations will be the first such occasion since it was closed in 1994.

The 21st FS at Luke AFB, AZ began receiving its initial complement of F-16A/Bs during January 1997. The squadron has been established to train Taiwanese aircrew. Its first four aircraft are production F-16s for the RoCAF carrying USAF serials and markings.

The 509th BW vice commander Colonel Jim Macon, together with Major Len Litton, flew the 1,000th B-2 mission from Whiteman AFB, MO on 21 November 1996.

The C-141B retirement process is continuing, with the 60th AMW at Travis AFB, CA scheduled to lose seven StarLifters during FY 1997.

ANG air defence units are continuing to switch from the F-16A/B (ADF) to the F-16C/D. The latest unit to transition was the 111th FS at Ellington ANGB, TX which received its first F-16C in September 1996.

QF-4S drone conversion

The Naval Air Depot (NADEP) at Cherry Point, NC completed its first production QF-4S conversion at the end of 1996. Previously, drone conversions were carried out to the F-4N. Approximately 30 F-4s are in storage at Cherry Point awaiting conversion.

Long-serving F-16

The F-16 Fighting Falcon officially logged its 5,000,000th flying hour in USAF service on 4 December 1996, when a 388th FW F-16C performed a demonstration flight at Hill AFB, UT.

Last Holloman QF-106

The final shootdown of a Convair QF-106 Delta Dart (QF-106B/57-2524) drone at Holloman AFB occurred on 20 February 1997. Det 1 of the 82nd Aerial Target Squadron flew the last terminal mission. The mission was an IR countermeasures effort and the aircraft was shot down over the White Sands Missile Range by an SA-18 'Grouse' (9K-38 Igla) operated by the US Army.

Since 1991, the detachment has flown 300 unpiloted QF-106 missions. Unpiloted flights are known in jargon as NULLO (not under live local operation). Of 367 missions flown in 1996, 40 were unmanned and 14 drones were actually shot down at nearby White Sands.

US forces evacuate Tirana

Under fire from SAMs and small arms, USMC CH-46E, CH-53E and AH-1W helicopters entered Albania on 13 and 14 March 1997 to rescue US citizens caught in the civil war being fought in the capital, Tirana. The USMC aircraft carrying out Operation Silver Wake were from HMM-365, embarked on USS *Nassau* (LHA-4) as part of the 26th Marine Expeditionary Unit.

V-22 developments

The first V-22 Osprey engineering and manufacturing development (EMD) aircraft (BuNo. 164939) made its first flight at Arlington, TX on 5 February 1997. The no. 7 Osprey was ferried to Patuxent River, MD on 16 March.

Longbow Apache

The first production AH-64D Apache Longbow made a 30-minute initial flight at Mesa, AZ on 17 March 1997, with chief pilot Jerry Keyser and production test pilot Walter Jones at the controls.

C-17 developments

The USAF's C-17 Globemaster III fleet has surpassed 50,000 total flying hours (this does not include more than 1,000 flying hours on T-1, the dedicated flight test aircraft). The 24 C-17s at Charleston AFB, SC and the five at Altus AFB, OK reached the 50,000-hour mark in March 1997. The aircraft at Charleston are jointly operated by the 437th AW and 315th AW (Reserve Associate) of AMC, and at Altus by the 97th AMW of AETC. The Air Force recently accepted aircraft P-30, which is undergoing airborne defensive system mods before final delivery in April 1997. Aircraft P-31 is scheduled for final delivery in May.

B-1B 'Bone' developments

Boeing's North American division is lobbying the Air Force to advance the schedule for the Conventional Munitions Upgrade Program (CMUP) for the B-1B bomber. The fleet has now reached Block C standard with the capability to employ CBU-87/89/97 cluster bombs. The B-1B force reached RAA (required assets available, a term replacing IOC, or initial operating capability) in Block C when three B-1Bs of the 37th BS, 28th BW at Ellsworth AFB, SD became combat-ready with CBUs on 17 September 1996.

The USAF is now testing two aircraft configured as Block D, which will provide the B-1B with GPS, communications improvements, and the Sanders ALE-50 towed decoy. The first Block D-configured aircraft (85-0068) was delivered from the Palmdale, CA factory to Edwards AFB on 18 March 1997. The second (84-0049) was scheduled to follow. Thereafter, the USAF plans to field a 'six-pack' of Block D B-1Bs, actually consisting of seven aircraft, which will attain RAA status by 31 March 1999. A future Block E will give the fleet a new computer and the WCMD (wind-corrected munitions dispenser). Farther away is Block F, which will upgrade the defensive system.

F-22 Raptor roll-out

With immense fanfare, the US Air Force rolled out its first Lockheed Martin F-22 Raptor EMD 'air dominance fighter' (serial no. 91-0001) at

Marietta, GA on 9 April 1997, followed by a maiden flight on 29 May. At the ceremony, USAF Chief of Staff General Ronald Fogleman faced down critics of the programme, saying, "Air superiority is not a God-given right of Americans. Somebody's got to pay attention to this. It's not a business you want to be second best in. You have to dominate … The F-22 is not an airplane you use to defend your airspace. It's an airplane that is used to dominate the other guy's airspace." The USAF estimates its 438 F-22s will cost $48.3 billion.

F-22 issues

In an effort to stem development cost over-runs on the Lockheed Martin F-22, the USAF has made changes to the quantity and composition of the pre-production programme. The first nine aircraft, identified by the manufacturer as 4001 to 4009, were to have been assigned to evaluation and development, with numbers 10 to 13 being pre-production verification (PPV) to be employed by the USAF for the initial operational test and evaluation (IOT&E) phase. The change involves elimination of the four PPV airframes, and the IOT&E stage being performed by aircraft 4008 and 4009 together with the first two low rate initial production (LRIP) aircraft. The Air Force had planned for 76 LRIP aircraft to be produced between 1999 and 2002, although this has been revised to 70 aircraft over five years.

The first development aircraft, 4001, made its first flight in May 1997, prior to being assigned to the AFFTC at Edwards AFB. The majority of subsequent development airframes will also join the AFFTC, before the 57th Wing at Nellis AFB, NV receives a small number for weapons evaluation. Once these organisations have completed their development, the F-22 will be cleared to join the operational squadrons early in the next century.

F/A-18E/F progress

As of 28 February 1997, the McDonnell F/A-18E/F Super Hornet had completed 421 flights and 680 flying hours. January marked sea trials aboard the carrier USS *John C. Stennis* (CVN-74), delivery of the third F/A-18E and the second F/A-18F to Patuxent River, and the start of 'clean' flutter tests. February saw completion of clean flutter tests, the start of loads testing, the start of high angle-of-attack testing, cold weather environmental control tests, and the beginning of weapon separation trials. The programme was expected to begin air-to-air weapon separation tests in March.

The fifth F/A-18E made the type's first flight with weapons attached on 21 February. During the 2.5-hour sortie flown by Northrop Grumman test pilot Jim Sandberg, the F/A-18E carried three 480-US gal (1815-litre) Aero Servo fuel tanks, two 1,000-lb Mk 84s, two AIM-9s, and two AGM-88Cs.

From 4 January until 8 March 1997, Shannon Airport, Ireland, hosted a major meteorological research project – FASTEX '97 (Fronts and Atlantic Storm Tracks Exercise). At Shannon, the US Department of Commerce based its (much modified) Gulfstream IVSP and WP-3DE Orion – both operated by the National Oceanic and Atmospheric Administration – along with an L.188C Electra operated by the National Center for Oceanographic Research. Other aircraft from France, Canada and the UK were involved to a lesser degree. Unseasonably good weather during January put a brake on activities, but the scientists got more than they bargained for the following month when unusually bad weather followed. The Electra was badly damaged by a lightning strike and limped back to Shannon for major structural repairs.

Left: Congressional F-22 programme cost estimates of $64.4 billion are at odds with the USAF's figures. The Air Force still has a serious battle on its hands to acquire and preserve funding for all 438 Raptors.

CH-47D upgrade

The US Army has given Boeing the go-ahead to modify two CH-47D Chinooks to 'production representative' standard for the Improved Cargo Helicopter (ICH) programme. No new designation has been announced for the ICH Chinook, but the next logical one would be CH-47F. A third, non-standard aircraft is already flight-testing ICH features. The programme, launched as part of the Pentagon's planning for the period 1998-2003, will eventually upgrade 300 of the Army's fleet of 431 CH-47D helicopters.

ICH involves modernising and improving the CH-47D fleet to ensure the US Army retains its heavy-lift capability until the Joint Transport Rotorcraft (the notional replacement for the CH-47 and CH-53E) begins service in 2015 or later. If the ICH effort proceeds as planned, unmodified CH-47Ds will remain in service until 2025, and ICH CH-47Ds until 2040.

The ICH programme calls for upgrading 300 Chinooks with fuselage remanufacturing, fuselage 'tuning' to reduce vibration effects in aircraft avionics and other systems, and installation of a digitally compatible databus to make cockpit instrumentation compatible with the Army's digital battlefield requirements and to improve navigation. The manufacturer claims that these improvements will reduce ICH Chinook operating costs to 22 per cent lower than the costs of operating a D model today. Conversely, the Army would face operating cost increases of 40 per cent if no improvements were added to the CH-47Ds flying now.

The first modernised ICH Chinook is to be delivered in 2003, followed by an increase to at least 24 deliveries per year until Army fleet requirements are met. Programme manager Sam Sutter says that "since [Boeing's] international customers tend to buy what the US Army operates, ICH will create a potential for more international Chinook sales, perhaps as many as 400 worldwide."

At Fort Rucker, AL, the US Army Aviation Center is conducting flight tests of a Chinook incorporating many of the improvements to be featured in the ICH. The aircraft, recently nick-named Bearcat III, completed Boeing evaluation of fuselage tuning and vibration reduction trials. The aircraft (86-1678) is a CH-47D (a former CH-47C) modified in 1986 to D model standard; it served in Germany, in Operation Desert Storm and in Maryland before being leased by Boeing

in March 1995. The US Army refers to this one-of-a-kind ship as the Vibration Reduction Test Aircraft (VRTA).

About 650 Chinooks are flying around the world. This total includes early Chinooks and those modernised to CH-47D standard, commercial Model 234s, and Boeing/Kawasaki co-produced CH-47Js (equivalent to the CH-47D). The worldwide Chinook population also includes Model 414 Chinooks (CH-47C) built by Agusta near Milan, Italy. Agusta's Chinook customers include Egypt, Greece, Iran, Italy, Libya, and Morocco. Boeing's Chinook customers include military and commercial operators in Canada, Argentina, the UK, Spain, Norway, Australia and Thailand.

The first of the two production-standard CH-47Ds is scheduled to reach Boeing's Philadelphia plant in May 1999 and to make its first flight in ICH configuration in December 2001. In late 1996, the manufacture of two production-standard ICH Chinooks was announced, at a cost of $750 million. Since then, available funding has been pared to $621 million.

E-2 Hawkeye

Northrop Grumman was scheduled to deliver to the US Navy the first of 36 E-2C Hawkeye 2s (BuNo. 165293) to be manufactured in St Augustine, FL. The E-2C Group II made its first flight on 22 March 1997 and was scheduled for delivery to VAW-120 at Norfolk, VA in April. The manufacturer has a firm commitment for 12 of the 36 planned (BuNos 165293/165304), and is also building two E-2Cs for the French navy with expectations for a contract for a third. One hundred and sixty-six E-2s were built for the United States Navy, Egypt, Israel, Japan, Singapore and Taiwan during 1973-94 at Calverton, NY before production shifted to Florida.

BRIEFING

Islamic Republic of Iran Air Force

Iranian air power on display

Since the end of its eight-year war with Iraq, in 1988, Iran has hosted a biennial military 'air show'. Such displays are routinely held in February, to commemorate the anniversary of the 1979 Islamic Revolution. The 1996 display took place at Tactical Air Base No. 1, Mehrabad, near the capital, Tehran. Though some time has passed since then (and though the show has been briefly reported by some Western sources), photographs recently obtained by *World Air Power Journal* give a clearer view of the aircraft and weapons on show at Mehrabad last year. They also provide a significant insight into the current operational status of the IRIAF and its acquisition of new aircraft and weapons.

Above: Iran is believed to have taken delivery of 14 MiG-29s in 1990 and a follow-on batch of up to 48 aircraft has been reported, but never confirmed. It is believed that four former Iraqi air force aircraft, which escaped to Iran in 1991, have been pressed into use with the IRIAF. MiG-29s in Iranian service are armed with R-60 (AA-8 'Aphid') and R-27R/T (AA-10 'Alamo') AAMs. On show in another section of the exhibition, dedicated to Iran's self-sufficiency agency, was a specially developed, podded, hose-and-drogue air-to-air refuelling system to enable Iranian 'Fulcrums' to operate with the IRIAF's Boeing 707 and 747 tankers.

Above and left: Iran took delivery of 105 Northrop F-5As and 140 of the more capable Sidewinder-armed F-5E. F-5 losses were heavy during the Iran-Iraq war, but it remains an important type in the IRIAF inventory. The F-5E at Mehrabad had a locally-modified wingtip missile launcher, required to carry AAMs heavier than the AIM-9. From its markings, the missile (to port) is clearly a Chinese-supplied PL-9 AAM, which resembles the MATRA R.550 Magic 1, also in Iranian service.

The 'star' at Mehrabad was arguably the Sukhoi Su-24MK 'Fencer-D' – the first occasion this type has been seen in IRIAF markings. Iran is believed to have 33 'Fencer-Ds' in service, including 24 ex-Iraqi aircraft. The freshly-painted aircraft seen above may be one of the refugee Iraqi aircraft. It is certainly a different sub-type, as it lacks the overwing fences of the aircraft below and is therefore a late-production 'Fencer-D' (Mod). The Su-24 below has the squared-off wing fences that can house chaff/flare dispensers. The aircraft above is carrying six low-drag GP bombs on a centreline pylon, all probably sourced from China's NORINCO.

Above and right: The Mehrabad display was held from 1 to 10 February 1996. The display area was divided into three sections, one for combat aircraft and a second for general defence equipment, including Iranian Zelzal and Naze'at FROG-7 SSM copies (mounted on Mercedes 305 trucks), Oerlikon 37-mm and ZSU-23-4 AA guns, plus Hawk and Rapier SAMs. The third area was devoted to the 'Self-Sufficiency Jahad of the Air Force and Aeronautics University', which develops indigenous spare parts and support equipment. Clearly visible in the line-up above is a Chengdu F-7 in a scheme closely resembling that worn by a line-up of similar aircraft pictured in World Air Power Journal Volume 29. These aircraft were described by a Chengdu spokesman as destined for "Pakistan."

Left: Visible in this view is the R-60 (AA-8 'Aphid') acquisition round carried to starboard on the modified F-5E. Other weapons arrayed around the IRIAF aircraft on show included AIM-54 Phoenix AAMs and AGM-65 Maverick ASMs, a range of Russian/Chinese-designed bombs and rocket pods, plus the locally-built Kite 'smart' munitions dispenser and Raad LGB. In the background is a group of (operational) IRIAF aircraft, including a Bell 214 Isfahan, Kaman HH-43 Husky, Boeing-Vertol CH-47 Chinook, Fokker F27 and Lockheed C-130 Hercules.

The F-14A Tomcat on show had been repainted in a new two-tone blue/grey camouflage scheme, replacing the desert scheme worn previously by Iran's F-14s, and echoing the scheme worn by the MiG-29. The Tomcat was displayed alongside AIM-54 Phoenix air-to-air missiles, though there was no indication whether these weapons were still operational.

The McDonnell Douglas F-4D/E Phantom was once the backbone of the Iranian air force and, of the 225 aircraft delivered, 40 are believed to be still operational. This F-4E is fitted with a TISEO (Target-Identification System, Electro-Optical) sensor that provides PGM (glide bomb and AGM-65) capability. The TISEO sensor is mounted in the port wing leading edge.

BRIEFING

Air assets in the Central African Republic
Mirage over the Savannah

The Central African Republic (République Centreafricaine) hosts the second-largest French garrison in Africa after Djibouti, the EFAO (Elément Français d'Assistance Operationnelle). The French troops occupy two bases in the country: Bouar, at the Cameroon and Chad borders, and Camp Beal (which is the HQ of the EFAO) at Bangui, the capital. Normally, French troops in the CAR consist of an airborne company (COMPARA), an armoured squadron equipped with AML armoured cars, a 120-mm mortar battery, a command and logistics company, and a headquarters unit. The Armée de l'Air is represented by a detachment of four Mirage F1CTs, two Mirage F1CRs and two Transall C.160s, plus a refuelling aircraft based at M'Poko Bangui International Airport.

Due to its geographical position in the heart of Africa, the CAR is a very important platform for French military operations. Bangui was used as rear base for Operations Manta and Epervier during the 1980s when French forces helped the Chad army to rout the Libyans. The base was also used more recently during Operation Turquoise in Rwanda in summer 1994. Recently, the EFAO was involved in maintaining order in the country after the third mutiny of the Forces Armées Centreafricaine (FACA). The mission of the EFAO was to protect and evacuate the Westerners, and protect economic installations.

The Central African Republic is ruled by President Ange Patasse, who was democratically elected in 1993. His leadership is weak and the country has collapsed in an economic crisis, induced in part by tribal rifts. President Patasse is a Sara (the people of the savannah) and was elected by the Sara and M'bara (people of the forest) plus other ethnic

groups, but not the Yakoma (people of the river). The former president, Mr Kolingba, was a Yakoma who, although they represent only 3 per cent of the population, generally ruled the country in the preceding years; more importantly, the Yakoma comprised 40 per cent of the army.

The first army mutiny occurred in April 1996 and was followed by a second in May. French forces restored order and, after a short but fierce fight, retook the radio building. The third mutiny started in November 1996 and can be considered as a true military uprising against the unpopular but democratically elected president.

The few heavy weapons of the FACA are in the hands of rebels who have their HQ in Camp Kassaï, to the east of Bangui. To avoid destruction of the city centre and to prevent direct conflict between the Sécurité Presidentielle and the Yakoma, which would have caused a bloodbath, French troops took up position in Bangui.

On 4 January 1997 a French paratroop officer and an NCO were killed by several AK-47 shots fired in their backs as they entered their vehicle after escorting an African negotiating team. This murder prompted strong French retaliation. On the night of 4/5 January, the 3e and 4e Compagnies of the 2e REP (Régiment Etranger de Parachutistes Legion), the 2e Compagnie of the 8e RPIMA (Régiment de Parachutistes d'Infanterie de Marine) and special forces of the COS (Commandement des Opérations Spéciales/Special Forces) launched a large sweep in the hostile suburbs of Petevo, Bimbo and Backongo. They were supported by a Puma helicopter armed with a 20-mm cannon. During the night, the helicopter was diverted to support Checkpoint Alpha 15 which was attacked by two

Above: A view across the ramp at M'Poko air base, Bangui. The two Mirage F1CTs seen here, in the foreground, both wear the badge of EC 1/30 'Normandie-Niemen'.

One of the two F1CRs of ER 2/33 'Belfort' departs for a recce flight. The blue comet indicates that this aircraft has won the 'comet' reconnaissance competition.

14.5-mm KPV HMGs firing from Camp Kassaï. The helicopter destroyed the two guns, and during the operation a dozen mutineers were killed, 52 were taken prisoner, and weapons including a 14.5-mm and a 12.7-mm machine-gun were captured. Seven French soldiers were lightly wounded. This operation forced the rebels to negotiate, and an African Peace Force will now monitor their disarmament, from Bangui.

M'Poko air base

Since 1996 the Mirage F1CT has replaced the Jaguar in Africa. The base of M'Poko, at Bangui's international airport, is the second-largest Armée de l'Air installation in Africa. Detachment 7/33 consists of four Mirage F1CTs and two Mirage F1CRs belonging to EC 1/30 'Normandie-Niemen' and ER 2/33 'Belfort'. They alternate every four months with aircraft from EC 2/30 'Alsace' and ER 1/33 'Savoie'. All

of these units maintain the traditions of famous Free French squadrons involved in World War II. Pilots and aircraft remain in Bangui for four months, including a 15-day stay in N'Djamena, Chad. This small detachment of six Mirages gives the Armée de l'Air indisputable air superiority in central Africa. Since the conclusion of the Cold War and the end of Soviet aid, the Angolan and Nigerian air forces (the only conceivable threats) have been unable to conduct serious air operations due to poor maintenance and lack of spares.

"Flying over Africa is a dream, but it isn't easy every time," said 'Barzy', a 30-year-old captain in charge of Détachement 7/33. Because of the heat, aircraft take off with a reduced fuel load, and pilots are particularly careful during landing. In flight, the Mirages can be refuelled by a C-135FR detached from Libreville, Gabon or N'Djamena, Chad. The Transall C.160NG is also used for air refuelling. The aircraft generally take off at 09.00 to avoid the heat of mid-day. On the taxiway, the pilot leaves the cockpit open and does not employ air conditioning, in order to avoid misting when the aircraft is airborne.

Two patrols of two F1CTs and one F1CR take off. The missions are similar to those undertaken in Europe but the aircraft can fly low –

The Dassault Mirage F1CT (T/tactique) is an upgraded ground-attack derivative of the Mirage F1C interceptor. The F1CT boasts an improved Cyrano IV radar, with added air-to-ground modes, plus a laser rangefinder – visible here in its fairing under the forward fuselage.

ESCADRILLE CENTREAFRICAINE

The state of the national air arm, the Escadrille Centreafricaine (Central African Flight), parallels that of the country: complete disarray. Lack of funding has left it with only a Rallye Guerrier and the presidential helicopter (an AS 350 Ecureuil) able to fly. A Cessna 337 and two Islanders (one belonging to the Ministry of Water and Forest) are on the inventory but are not in flying condition due to lack of spares. Pilots were trained

in France and are proficient, but they suffer from a severe lack of flying hours.

Said one of the air force's pilots: "The big countries forget Africa. In the past we had a perfect aircraft, well adapted to Africa – the C-47 Dakota – but slowly this remarkable aircraft disappeared due to incompatible fuel and lack of spares. We need an unsophisticated aircraft. Even a CASA CN.235 is full of black boxes and too complicated for an African airfield."

250 ft/75 m – without regard for people on the ground. Maps are imprecise and are not updated, but the Mirages are equipped with GPS and inertial navigation system. One of the main problems encountered is the lack of a large divert airfield in case of emergency. Only M'Poko airfield and a private airfield built near the hunting lodge of former Emperor Bokassa in the north of country can be used for emergency landing. In the event of a serious problem, pilots are forced to eject, but happily that has not happened with the Mirage F1.

Normal configuration is two 1200-litre (265-Imp gal) fuel tanks and two 250-kg bombs. Rocket pods for 68-mm (2.7-in) weapons can also be carried, but normally the 30-mm cannon is perfectly adequate for the 'soft' targets likely to be encountered in that part of Africa. Air-to-air missiles (MATRA R.530 or R.550 Magic), ECM pods and chaff launchers are stocked in

M'Poko but are rarely seen on the aircraft due to the complete lack of airborne opposition, and to avoid wear from the equatorial climate. During recent events at Bangui, the Mirage F1CTs made a few low passes over Camp Kassaï (the main rebel base) but did not use their weapons. Mirage F1CRs made a number of reconnaissance flights and took photographs of rebel positions, but did not employ their strike capacity. They also photographed the cut made to the Bangui access road, and the landing zone for helicopters and paratroops. The rebels had only a few 12.7-mm and Russian 14.5-mm KPV heavy anti-aircraft guns. No SA-7s have been observed, but in Africa a large number of these shoulder-launched missiles are universally available.

"Maintenance of the aircraft is relatively easy and the F1 handles the heat well," said Major Bayard, who is in charge of the technical aspects of Det 7/33. Maintenance

personnel take care to check daily all the small intakes of the aircraft, especially the pitot tube. The cause of this meticulous operation is the mason wasp. These African insects get into an aircraft's apertures and begin to build their nest. From outside the nest is not obvious, but when the pilot is on the taxiway and ready to take off, all the instrument panels can malfunction due to interference from the wasp's handiwork. Snakes are also common in the area, and during the Jaguar's stay one was once found in an air intake.

Two Transall C.160s belonging to the GTD (Groupement de

Transport Détaché) are detached to the base, a C.160NG of ET 1/64 'Béarn' and a C.160 of ET 3/61 'Poitou'. The aircraft are used for airborne drop, assault landing and cargo-carrying. The C.160NG also has a tanker capacity and often works with the Mirage F1s. This aircraft is equipped with a new (but 'bolt-on') navigation system consisting of a coupled GPS/INS.

Army aviation (Aviation Mégère de l'Armée de Terre) is represented in Bangui by four Pumas belonging to the 5e RHC (Régiment d'Hélicoptère de Combat). One of these helicopters is piloted by a member of the Commandement des Opérations Spéciales and, as detailed above, on the night of 4/5 January he took out the rebels' heavy weapons. As these recent events have proved, even with a reduced number of aircraft, the French presence in Bangui is still an important factor in the stabilisation of central Africa.
Yves Debay

Below: The two Transalls of the GTD provide logistical and air-to-air refuelling support for the AA in the Central African Republic. The aircraft nearest the camera is fitted with a refuelling HDU.

Above right and right: The cannon-armed SA 330B Pumas of the ALAT's 5e RHC have made an important contribution to the successful outcome of recent French military operations in the CAR.

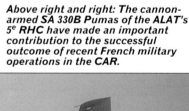

Mil Mi-9 'Hip-G', Mi-8TPS, Mi-8PS and Mi-8MB

Battlefield C² post, VIP transport and casevac

The Mi-9 'Hip-G' is an extensively upgraded version of the Mil Mi-8VzPU (the correct designation of the 'Hip-D' is Mi-8VzPU; see 'Vozdushnyy Punkt Upravlyenya, Airborne Command Post', *World Air Power Journal* Volume 20) and fulfils the same role. Initially, this variant was designated Mi-8IV (*Ivolga*/'oriole'), but later – given its specialised nature – received the designation Mi-9. (Similarly, the much upgraded aerial command post version of the Mi-6VKP 'Hook-B' was given a special designation, Mi-22 'Hook-C'.)

The 'Hip-G' is primarily used by army commanders at the divisional level, but its use is apparently not restricted to the Soviet and Russian

ground forces. In Poland, a single 'Hip-G' was operated by the headquarters flight of the 149th BAP (Bomber Aviation Division), based at Szprotawa (subordinated to the Soviet – and latterly Russian – 4th Air Army), in addition to the more typical An-2. In the former German Democratic Republic, single Mi-9s were observed and photographed during 1992-93 at Damgarten (01 blue) and Grossenhain (01 red), away from army aviation bases. These aircraft may have been operated by the headquarters flights of the 16th IAD (Fighter Aviation Division) and 105th IBAD (Fighter-Bomber Aviation Division), respectively.

The fuselage of the Mi-9 is a

combination of the fuselage of a basic Mi-8T and the clamshell doors and rear fuselage section of the civil Mi-8P passenger variant and military Mi-8PS (see below). Basic dimensions are the same as those of the Mi-8T/Mi-8S: fuselage length (without rotors) 18.31 m (60.07 ft), total length 25.28 m (82.9 ft), height 5.65 m (18.54 ft), rotor diameter 21.29 m (69.85 ft). Empty weight is 7500 kg (16,535 lb) (7160 kg/15,785 lb for Mi-8T; 7420 kg/24,345 lb for Mi-8PS), take-off weight is 11000 kg (24,240 lb) (11100 kg/24,470 lb for Mi-8T; 10400 kg/22,930 lb for Mi-8PS), maximum take-off weight is 12000 kg (26,455 lb) (same for Mi-8T/PS).

The fuselage of the Mi-9 is

divided into four compartments: flight deck, communications section, operational control centre and a section for the storage of auxiliary equipment. In addition to a flight crew (two pilots and flight engineer), the Mi-9 has a crew of three communications operators and three operators.

Aft of the flight deck, the cabin of the 'Hip-G' is divided by bulkheads with doors into three compartments. From nose to tail, these are: a communications section (between ribs 1 and 5), an operational control centre (between ribs 5 and 10), and a technical section (between ribs 10 and 16). The communications section is the nerve centre of the *Plazma*-1 information system and comprises three work stations, for a radio engineer (station 6), a radiotelegraphist (station 5) and a commander of the communications section (station 4), who operates the four-channel AK-21 radio communications switchboard.

Mi-9 equipment fit

The Mi-9 is not equipped with the R-833, R-842 and R-852 (R-852 is an emergency radio compass) radios and ARK-U2 radio compass fitted in other versions of the 'Hip'. Instead, in addition to the standard R-860 and R-856 communications radios of the 'Hip', the communications equipment of the Mi-9 consists of the following special mission equipment and associated antennas: R-886 VHF radio (two longitudinal blade antennas under the fuselage, designated R-886D and R-886E, sometimes erroneously referred to as R-826); R-802VYa UHF transmitter (two antennas: AShS-1G located between the blade antennas

This rear view of the Mi-9 'Hip-G' illustrates the 'hockey stick' ASM-405M2 antenna of the R-405MPB direction-finding equipment (port) and the ASh-1 antenna of the R-860 UHF radio (starboard).

This starboard view of an Mi-9 clearly shows the outputs for the (from right to left) R-405 and R-111 aerials and TA-57 and P-170E telephone equipment, used when the aircraft is functioning as a command post on the ground.

This underside view shows the starboard fairing for the wire antenna for the R-886 VHF receiver and – in the foreground – wire aerial for the R-111 VHF radio.

Another close-up view, this time of the port underside fuselage of the 'Hip-G', reveals the port fairing for the wire antenna of the R-886 VHF radio receiver.

Yellow 33 (c/n 98448483) is one of two Mi-9 'Hip-Gs' operated by 248 OVE at Minsk-Stepyanka (Lipki) in the Republic of Belarus.

under the forward fuselage, AShS-1 on top of the base of the tailboom); R-111 VHF transmitter (the wire aerial is located outboard of the starboard blade antenna and is normally folded, but can be extended for inflight operation after the aircraft has lifted off and ground separation is at least 2 m/6.5 ft).

The R-405MPB (R-405) direction-finding equipment is served by three antennas: the ASM-405M2 antenna is the ice-hockey stick-shaped antenna which protrudes from the port clamshell door and operates in the 60-65 MHz range; a second ice-hockey stick antenna, located under the tailboom, is the ASM-405-M, which operates in the 65-70 MHz band (88-154). The third antenna is the ASD-405, which is located on top of the fuselage between the R-802 and R-832M antennas. The antenna protruding from the starboard clamshell door is the AShS-1 antenna for the R-860 UHF radio, which is located on top of the fuselage in other versions of the 'Hip'. The wire aerial for the R-856A (R-856MB) (replaces R-842 of other variants) and AShD-UD broad-band antenna for the R-832M VHF emergency radio compass are located on top of the tailboom.

Operator stations

The main section of the cabin accommodates work stations for three operators (station 1 and 2 at starboard side, station 3 on port side). They are seated on swivelling chairs next to an observation window, below which a telephone is located. Their two tables can be joined to form one larger table measuring 80 x 200 cm (31.5 x 78.7 in) for work with large-format tactical maps. On the cabin walls next to their respective work stations are fixed three plotting charts/data panels, measuring 86 x 86 cm (33.8 x 33.8 in) (between stations 1 and 2) and 56 x 55 cm (22.0 x 21.6 in) (over table of station 3 and fixed to bulkhead behind operator 2).

On the bulkhead across work station 3 is an equipment rack for the MN-61PB tape recorder and AK-11 apparatus, above which is

The Mi-9 is readily distinguished from standard 'Hip' versions by the pair of 'hockey stick'-shaped antennas protruding from the port clamshell door and tailboom.

placed a light metal rectangular case with two compartments for document folders (sized 220 x 330 mm/8.7 x 12.9 in), one section for three tubes (diameter 120 mm/4.7 in) for 850 x 850 mm (33.5 x 33.5 in) tactical maps, and storage space for rations for nine crew members.

The third section houses the Al-8 auxiliary mobile power unit (APU) with GS-24A DC generator (14-60 kW), which provides ground power when the two antenna masts are deployed on the ground. The outlets for the R-111 and R-405MPB antennas and telephone sets TA-57 and P-170E are located on the starboard side of the fuselage.

On the port side of the equipment storage section are located racks for remotely controlled com-

Above and right: The Mil Mi-8PS (Passazhirskiy-Salon) VIP transport has also been referred to as the Mi-8P or Mi-8S. Note the blade aerial under the forward fuselage, associated with the R-863 command radio, and the wire aerial of the R-111 VHF radio, similar to that of the Mi-9 and Mi-8TPS. The Mi-8PS has been seen with and without a Doppler box under the tailboom.

Above and right: This is a Mil Mi-8TPS specialist transport. Note the blade aerial under the forward fuselage, associated with the R-863 command radio, as well as the stepped Doppler box under the tailboom. The interior of the aircraft is seen from the starboard side, looking forward.

munications equipment, and storage space for a trolley with Al-8. On the starboard side (between ribs 10 and 16) are a storage bin for telescopic antenna masts for the R-111 and R-405 antennas (and cables), with a bunk on top

providing resting space for one crew member, and (between ribs 10 and 11) a rack for equipment referred to in manuals as '19-18' (a scrambler?). On top of the cover of the storage bin, 10 sets of NBC gear (comprising coats, boots, gloves and protective masks) can be stowed and secured with straps.

The rear cargo doors of the 'Hip-G' are smaller than those of other versions of the 'Hip' and are cut off squarely rather than transversely, and feature a door in the middle for easy deployment of the ground power unit. Inside, a starboard clamshell door provides storage space for 12 litres (3.2 Imp gal) of drinking water, batteries two and five, instruments for NBC detection, fire extinguisher OU-2, and spare parts for the communications equipment. Inside the port door are transformer PO-750A,

BRIEFING

Right: This is a Mil Mi-8MB Bissyektr ambulance version. This aircraft is operated by 248 OVE, based at Minsk-Stepyanka in Belarus. Note that nation's flag over the side door.

Below and below right: This is a view from the starboard side (looking rearward) of the interior of an Mi-8MB ambulance. The required life support equipment for the Mi-8MB is located above what appears to be an extra fuel tank, inside the cabin (below right).

voltage regulator R-27BT, and transformer PO-3000 series 3.

For obvious reasons, no internal fuel tank is in the cabin. Therefore, fuel capacity is limited to the two external tanks of 1140 litres (250 Imp gal) (port) and 1030 litres (225 Imp gal) (starboard). With a cruising speed of 120 km/h (75 mph), the Mi-9 is quoted to have an endurance of 3 to 3.5 hours.

The antennas for the R-405 direction finder and R-111 communications radio can be erected on telescopic masts when the Mi-9 is deployed as a command post on the ground. The antennas can be erected in two variants: the 16.5-m (54-ft) mast for the R-405M at an angle of 45° to the centreline of the aircraft, and the 11-m (36-ft) mast for the R-111 at an angle of 30° to the aircraft's centreline, at distances to the airframe of 310 m (1,017 ft) and 233 m (765 ft), respectively. Or, the cables can be laid out at 90° angles to the centreline and the masts placed at distances to the helicopter of 295 m (820 ft) (R-405) and 260 m (853 ft) (R-111). The antenna of the R-405 direction finder comprises a number of Z-shaped aerials for the decimeter band and a screen-shaped *volnovoi kanal* antenna for the meter band. A clearance of 5 m (16.4 ft) between rotor and mast-stays is mandatory. The two TK-2 reels with 1000 m (3,280 ft) of telephone cable P-274 can be stored in a rack on the port side of the equipment compartment.

Mil Mi-8TPS

The Mi-8TPS has no separate NATO ASCC designation, and is not easily distinguished externally from the basic Mi-8T 'Hip-C' variant. This variant is sometimes referred to as Mi-8TP or Mi-8PS (*Passazhirskiy i svyaz*, 'passengers and liaison/communications'), but the correct designation is Mi-8TPS (*Transportnii Polu-Salon*, 'transport semi-salon'). The main external differences are the blade aerial under the forward fuselage, and the stepped fairing of the combined Doppler aerial and radar altimeter typical of aircraft produced at the Ulan Ude factory in the early 1990s (and similar to that of the Mi-171). Another feature of the Mi-8TPS is the five vibration dampers on the rotor head.

The cabin of the Mi-8TPS features a communications station behind the cockpit rear bulkhead, behind the pilot's position, straight across the port side sliding door. The communications equipment of the Mi-8TPS comprises R-842M HF, R-860 VHF, R-111 UHF and R-832 VHF radio transmitters, thus sharing the latter three with the Mi-9. The blade aerial under the forward fuselage is associated with the R-863 command radio, and is also seen on many Mi-8PS VIP transport helicopters (see below). The primary task of the Mi-8TPS is liaison while providing secure inflight communications for the commanders on board. The main section of the aircraft features a command station with two swivelling chairs on the starboard side, and a row of seats along the fuselage on the port side.

Mil Mi-8PS

Like the Mi-8TPS, the Mi-8PS (*Passazhirskiy-Salon*, also often referred to as Mi-8P or Mi8S) has no separate NATO ASCC designation, but is easily distinguished externally from the basic Mi-8T 'Hip-C' by the square windows. This variant is mainly used for transporting high-ranking officers and features an expanded communications suite and a VIP interior.

Mil Mi-8MB

A commercial ambulance version of the Mi-17, designated Mi-17-1VA, was displayed at the 1989 Le Bourget Aerosalon in France. Small numbers of a military ambulance version of the basic Mi-8T, designated Mi-8MB (*Bissyektr*), are in use with the armed forces of the former Soviet Union. In Afghanistan, two such aircraft were operated by 50 OSAP (Independent Mixed Aviation Regiment). Based at Kabul International Airport, these helicopters acted as 'plane guard', since aircraft taking off and landing at this airport were under threat of being shot down by shoulder-fired SAMs as soon as they crossed the airfield perimeter.

One of the accompanying photographs (top of this page) depicts one of these Mi-8MBs serving with 248 OVE (Independent Helicopter Squadron) of the air force of the Republic of Belarus, and was referred to as an Mi-8T *sanitarnii* (ambulance or medical) by its crew. The aircraft is equipped with two stretchers (provision for three) and life-support systems, which are fitted over the internal fuel tank. It should be noted that this aircraft was not fitted with a winch over the sliding door on the port side of the fuselage, as seen in many Mi-8Ts and Mi-8MTs, and as such is unlikely to be operated as a true search and rescue aircraft, but more likely in conjunction with a dedicated SAR machine.

Frank Rozendaal

Douglas A-3 Skywarrior
Hughes flying labs

Well before its retirement from the US Navy in 1991, the A-3 had gained favour among defence contractors and aerospace companies as a flight-test and research platform. During the last 30 years, the A-3 has flown such projects for the Army, Navy/Marines and the Air Force, serving contractors such as Westinghouse, Raytheon, Thunderbird Aviation and Hughes Aircraft. Raytheon still operates the type from its facility in Hanscom Field, Massachusetts, but the largest fleet belongs to Hughes Aeronautical Operations, the flight test unit of Hughes Aircraft located at Van Nuys Airport, in Los Angeles.

Hughes Aeronautical Operations has modified and/or operated more than 100 different aircraft types since the unit was established in 1948, ranging from the B-58 Hustler to the DC-10, as well as a myriad of fighter types and corporate jets. Having such vast experience with so many aircraft types, it is quite a tribute to the A-3 that Hughes has selected it as its primary flight-test platform for the 1990s and beyond. Hughes began operating the A-3 in the mid-1960s and recently increased its fleet to 12 A-3s as it acquired several aircraft formerly operated by Thunderbird Aviation. Hughes's fleet as of January 1997 consists of two EA-3Bs, three TA-3Bs, and seven RA-3B variants.

The team at Hughes Aeronautical Operations considers the A-3 uniquely suited to the task of flight test. Its design as a nuclear bomber required that the crew be able to arm the weapon in flight, hence the A-3 was designed with a pressurised area in the fuselage behind the crew compartment providing access to the bomb bay. EA-3s have an even larger and better pressurised cabin to accommodate the electronic warfare crew. These pressurised cabins are one of the things that set the A-3 apart from other tactical military jets. Calling the aircraft "a great flying lab," Hughes test pilot Ron Woltman points out that the A-3's large crew compartment and an 'airline'-like cabin pressurisation schedule permit engineers and a support team to fly along on the test flight, actively participating first-hand in a 'shirt-sleeve' environment rather than relying solely on remote telemetry data or a post-flight debrief. Some corporate jets can be modified to carry engineers in the cabin and pods under the wings, but they cannot match the perfor-

Hughes 79 is seen here landing at Van Nuys with its essential brake-chute deployed. The carrierborne A-3 was not noted for its brakes.

mance of a military jet like the A-3, especially when flying low level at high speed. The A-3 can reach 480 kt (551 mph; 887 km/h) at sea level – fast enough to work with most fighters out of afterburner, according to Woltman.

The ability of the 'Whale' to fly fast and low enables it to do captive missile testing. This involves hanging a missile on a wing pylon (or nose pylon in the case of one unique Hughes A-3) and flying the aircraft so as to simulate a cruise missile in flight: low and fast. This type of testing is especially useful in examining sensors and guidance systems since the engineers can ride with the 'captive' missile in flight. The Tomahawk and Harpoon were tested this way. The A-3 is also quite capable of firing a missile. The first AIM-9 Phoenix ever fired was launched from a Hughes A-3.

In addition to speed, the A-3 has an impressive 2,500-mile (4025-km) range and five-hour endurance. With inflight refuelling, range and endurance can be stretched even further. Hughes Aeronautical Operations can provide inflight refuelling support to its flight-test aircraft by providing 'buddy tankers' from its own fleet. Two of Hughes's A-3s are modified to act as tankers with refuelling pods under the wing, and all aircraft can be configured to receive fuel via inflight refuelling, although the booms are not always installed.

Safety is among the many attributes that have kept the A-3 flying. "It was built as a bomber with one purpose in mind," Woltman pointed out, "to get to the target and back." It has many redundant systems and manual backups; Woltman added, "everything on the airplane can quit, you name it [referring to

The aircraft seen right is NRA-3B 142667/N576HA – note its unique missile pylon on the nose. Below is Hughes 78 (144825/N578HA), the former 'Snoopy'-nosed A-3 at PMTC.

hydraulic and electrical systems], but as long as it's got at least one engine running…it'll get you home. Except for the A-6, I don't think there are many tactical jets that can stand up and say that!" The A-3 uses the reliable J57 engine, the same as used in the F-8.

Except for the recent arrivals from Thunderbird, all of Hughes's A-3s have received a standardised modification package which has rendered them "optimised as test-beds," according to Kearny Bothwell of Hughes Public Affairs. The aircraft have an upgraded avionics suite including Omega and GPS navigation systems. VHF radios complement the military UHF units and the aircraft carry dual VOR/ILS systems along with TACAN navigation systems. They are capable of providing 60-Hz AC, 400-Hz AC, and 28-V power to flight-test equipment, allowing the use of commercial off-the-shelf equipment without the need for modifications to either the test equipment or the aircraft. Stan-

dardised equipment racks are installed and plumbed with cooling air, while seats and ICS (Intercockpit Communications Systems) facilitate communications for the flight-test crew. The wings are internally strung with a wide variety of wiring, video co-axial, and digital bus cables, making it easy for customers to hang external stores on the pylons without major modification expense (not all A-3s have wing pylons but all of Hughes's do.) These standardised modifications translate into minimum start-up time and costs at the beginning of a test programme.

Excelling as it does in its current role, the 'Whale' will be earning its keep into the next century. Although the S-3, with its rugged military build and its pressurised cabin, might be a replacement candidate for the A-3 someday, it still lacks the A-3's speed. As long as there is a need for speed in a 'flying lab', it looks as if the flight-test community will keep the A-3 flying for years to come. **Dave Cibley**

BRIEFING

In addition to the standardised modifications, several aircraft have been uniquely modified. This is a run-down of Hughes's current Skywarrior stable:

144867

The most senior member of Hughes's current line-up of A-3s, N577HA – better known as 'Hughes 77' – joined the company in 1969. This NTA-3B was fitted with an F-111B nose in place of its own, in the early 1970s, to evaluate the AWG-9/AIM-54 radar/missile system for the naval F-111. Later, when the F-111B programme was cancelled due to preference for the F-14A, the F-111 nose was replaced with one from a Tomcat, and testing continued. The F-14 nose remained on 'Hughes 77' until a recent project required the installation of another F-111 nose. The two radomes are now interchangeable on this aircraft, making for a very flexible test-space up-front. 'Hughes 77' is also modified to carry a radar in the tail, which can be directed 90° to either side, allowing it to conduct radar testing in any direction 360° around the aircraft. '77' reportedly has been used in radar cross-section testing, but Hughes refuses to confirm or comment on those reports.

146454

'Hughes 74' is a former VQ-2 EA-3B which has been modified with an F-15 nose section. Hughes will not discuss the reason or details of the modification except to confirm that the nose was 'sawed off' an Eagle in the Davis-Monthan 'boneyard'. Number 74 is one of two EA-3s in Hughes's stable.

144865

The other EA-3 variant is Number 75, a former TA-3B which was operated as a VIP transport with VR-1 until the late 1970s and later was converted to EA-3 status in the early 1980s. It, too, ended its Navy career with VQ-2 and is now being used for research under contract by Livermore Labs. Both of Hughes's EA-3s are veterans of Desert Storm, in which they were used by VQ-2 to detect and locate electronic emissions from SAM sites and to co-ordinate HARM strikes.

142667

'Hughes 76' is an NRA-3B formerly assigned to PMTC (now NAWC-WEPS) at nearby Point Mugu. This aircraft still carries a unique missile pylon under the chin which was used for captive missile testing during its career as 'Bloodhound 71' at the Navy's Pacific Missile Test Center. '76' has no 'cats' or 'traps', meaning it has never operated from a carrier. It has been modified as an inflight-refuelling tanker.

144825

'Hughes 78' is the once famous 'Snoopy'-nosed A-3 from Point Mugu. The 'Snoopy' nose was removed in 1989 in favour of a standard A-3 refuelling probe. This ex-'Bloodhound 75' and its sister 'Hughes 76' are still commonly used by Point Mugu to carry external stores for short one- and two-day programmes. Like Number 76, it has no 'cats' or 'traps' and has been modified as an inflight-refuelling tanker.

144858

'Hughes 79', a TA-3 pilot/navigator trainer, is the highest-timed A-3 still flying, with over 13,000 flight hours.

144846

Assigned Hughes N-Number 547HA, this aircraft is used for spares. It had been stored at Davis-Monthan from 1971 to 1981, and was recently acquired by Hughes.

142256

This NRA-3B was with PMTC and Patuxent River before being transferred to Westinghouse in 1971. It was last used as an S-3 avionics testbed until 1993.

144856

This aircraft was rebuilt after a crash at San Clemente Island in August 1985, using the tail from EA-3B BuNo. 146449. It was acquired from Thunderbird late in 1996.

146446

This aircraft, modified as an ERA-3B in 1970, is one of two CLE wing photo A-3s built (BuNo. 146447 is the other). It was acquired from Thunderbird late in 1996.

144832

Reactivated to flight status from Davis-Monthan in early 1980, it was converted to an ERA-3B for FEWSG support. It was acquired from Thunderbird late in 1996.

142668

Reactivated to flight status in early 1981, this too was converted as an ERA-3B for FEWSG support. It was acquired from Thunderbird late in 1996.

Douglas A-3 Skywarriors – Hughes, Van Nuys, CA

BuNo.	Type	Last USN unit	Previous MODEX	Registration	Hughes no.	Wing design	Comments
146454	EA-3B	VQ-2	004	N574HA	74	CLE	F-15 nose. Desert Storm mission markings
144865	EA-3B	VQ-2	011	N575HA	75	CLE	VIP transport assigned to VR-1 until late 1970s as a TA-3B. Was converted during Navy service from a TA-3B.
142667	NRA-3B	PMTC	BH 71	N576HA	76	Basic	PMTC testbed with wing and chin external stores pylons. No cats or traps. Modified an inflight-refuelling tanker.
144867	NTA-3B	VAH-123	NJ 320	N577HA	77	CLE	VAH-123 until 1969. With Hughes since 1969. Modified for F-14 or F-111 radome. AUG-9/APG-71 radar development testbed
144825	NRA-3B	PMTC	BH 75	N578HA	78	Basic	PMTC Testbed. No cats or traps. Old PMTC 'Snoopy'-nosed aircraft. Modified as inflight-refuelling tanker.
144858	TA-3B	VAQ-33	GD 121	N579HA	79	CLE	A3 pilot/nav trainer from VAQ-33. Over 13,000 flight hours and landings (highest time A-3 still active).
144846	ERA-3B	VAQ-34	GD 210	N547HA	None	Basic	Stored DMAFB 1971-1981. Mod to ERA-3B 1981.
144856	TA-3B	VAQ-33	GD 121	N160TB	None	CLE	Crashed on landing at San Clemente August 1985. NARF Alameda cut tail from aft cabin BH (Sta. 475) and spliced on the tail from EA-3B 146449.
146446	ERA-3B	VAQ-34	GD 213	N161TB	None	CLE	VAP-61 aircraft until 1969. Modified to ERA-3B in 1970. One of two CLE wing photo A-3s built. (146447 is the other CLE wing RA-3B.)
144832	ERA-3B	VAQ-33	GD 102	N162TB	None	Basic	Reactivated to flight status from Davis-Monthan in early 1980 and converted to ERA-3B for FEWSG support.
142668	ERA-3B	VAQ-34	GD 100	N163TB	None	Basic	VAP-61 until 1973, VQ- 1 until 1975. Stored at DMAFB until 1981. Reactivated to flight status early 1981 and converted to ERA-3B for FEWSG support.
142256	NRA-3B	Westinghouse		N256HA	None	Basic	PMTC and Patuxent River testbed transferred to Westinghouse in 1971. Last used as S-3 avionics testbed until 1993.

Magyar Honvédseg Repülo Csapatai MiG-29s
Hungarian missile trials in Poland

In the autumn of 1993, 28 MiG-29B and UB aircraft arrived at Kecskemet air base to re-equip a full fighter wing, a development unprecedented in Hungary's small air arm. The 'Puma' and 'Dongo' squadrons of the 59 HRE 'Vitez Szentgyorgyi Dezso' (Tactical Fighter Regiment) had previously flown the MiG-21bis. The exceptional performance characteristics and advanced weapon system of the MiG-29 set new horizons for air combat tactics. It became obvious that its advanced weapons system should be tested under live conditions as soon as possible.

Hungary's small size and dense population precluded trials at home. Common practice in the 1970s was to use either the desert range near Astrahany in the former Soviet Union, or to temporarily occupy the skies over the Baltic Sea in Poland. Soviet ranges provided realistic firing training conditions, but the unpredictable situation following the collapse of the Soviet Union – and the gargantuan increase in charges – have led to the loss of this valuable training facility. Poland remained accessible, and thus an agreement was struck to allow Hungarian MiG-29s to use Polish firing ranges in 1996. All recognised that facilities would not be ideal – it was generally accepted that shooting at a flare while it is descending on a parachute gives little more than the experience of

An armed 'Dongo' squadron MiG-29 'Fulcrum-A' departs Minsk Mazowiecki, home to the Polish air force's premier fighter unit, 1 PLM.

the 'sound and feel' of a missile leaving the launch ship.

The standard air-to-air load-out of Hungarian MiG-29s consists of two R-27R (AA-10 'Alamo') and four R-73 (AA-11 'Archer') missiles. Although they are wired to carry the R-60MK (AA-8 'Aphid') 'pocket' dogfight missile, neither it nor its launcher was purchased with the aircraft. However, old R-60s were selected for trials because the SARH R-27R was not suitable against the intended target, and the R-73 is much more expensive than the R-60. The latter were readily available as standard armament of the MiG-21bis and Su-22M-3 aircraft in service, and many of these missiles were then close to the end of their operational life.

Right: A total of eight MiG-29A/UBs from the Hungarian air force's 59 HRE (Harcaszati Repülo Ezred/Tactical Fighter Regiment) deployed to Poland for the type's first live missile trials in 1996.

Originally it appeared that younger pilots would be selected for the trials in order for them to gain experience, but in the end it was the seasoned pilots who took off. Their knowledge ensured that they could concentrate on the evaluation of the weapons system and could judge its usefulness.

Airlift was provided by the Szolnok-based Mixed Air Transport Brigade (89 VSD). The first An-26 carrying missiles and officers

co-ordinating the deployment departed for Minsk-Mazowiecki on 11 May 1996. This air base near the Polish capital is the home of the 1st 'Warszawa' Fighter Regiment flying MiG-29s, and provided all the equipment necessary to operate the type. The next days found the An-26s busy carrying ground crew, air controllers and equipment. The Hungarian MiGs (six MiG-29As and two MiG-29UBs) arrived on Monday morning.

Some firings were made from two-seat MiG-29UBs (top). In the view above the live R-60 (AA-8) can be seen in the backseater's rear-view mirror, just prior to launch (right).

Careful selection of pilots and detailed planning of deployment was followed by training sorties against an Mi-8 helicopter cruising at 3800 m (12,465 ft). The MiG-29s carried practice R-73 missiles, so-called 'imitators' that comprise a seeker head and data recorder. They locked on each and every time, even though the helicopter was a less than ideal target.

Sparkling sunshine greeted the airmen at Minsk-Mazowiecki the next morning. However, their Su-22M-4 'target' (carrying eight flares) was grounded due to thick fog at Taszar, their home base. A weather reconnaissance Polish MiG-29UB, with mixed crew from the two nations, confirmed the situation. The fog cleared at noon, though, and the 'Fitter' was able to depart. Hungarian pilots, being already kitted out, had only to put on the unaccustomed survival vests, inspect their aircraft and climb into the cockpits. With five-minute separations, flight leads and wingmen took off at military power, turned right and headed north, trailing characteristic black smoke. The approach to the target area took 27 minutes at 8800 m (28,870 ft) flying at 900 km/h (560 mph). The clear weather offered exceptional visibility and the Baltic coast was visible, at altitude, from 120 km (75 miles). At 40 km (25 miles) from the target area they checked the pre-briefed identification points. The Su-22 dropped one flare for each flight. A few seconds after release the flares' parachutes deployed and the device ignited. The approaching MiG pilots acquired them visually and made heading corrections. Exact distance data was regularly given by ground air controllers. Thumbing the *Glavnij* (main) switch, the pilots activated the MiG-29s' weapon systems, designated the target using one of the four aiming modes, launched the missiles and, because of the high closure rate, immediately disengaged. Gentle turns gave them an opportunity to observe the results. The two waves of four-four flights hit all eight flares.

Target acquisition elements of the MiG-29's fire control unit are the RP-29 pulse-Doppler radar and the OEPS-29 electro-optical system, complemented by a helmet-mounted target designator. The radar was dropped from the trial. The OEPS-29 suite consists of an IRST sensor and a laser rangefinder. The helmet-mounted sight can designate off-boresight targets in air combat, and in the rapid selection of targets flying in close formation. The IR-homing missiles are able to lock on independently without aid from the IRST, but when aided by the above system the process becomes selective and much faster. During the Polish firings trials, four acquisition modes were tested.

TP (IRST): In this primary mode of the OEPS-29, visual target acquisition is not necessary. The IRST system detects the targets, which are displayed as plots simultaneously on the HUD and CRT screens. The pilot designates one to track, and the laser rangefinder measures its distance. The IR-homing missiles lock on to the selected target automatically.

TP-BB (IRST close air combat): During close-in engagements the pilot manoeuvres so that the target is kept in a zone displayed on the HUD. Then, by pushing a button on the throttle, he initialises the process explained above.

Optika (optic): Following visual acquisition, the pilot directs the missile heads by moving the designator circle projected onto the HUD over the selected target by a small joystick on the control stick. The missiles will lock on the target in the designated area. If the electro-optical sight and the radar are on, they also try to engage the target, but this is not necessary for a successful launch.

Shlem (helmet-mounted sight): The pilot designates the target using the sight mounted on his helmet. The missile seeker heads, the electro-optical system and the radar follow the movement of the pilot's head and turn in the appropriate direction. The missile can be fired when the seeker locks on, however, exact launch parameters (e.g., target distance) will be available only if the radar or electro-optical sight is tracking the target.

In case the radar, the electro-optical system and helmet-mounted sight should fail or be confused by defensive measures, the pilot is still able to launch IR-homing missiles successfully. This mode is called Setka (mesh – refers to the crosshair). A simple crosshair is projected onto the HUD. It requires only one functioning 'bulb' in the HUD. The pilot uses this rudimentary sight to aim. The lock-on of the missile head is signalled acoustically, but the target distance is estimated visually. **Zoltán Németh, Zoltán Buza**

Although all of Hungary's MiG-29s wear a regiment (wing) badge on their fins, the squadrons maintain distinct identities. 1 HRS (Harcaszati Repûlo Széazad/ Tactical Fighter Squadron) is 'Puma' squadron, and 2 HRS is 'Dongo' (wasp) squadron.

White 'hunchbacks'
Ukrainian Mi-24s with the UN

Since March 1996 Ukrainian army aviation helicopters have been playing an instrumental part in the UN mission to keep the peace in the Eastern Slavonia region of Croatia. When tension has been high, the presence of Ukrainian gunships has calmed the situation. In May 1996 overflights by the heavily armed Mi-24s forced Serb para-militaries, allied to the notorious Serbian warlord Arkan, to flee the UN-administered region.

The United Nations Transitional Administration in Eastern Slavonia (UNTAES) was established in January 1996 and given the two-year mission of peacefully returning the region to Croatian rule. It had been seized by the Serbs in the 1991 war. Some 5,000 'Blue Helmets' from Belgium, Russia, Pakistan and Jordan, under the command of a Belgian major general, have overseen the demobilisation of 12,000 Serb soldiers and the removal of several hundred tanks, artillery pieces and other heavy weapons back across the Danube to the Federal Republic of Yugoslavia.

"The UN has learned that peacekeeping with a smiling face doesn't work in a war zone," said a senior UNTAES commander. UNTAES deployed with tanks, artillery and armoured vehicles, and was backed by the Ukrainian assault helicopters. The Serbs took notice of the UN's heavy firepower and quickly complied with the orders of the peacekeeping force.

Right and below: Ukraine has deployed the highly specialised 'Hind-G2' alongside its dedicated gunship Mi-24Ps in Croatia. The Mi-24K 'G2' can be equipped with a massive 1300-mm camera system, intended for artillery spotting and target reconnaissance. The camera is aimed through the extra window in the starboard cabin.

Far right: All of the Mi-8M 'Hip-Hs' have additional cockpit armour and full defensive countermeasures.

Based at Klisa airport, 15 km (9.3 miles) north of of Vukovar, is the 17th Ukrainian Helicopter Squadron, with six Mi-24s supported by six Mi-8MTs. The Mi-24 force comprises four 30-mm cannon-armed Mi-24P 'Hind-Fs' and two Mi-24K 'Hind-G2s'. Just under 250 army aviation personnel are assigned to the squadron, serving six-month tours in Croatia. Personnel are drawn from a number of bases throughout the Ukraine to form the UN contingent, but the bulk of the aircrews come from bases near Lvov, in western Ukraine, and Kerch, in the Crimea.

"We send only the best pilots and engineers here," said squadron commander Colonel Vladimir Pastukhov. Like most of his 30 pilots, the colonel learned his trade in the former Soviet army and spent eight months flying combat missions in Afghanistan. He has been flying the Mi-24 for 19 years but is also qualified on the Mi-8.

The UNTAES Force HQ in Vukovar has a Western command structure and the Ukrainians faced a steep learning curve to fit in with NATO procedures. "This is a new page in my life, 95 per cent of everything here is new,"said Colonel Pastukhov. "The only thing routine is the helicopters."

The flight line at Klisa looks like any other UN or NATO base in the former Yugoslavia, with flight operations being run from a prefabricated base made up of Corimec containers. Inside the offices, Western-manufactured computers and fax machines sit with Soviet-era field telephones. A Ukrainian contingent is also based in the Heli-Cell at Force HQ to co-ordinate daily taskings.

English is the working language of the UNTAES, so a large contingent of translators had to be drafted in from throughout the Ukraine's armed forces to ensure a smooth integration. Some interpreters have even been brought from the Ukrainian navy. Every helicopter flies with an interpreter onboard to facilitate contact with the Belgian tactical air control parties or NATO fighters.

Since the Ukrainians deployed to Klisa in March 1996, they have flown 2,500 hours and carried 7,000 passengers. "The Mi-8s fly cargo, reconnaissance, quick-reaction and medevac/casevac missions," said Colonel Pastukhov. "During the first rotation there were two squadrons – the 17th for attack and the 8th for transport – but now we have combined into one."

Ukrainian airborne operations are run from the base at Klisa, near the battered town of Vukovar, in Croatia.

The Mi-8s undertake regular night training with Belgian special forces troops from the Para-Commando Brigade. Two or three times a week the Mi-24s stage joint close air support exercises with Belgian TACPs, and other exercises with UN troop contingents.

In line with the UNTAES 'no nonsense' policy the Ukrainians have brought a full selection of weaponry with them, including AT-6 'Spiral' ATGMs for the Mi-24s and 80-mm rockets for both types of helicopters. The Mi-8s and Mi-24s regularly fly with full defensive aid suites (L-166V-11E Ispanka IR jammers, ASO-2V chaff/flare dispensers and RWRs).

The Ukrainians' Mi-24s are budgeted by the UN to fly up to 70 hours a month, which represents a major leap in their operational tempo. "Some Ukrainian pilots only fly 25 hours a year back home, so this a big thing for them, a great training opportunity," said a senior Belgian officer.

Tim Ripley

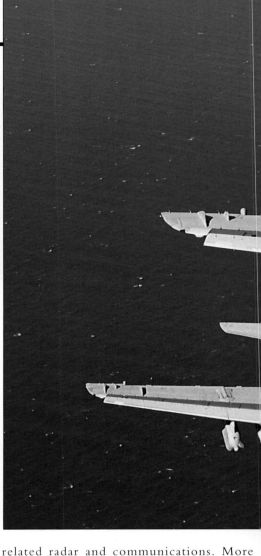

Grumman
EA-6B
Prowler

The EA-6B will soon be the only true SEAD platform available to the US armed forces. As their Air Force counterparts have been retired – the result of a deliberate and controversial policy of 'jointness' – Navy and Marine Prowlers have assumed a unique position as the United States' only combined active/passive anti-SAM and anti-radar aircraft. With the growth of SAM and radar technology, many have argued that US warfighting capabilities in this area should be expanded, not contracted. These voices are met by the perennial question of how to balance ever-shrinking defence budgets while countering the known threat. Against this background it remains to be seen how a uniquely US Navy asset will meet the needs of the US Air Force, and others.

In a figurative way, if not literally, the Prowler is the final product of the 'Grumman Iron Works', the dynasty that created the US Navy's great carrier warplanes for six decades. Located in eastern Long Island, the Naval Industrial Reserve Facility at Calverton (the Grumman Calverton facility or 'Iron Works') served as the final assembly point for the EA-6B. Plants 6 and 7 dominated the landscape. The ¼ mile-long Plant 6 served as the final production line, with Plant 7 serving as the operational hangar facility during flight test and sell-off. Today the great name and traditions of Grumman have been subsumed into the larger Northrop Grumman corporate body and the 'Iron Works' has been shut down – a victim of massive cutbacks in the defence manufacturing base in the US, and worldwide. Grumman no longer builds aircraft, but continues to support its aircraft in US military service while retaining its status as an important aerospace defence contractor.

The story of the A-6 Intruder and EA-6 Prowler has already been told in *World Air Power Journal* Volume 12, but since then important

changes have occurred that have affected the fortunes of both aircraft. The EA-6 has always lived in the shadow of A-6 Intruder, which is rightly seen as one of the best attack aircraft ever built. However, the close of 1996 saw the end of the A-6 Intruder's 31-year combat career with the US Navy. The Intruder was deemed to be too expensive to operate in a Navy forced to cut back its front-line types and one whose deep-strike mission had become less important in a post-Cold War world. So, as 1996 slid into 1997, the last Atlantic and Pacific Fleet A-6 squadrons made their final cruises before retirement. The sense of loss that came with the end of the A-6's career was only heightened by the sight of surplus airframes being poured into the Atlantic Ocean, off the Florida coast, to form an artificial reef.

Yet, as the A-6's star waned the EA-6B's ascended. The same budget stringencies that ended the Intruder's career pushed the EA-6B onto centre stage. Since it entered service in 1971 (as an EKA-3B Skywarrior replacement), the Prowler has jammed and confused SAM-

related radar and communications. More recently it gained the capability to attack and destroy those same emitters with the HARM missile. Now the Prowler is set to become the only US combat aircraft with this capability and the world's premier active/passive SEAD (suppression of enemy air defences) platform.

The Prowler has undergone many changes (the addition of HARM capability a decade ago was just one), but operations in Bosnia marked a number of milestones. For the first time, the Prowler was the sole jamming aircraft in the theatre, and its missions were truly 'joint', an integrated effort by the US armed services such as had been attempted in Desert Storm but not achieved. More than ever, the aircraft will become a showpiece for 'jointness' – operations carried out by different branches of the armed forces working together under a single command. The competition rather than co-operation of US service branches in Vietnam and in the 1980 hostage rescue attempt in Iran prompted Congress to enact the Goldwater-Nichols Law of 1986, which mandates 'jointness' and makes it indispensable to US strategy. The creation of US Navy joint-service 'expeditionary' Prowler squadrons is controversial, however, and many wonder if the Air Force was right to retire its F-4Gs and EF-111As.

During the Gulf War, most SEAD was provided by individual services for their own strike forces. Overall SEAD assets in the Gulf region included 102 Air Force aircraft with dedicated roles (F-4G, EF-111A), and 39 dedicated Navy aircraft (EA-6B), plus 308 ARM-capable Navy and Marine aircraft (A-7E, A-6E, F/A-18). Although Joint Forces Air Commander (JFAC)

Above left: The key to the EA-6B's success as a jamming system – and one of the reasons it survived and the EF-111A did not – is its four-man crew. Having three dedicated ECMOs, plus a pilot, allows a far greater division of duties between the crew than in other comparable aircraft. This 'lessening' of the workload allows everyone to do a better job once in action.

Above: The USMC's Prowler force has now stabilised at four squadrons, all of which were formerly components of a single unit, VMAQ-2. These aircraft are from VMAQ-1 'Banshees', which formed in July 1992.

Right: Combining a USAF mission with a Navy aircraft and operating procedures led to some early problems between the two communities. The Marines sit outside this structure and have always combined sea- and land-based operations.

General Charles Horner's Air Tasking Order orchestrated the complex operations, in practice they were hardly 'joint': most Air Force strikes were covered by Air Force SEAD and all Navy/Marine strikes were covered by Navy/Marine SEAD. The Navy and Marine Corps also provided most of the support for coalition air forces, which had no SEAD capability. Sixty per cent of Desert Storm SEAD sorties were flown by Navy and Marine Corps aircraft.

The Prowler's electronic warfare mission has evolved over the years. To the theatre commander, the EA-6B ranks as a 'high value asset' in both of its jobs. The first of these is electronic support measures (ESM): the gathering of intelligence on SAM sites, radar and C^3 (command, control and communications) locations. The Prowler flies this mission 'buttoned up', with its jammers off, collecting electromagnetic emanations but putting out as few as possible. The intelligence it gathers is often employed by theatre analysts in conjunction with the 'take' by other platforms like the RC-135 Rivet Joint, EP-3 Aries II, and ES-3 Viking. The Prowler's second job is SEAD: the neutralisation, denigra- tion or destruction of radar/missile threats with jamming ('passive' SEAD) and/or HARMs ('lethal' SEAD). SEAD includes the added duty of jamming/denigrating communications.

The EA-6B's electronic warfare (EW) mission is part of what the Pentagon calls

Command & Control Warfare (C^2W), as defined in Joint Chiefs of Staff Memorandum of Policy No. 30, dated 8 March 1993. In this context, the EA-6B is not just a Navy weapon but is the US joint services' primary tool in suppressing and defeating an enemy's air defence network, opening a way for joint operations to interdict far behind battle lines. During a major conflict, the theatre commander and officers at the national command level develop a C^2W plan that encompasses five components – operational security, military deception, psychological operations, electronic warfare, and physical destruction. The goal, as written in the policy document, is to "influence, degrade or destroy adversary C^2 capability while protecting friendly C^2 capabilities." To the EA-6B crew, this means neutralising an enemy's air defences.

EA-6B versus EF-111A

The EA-6B will soon be the only EW aircraft able to jam, deceive, disrupt, and shoot. The US Air Force retired the McDonnell F-4G Advanced Wild Weasel in 1994 and the EF-111A Raven, or 'Spark Vark,' is slated to retire in 1998. The EA-6B and EF-111A use similar capabilities to jam radar signals, since both use variants of the ALQ-99 tactical jamming system (TJS). The Raven, however, has never been modernised and remains equivalent to the ICAP EA-6B of the early 1980s, while today's upgraded ICAP II Block 89 EA-6B has a newer TJS suite and is effective over a greater frequency range, making it more a threat to recent Russian-bloc SAM radars. The EF-111A has never had a communications jamming mission like the Prowler and lacks the USQ-113 communications jammer that gives current Prowlers their capability to foul VHF and UHF communications. Ravens could have been upgraded for the lethal SEAD role with missiles, but they never were, and remain unarmed.

The EF-111A has greater range and is faster, enabling it to keep up more easily with a fast-moving strike package. The US joint services have elected to surrender these advantages in exchange for the EA-6B's ability to operate from carriers, employ HARM missiles and degrade communications. In fact, the EA-6B is fast enough to keep up with most strike packages, particularly en route when acting as 'shooters'. Loaded with ordnance, the F/A-18 and F-16 seldom exceed 520 kt (596 mph; 960 km/h) except in the delivery phase, where the Prowler would not participate (it would be just another target if in that close). Prowlers are faster and accelerate much better than the A-6E Intruder. Range is less, however, since the J52-P408 burns more fuel than the P-6 or P-8 in the A-6.

A joint study completed in 1994 showed that the systems operator in the two-seat EF-111A was overburdened with his dual tasks of navigation and EW; the Navy developed the Prowler as a four-seat aircraft after experience with another two-seater (the EA-6A Intruder) indicated that a larger crew could divide tasks more effectively. Today, Navy doctrine holds that the larger crew doubles the capability to analyse an adversary's radar and radio transmissions and to act against them. The EA-6B frequently flies with a three-person crew since the automation of the system really requires only a pilot and two ECMOs.

Individual air wing tactics and squadron tactical memoranda require the fourth person, and another set of eyeballs can be valuable – but a crimp on manpower may make it reasonable to leave the relatively marginal fourth crew member on the ship planning the next sortie rather than bagging flight time if the operational tempo is high. Still, a three-person crew retains the advantage over the EF-111A.

The US Air Force retains a lethal SEAD capability with its General Dynamics F-16C/D Block 50D Fighting Falcon, equipped with the Texas Instruments AN/ASQ-213 HARM targeting system (HTS). The HTS F-16 is fast enough to escort a strike package and can fire HARMs to suppress radars. HTS raises the 'shooter' aircraft from the ranks of those which fire HARM in only a 'range unknown' mode (F/A-18 Hornet, non-HTS F-16) to those which give the missile at least some bearing information plus range, firing in the 'range known' mode – but the 'bearing' provided by the F-16 is approximate at best.

The HTS F-16 has less reach and accuracy than the Prowler and has no capability to jam or disrupt emissions; its role is also an intensive tasking for a single pilot. To the commander in the combat zone, the HTS F-16 is a part-time EW asset which will escort strike packages when the Prowler cannot, but will also be used as a traditional air-to-ground fighter-bomber much of the time.

Today's EA-6B ICAP II Block 82 or Block 89 Prowler bristles with electronic equipment from

nose to tail. The Prowler carries jamming gear externally and receiving equipment internally. Four wing stations and one centreline station can carry AN/ALQ-99F TJS pods, although fewer are usually employed: a typical configuration is three jammer pods on stations 1, 3, and 5, with external tanks on inboard pylons 2 and 4.

Jamming systems

Two high-powered noise jammers and a tracking receiver are found in each TJS pod, electrical power for which is provided by an external turbine generator on the front, which spins in the slipstream. A forward antenna for self-protection by the deception jamming suite protrudes from the base of the air-refuelling probe in front of the windshield. (The EA-6B's refuelling probe is canted to the right at 12° for better pilot visibility, unlike that of the A-6 Intruder.) A fibreglass-coated fin-cap encloses the principal array of system integration receivers which detect hostile transmissions and relay data to the central computer.

In international use, letters of the alphabet (A through J) are used to define specific radio frequency ranges. EA-6B crews have their own terminology for the wavelengths of the spectrum, however. In American military usage, band numbers 1 through 9 are used to define radio frequency ranges – but the exact definitions remain classified. On the EA-6B, the fin-top receivers cover bands 4-9 while bulged fairings

EA-6B Prowler variants

Prototypes

First flew on 25 May 1968. Five prototypes flight tested, most with partial or no EW suite.

Standard

The initial model, now known as the 'standard'; identified in Grumman documents as **BASCAP (BASic CAPability)**. First production delivery July 1971. Twenty-three aircraft built.

EXCAP (EXpanded CAPability)

Version for the late 1970s. Twenty-five aircraft upgraded to this standard. Standard and EXCAP had jammers operated by ECMO-1 and -2 on the right side while ECMO-3 ran ALQ-92 communications jammer.

ICAP (Improved CAPability)

Retroactively called **ICAP I** (or **ICAP-1**). Multi-band exciter (MBE). Forty-three aircraft upgraded to this standard. ICAP put all TJS controls in back with ECMO-2 and -3, freeing ECMO-1 for navigation only.

ICAP II (or ICAP-2)

Retroactively named **ICAP II Block 82**. Provided additional jamming capabilities. First flight 24 June 1980. All surviving aircraft upgraded. First production aircraft delivered 3 January 1984. ICAP II introduced a new generic pod with a universal exciter (replacing MBE) which covered frequency bands 1 through 9, allowed mixing of transmitter bands within a pod, and provided new modes of operation and software control modulations. The new system was designated AN/ALQ-99F. Each pod is capable of jamming in two frequency bands simultaneously. Since the 1980s, the 'base' on which Prowler improvements were contemplated. Introduced advanced AN/AYK-14(V) Standard Navy Airborne Computer, known to Prowler crews as the 'Yuck 14'. ICAP II employs the AN/ASN-130 navigation system and the AN/ASN-123 tactical display. ICAP II aircraft can be linked together via TACAN datalinks enabling EA-6Bs to work together in a co-operative effort against an adversary. Introduced Carrier Airborne Inertial Navigation System (CAINS). Subvariants of ICAP II include **Block 82** (70 aircraft), **Block 86** (14 plus 56 aircraft, no longer in service), and **Block 89** (43 aircraft).

ICAP II Block 82

Retroactive name of surviving ICAP II aircraft. Recognition feature: vertical VHF UHF antennas. No antenna under chin. Two verticals on turtleback. The version used by all USMC squadrons. Introduced AGM-88A/C. First HARM-capable aircraft delivered 21 January 1986. Seventy aircraft, including 15 former EXCAP aircraft.

ADVCAP (ADVanced CAPability)

Also called **Block 91**. Three prototypes tested. Would have introduced Receiver Processor Group (RPG) for the TJS, dual AYK-14, XN-8 VHSIC computers, a communications countermeasure system AN/ALQ-149, third ECMO suite in right front seat, AN/ARN-118 TACAN, two additional external AN/ALE-41 chaff dispensers or two internal ALE-39 chaff and flare boxes, GPS, and disc-based onboard loader/recorder. Activation of two additional pylon stations outboard the wing folds. J52-P-409 turbojets. Vehicle enhancements for improved aerodynamics inclusive of the development of a Navy Standard Automatic Flight Control System (SAFCS). A subvariant identical to ADVCAP but without newer jamming sub-system was approved for export.

ICAP II Block 86

First EA-6B given the 'Block' title, determined by the fiscal year it was ordered (incorrect use of 1 October 1962 joint services designation system). Compared to predecessor ICAP II (retroactively called Block 82), Block 86 – in use until January 1997 – has new radios (ARC-182 VHF/UHF, KY-58, ARC-199 HF/KY-75), enhanced signal processing (CIU/E), integration of the ALQ-126 of the self-protection system B variant and a digital fuel quantity system. Other front cockpit improvements. ALQ-99 receiver system slightly modified with 'parallel encoders' to increase signal processing capability. Fourteen upgraded aircraft. Fifty-six new airframes were delivered to Block 86 standard. All survivors upgraded to Block 89 by 1997.

ICAP II Block 89

Recognition feature: one swept-back antenna on chin and two or three on turtleback. Main changes: 'safety of flight' items, such as halon fire extinguishers for the engine bays and fire-hardened control rods and cables. One aircraft new-built to this standard (BuNo. 164403, 170th and last EA-6B built) delivered to NATC Patuxent River, Maryland in September 1991. Forty-three aircraft were modified to Block 89 standard.

ICAP II Block 89A

Probably to be funded in FY 1998 (beginning 1 October 1997). Minor changes, principally an electronic flight instrumentation system (EFIS). Improved cockpit instrumentation; Litton embedded GPS/INS missionised integration. First two airframes identified for conversion to Block 89A are a 'validation' (val) aircraft and a 'verification' (ver) aircraft, with the pair becoming 'valver' aircraft. Modifications will be done by NADEP Jacksonville, Florida with deliveries starting in 1998. The two valver airframes (P-4, BuNo. 156481, a Block 82; and P-62, BuNo. 160434, a Block 89) currently at Northrop Grumman. Contract for installation of GPS on these two aircraft issued September 1995.

ICAP III

Notional future version.

SPECIFICATION

Grumman EA-6B Prowler

Type: four-seat tactical jammer and electronic warfare aircraft
Powerplant: two Pratt & Whitney J52-P-408/408A turbojet engines each rated at 11,200 lb (49.82 kN) thrust
Performance: never-exceed speed 710 kt (815 mph; 1311 km/h); maximum speed 541 kt (621 mph; 999 km/h); cruising speed 418 kt (480 mph; 772 km/h); service ceiling 37,600 ft (11460 m); ferry range (with five drop tanks) 1,747 nm (2,009 miles; 3233 km); approach speed 122 kt (140 mph; 225 km/h); minimum landing speed 122 kt 140 mph; 225 km/h); minimum landing distance 2,185 ft (665 m)
Weights: empty 32,574 lb (14775 kg); internal fuel 15,574 lb (7064 kg); external fuel 10,025 lb (4547 kg); ferry configuration 60,045 lb (27235 kg); maximum take-off gross weight 61,043 lb (27688 kg); maximum 'bringback weight' (carrier landing) 45,500 lb (20638 kg)
Dimensions: span 53 ft 0 in (16.15 m); span (folded) 25 ft 10 in (7.87 m); aspect ratio 5.31; length 59 ft 10 in (18.24 m); wheel base 17 ft 2 in (5.23 m); height 16 ft 3 in (4.95 m); wing area 528.90 sq m (49.13 m²)

---

on the side of the fin cover bands 1-3. On the trailing edge of the fin-top 'football' is the 'beercan' fairing for the aft-facing ALQ-126 DECM system. The Prowler's search and navigation radar is the Norden APS-130, a downgraded version of the Grumman A-6E Intruder's APQ-156, with attack functions deleted. The radar provides accurate ground mapping. The APS-130, which is considered almost unbreakable, replaced the original APQ-129, which provided a better picture but was plagued by serious 'down' rates.

AN/ALQ-99

Early Prowlers, including those of the Vietnam era, faced significant limits because each AN/ALQ-99 pod had to be dedicated to a predetermined band. Thus, there were low band (1-2) pods, band 7 pods, and so on. This made life difficult for maintainers and meant that, once launched on a mission, a Prowler could be employed only against SAM missile radars on predetermined wavelengths, and was useless against an unanticipated threat. Early Prowlers were unarmed, although missile armament was always a conceptual feature on the aircraft.

The ALQ-99F jamming system is made up of the receivers, central processing computer, and up to five (normally three) pods. They can operate in full auto (detection and automatic assignment of jamming power) and manual (ECM operators manually search the spectrum and assign jamming) modes.

The wing of the Prowler, with its four carrying stations (the total becomes five when a centreline station is counted), looks identical to that of the A-6 Intruder and has similar dimensions, but has a different internal structure. The keel centre-section area was designed as a renewable resource rather than a permanent fit. Changing out a wing centre-section requires so little effort that it can be done in just hours at the depot level. The Prowler wing spans the same 53 ft (16.15 m) as the Intruder, but its internal structure is quite different. These differences are intended to make the wings sturdier than those of the Intruder because of the 'bringback weight' of external pods carried by the Prowler. The Navy operations manual, NATOPS, allows a Prowler 'bringback weight' of 45,500 lb (20640 kg), or some 9,500 lb (4310 kg) heavier than that allowed for the Intruder.

The EA-6B is powered by two Pratt & Whitney J52-P-408 or -408A turbojet engines rated at 11,200 lb (49.82 kN) thrust at take-off and 9,300 lb (41.37 kN) thrust in normal flight. The original EA-6B powerplant was the A-6A's J52-P-8 engine, modified to P-408 standard beginning in 1973 with the addition of variable inlet guide vanes, allowing an increase in thrust.

The Prowler can carry up to four ALE-41 external, pod-mounted chaff dispensers. They are widely disliked, assumed to conflict with EW functions, and rarely used.

The 170 Prowlers manufactured at Calverton have been repeatedly improved with upgrades to existing aircraft and manufacture of new variants. All but two variants have been retired, those in service today being ICAP II Block 82 and ICAP II Block 89 Prowlers.

The Prowler's fuselage is borrowed from the A-6 Intruder and lengthened by 54 in (137 cm) to accommodate four crew positions. Crew

Above: VMAQ-3 'Moondogs' now uses an 'MD' tailcode (reflecting the squadron name) instead of the original 'AB' codes seen here.

Right: All of the aircraft in this quartet of EA-6Bs carry an identical load-out of two fuel tanks, a single ALQ-99F jamming pod and HARM missile. This is clearly a training load-out. Any operational mission would be flown with at least two pods, and three would be the norm – particularly if tanker support was available.

consists of one pilot (front left seat) who is a naval aviator and is always in charge of flying the aircraft (although any crew member may be a mission commander), and three electronic countermeasures officers located as ECMO 1 (front right), ECMO 2 (rear right) and ECMO 3 (rear left). The crew sits in pairs beneath two separate clamshell canopies which are pneumatically actuated and open to 35°. All four occupy roomy cockpits and are strapped into Martin-Baker GRUEA-7 zero-zero ejection seats. The two officers in the rear seats face an instrument panel that rises well above head level: they have visibility to the side but not forward.

Prowler crew roles

ECMO 1 is the navigator and handles communication. He can hear what the back-seaters do but has no oscilloscope to follow the action, and usually provides an extra set of eyes for the pilot, not just outside the aircraft but in performing instrument scans. Obviously, communication is vital to the success of a combat sortie or a military campaign. Typically, ECMO 1 monitors two communications nets. 'Net 1' consists of AWACS (Airborne Warning and Communications System) aircraft, escort fighters, and any other friendly assets committed to the air-to-air situation. 'Net 2', or the EWC&R (electronic warfare communications and reporting) net, comprises the EC-130 command, other EW aircraft, Joint Stars, and (in the Bosnian example) CAOC – NATO's Combined Air Operations Center, at Vincenza, in Italy. ECMO 1 is thus kept very busy flying, navigating, and communicating; although not otherwise part of the SEAD mission, he has a key role in the employment of HARM.

ECMO 2 and 3 are the warfighters who detect a signal and designate a potential target. ECMO 1, who has the HARM control panel, sends the target 'packet' to the missile; this provides the pilot with steering cues (vertical and horizontal needles) on his attitude reference gyro, which is otherwise used during carrier landings. When the aircraft is in the launch window the pilot gets a cue that he can shoot, and pulls a trigger located on his stick handle.

The naval flight officers (NFOs) who fill the ECMO jobs rotate from one seat to another. The squadron scheduling officer is likely to arrange a rotation in which an ECMO returns to the same seat every third flight. This is considered a drawback for new ECMOs who spend every third flight as ECMO 1, where they acquire relatively little useful experience.

Introduction of HARM as an operational Prowler weapon in 1986 was the biggest single

VX-9 was established in 1994, as the USN's sole test and evaluation unit, combining the former VX-4 and VX-5. This 'Evaluators' Prowler is seen arriving at its Point Mugu home, demonstrating the efficacy of the EA-6B's tail skid.

Left: **Eve of Destruction** *is a Desert Storm veteran serving with VAQ-141. The Prowler can carry 30-round AN/ALE-29A or AN/ALE-39 chaff/flare dispensers in the aft extendible (avionics) equipment platform, or 'birdcage'. The AN/ALE-39 differs from its forebear by having the capability to also deploy expendable active countermeasures (jammers).*

Right: VAQ-133 'Wizards' inherited the mantle of an earlier Navy unit of the same name, when it was re-established as the first joint expeditionary EW unit in April 1996.

Below: The EA-6B and F-14 are the last survivors of Grumman's great naval combat aircraft dynasty. Both have had to adopt new roles in order to survive in a world of ever-shrinking budgets.

change in the history of the EA-6B, transforming it from a passive weapon like the EF-111A into a 'shooter'. The current HARM version is the Block IV model of the TI (Texas Instruments) AGM-88C1 HARM, replacing the Block I and II versions employed during Operation Desert Storm. In the early 1990s, the US Navy explored a second source competition anticipating an AGM-88C2 low-cost HARM seeker built by Loral Ford (at the time) which would have been in magazines along with TI-built missiles. The proposed C2 passed all tests, but never went into production. TI kept lowering the cost so the issue became moot. In the world of HARM, block numbers designate hardware, software and CLC changes (the missile's serial for proper configuration management).

HARM engagement

HARM employs a broadband anti-radar homing seeker and a computer-controlled seeker and autopilot. The 13-ft 8-in (4.17-m) missile weighs 800 lb (360 kg), reaches Mach 2.0 and employs its passive radiation homing capability to deliver a fragmentation warhead to targets up to 50 miles (80 km) away.

The three modes of the HARM, Block II/IV are Pre-Briefed (PB), Range-Unknown (RU), and Range-Known (RK), the last being the most accurate. The modes give different ranges, flight profiles, time of flight, acquisition angles, and target specificity.

HARM can be carried on four of the Prowler's five attachment points: the centreline point is not used because of potential damage to the fuselage in a launch. Published reports of a dual HARM launcher enabling two missiles to be hung from a single point are in error.

Since ECMO 1 has the master arm switch as part of the HCP (HARM control panel) at his right knee and the pilot has the trigger on his stick, the HARM is, as one crewman describes it, "fired by a committee." Any one of the three ECMOs can designate the missile, assign the target, feed data, and tell the HARM what targets to pursue. In a well-orchestrated attack, the backseaters locate and designate the target, ECMO 1 throws the master arm switch (making the pilot's trigger 'hot') when prompted on the intercom, and the pilot shoots. The missile launch involves a tremendous amount of noise and smoke, readily obvious to all crew members.

HARM is regarded as a success story, a military system that arrived on time and worked right. Every shooter in a carrier air wing uses the same Block IV AGM-88C1 version (only training rounds retain the earlier AGM-88A designation), although interfaces and operations methods for each aircraft are different. The F/A-18 (and previously the A-7 and A-6) use the weapon as a sensor and process the data through a pre-programmed command launch computer (which is reconfigurable if new threats emerge), which programmes the HARM for a specific set of threats and particular flight profile. The EA-6B, however, uses its ALQ-99 system as the sensor, and then programmes the HARM for post-launch performance much like the F-4G did (first with the APR-38 and later APR-47 systems). By developing the system for both types of capability in order to be compatible with the Air Force Weasels, the Navy has a much more flexible system which adapted well to the EA-6B's capabilities.

The Prowler has an excellent safety record (0.5 mishaps per 100,000 flying hours), but for all its capabilities remains a challenge to technicians and maintainers. A mechanic claims the Prowler is known below decks as 'The Bridge Club' (a reference to its four-member crew) and remarks that keeping the EA-6B in operation involves "all the headaches of keeping all these systems working properly, a David and Goliath kind of task. There are also the weekly, monthly, etc. inspections where we have to take off a bunch of panels to look for stress cracks and corrosion." Taking a bath is also a challenge: "Washing this beast is a definite task to be reckoned with."

SEAD mission

First deployment with HARM by the EA-6B was made by squadron VAQ-140 'Patriots' aboard USS *John F. Kennedy* (CV-67) in 1988. The carrier had the 'all-Grumman air wing' tried by the Navy for a time, equipped with F-14 Tomcats and A-6 Intruders but only an *ad hoc* detachment of the Vought A-7E Corsairs which

The Prowler's adoption of HARM (from the 13th production ICAP II aircraft, and then retrospectively) transformed the aircraft into a truly versatile combat aircraft. Early fears that the missile's own autonomous seeker might be jammed by ALQ-99 proved groundless.

were then the service's only other HARM shooters. The Prowler detachment thus provided a capability not found elsewhere on the ship.

HARM in combat

The Prowler first used HARM missiles in combat during Operation Desert Storm. There, mission planners equipped the Prowler for SEAD combat mission by making typical trade-offs: all five hardpoints can accommodate ALQ-99 pods or fuel, while four of the five can be used for HARMs. Thus, the EA-6B could carry five ECM pods for an exceedingly short-range sortie against a complex air defence threat. Typically, the EA-6B Prowler is loaded with three ALQ-99F pods and two external tanks of fuel. Much depends on circumstance. For example, during the Gulf War, carrier aircraft operating from the Red Sea had easy access to plenty of Air Force tankers for frequent

refuellings, so carried two HARMs, three ECM pods, and no external fuel. In contrast, Prowler crews flying from the Persian Gulf had less access to aerial refuelling, so carried three pods, one drop tank, and one HARM. In current operations, mission planning is driven almost exclusively by the availability of tankers for the strike force and its accompanying Prowlers; with its dedicated KA-6D Intruder tankers now retired, the Navy is more dependent than ever on the S-3B Viking with its buddy store (the

Viking remains capable of flying its primary ASW mission while serving as a tanker) and Air Force refuellers.

Inter-service differences over SEAD were never more evident than in Desert Storm. As one naval aviator describes it, "The USAF planned to employ HARM to clear specific targets in specific corridors to and from targets. The Navy figured you should kill whatever threat is emitting (although, in fact, Navy SEAD was passive until HARM came along). The

Inside the Prowler

The pilot's cockpit in today's EA-6B is dominated by the APS-130 screen. Above it are the primary flight instruments. Canopy jettison and hook controls are above and to the right. To the left of the radar are the engine RPM/TGT, oil and hydraulic indicators. Radar controls, emergency switches and throttles are on the left console. Radio, wingfold, and auxiliary controls are on the centre panel.

ECMO 1 also has an APS-130 display. Above it is the ALQ-92 display (removed). To the left of these screens (in a vertical stack) are the station select (jettison), nav/TACAN and ECM dispenser controls. ALQ-92 frequency controls and the chaff programmer are located to the right of the main panel. ALE-41 controls, radio/ICS switches, KY-28 and interior light switches are all on the side console.

The ECMO 3 station (behind the pilot) has environmental and radio/ICS controls on the left (side) console. Above them are the bearing/distance/heading controls and indicator panels plus TJS receiver controls for the ALQ-99F system. The main instrument panel has the large digital display indicator (DDI) screen at its centre, with signal activity lights above, video display and DDI controls below.

ECMO 2/3 stations are largely identical. Both share a central instrument panel containing a UHF frequency/channel indicator, Mach /airspeed indicator, cabin pressure indicator, altimeter, eject warning light, canopy controls, TJS master controls and access to the onboard computer. Below these, on the central console, are TJS pod power and digital recorder controls.

EA-6B Prowler units

VAQ-128

Likely to be named 'Golden Prowlers'. A squadron with this designation (carrying on the traditions of A-6 Intruder Fleet Replenishment Squadron VA-128 'Golden Intruders') is expected to become the fourth Prowler expeditionary squadron in 1997.

VAQ-129 'Vikings' or 'New Vikings'

Callsign EAGLE. Began as VAH-10 operating the A-3, and was established 1 May 1970. Created by the redesignation of VAH-10, also the 'Vikings', which had three EKA-3B detachments at the time of the designation change. Acquired current designation on 1 September 1970. Began operating A-6As in 1970, and EA-6Bs in 1972. Acted as the FRS for the EA-6B type. In continuous existence as a Prowler unit.

VAQ-130 'Zappers'

Callsign ZAPPER, formerly ROBINSON. Established as VW-13 on 1 September 1959, operating the Martin P4M-1Q Mercator. Redesignated as VAQ-130 on 1 October 1968 to become the first EA-6B operator. Operated EKA-3B until 1970. During Desert Storm, was commended for its operations against Iraqi targets. Currently operates EA-6B ICAP II Block 89, authorised strength of five. Saw combat in Bosnia.

VAQ-131 'Lancers'

Callsign SKYBOLT. Established and called to active duty as VP-931 on 3 September 1950; redesignated as VP-57 on 4 February 1953; became VAH-4 on 3 July 1956 and VAQ-131 on 1 November 1968. Had combat experience in Vietnam, Grenada, Lebanon, and Desert Storm.

VAQ-132 'Scorpions'

Callsign SWAMP FOX. Began life as VAH-2 on 1 November 1955, equipped with EA-3. Picked up current designation on 1 November 1968. Was the first EA-6B squadron to deploy, in 1972. The squadron saw combat in Vietnam and Desert Storm.

VAQ-133 'Wizards'

Callsign MAGIC. Established on 1 April 1996 as one of the new Prowler expeditionary squadrons to support USAF electronic combat needs. Retains nickname and traditions of an earlier Navy squadron with same designation, disestablished in 1992. Neither squadron bearing this designation has been in combat. VAQ-133's authorised strength is five EA-6B ICAP II Block 82 aircraft, although six side numbers are set aside for its use (630-635). When it began operations, the squadron had three aircraft. Deployed to Iwakuni, Japan in January 1997.

VAQ-134 'Garudas'

Callsign GARUDA. Established 17 June 1969. In continuous existence. Expeditionary squadron. Retained 'NL' tailcode now used as expeditionary tailcode for 'Prowlers' (formerly CVW-15 on Vinson). Saw action during US withdrawal from Vietnam, 1975.

VAQ-135 'Ravens' or 'Black Ravens'

Callsign BLACK RAVEN. Established 15 May 1969. In continuous existence as a Prowler squadron. Saw action in Operations El Dorado Canyon against Libya (1986) and Praying Mantis against Iran (1988). Made two HARM shots in Iraq after Desert Storm.

VAQ-136 'Gauntlets'

Callsign IRONCLAW. This was the first Prowler squadron which had not previously flown the 'Whale' (Douglas EKA-3 Skywarrior). Participated in Operation Desert Storm. Overseas since 1980 in Japan. Home-ported with CVW-5 at Yokosuka, Japan.

VAQ-137 'Rooks'

Callsign ROOK. Was re-established for Navy operations in the 1990s. The earlier squadron with the same name and designation saw action in Lebanon, against Libya (Prairie Fire), and Desert Storm.

VAQ-138 'Yellowjackets'

Callsign RAMPAGE. Established on 27 February 1976, and in continuous existence since then, but has not seen combat.

VAQ-139 'Cougars'

Callsign GHOSTWALKER. Established 1 July 1983. Deployed during Operation Desert Shield, but has not seen combat.

VAQ-140 'Patriots'

Callsign STINGER. Established 1 October 1985. In continuous existence as a Prowler squadron. Deployed during Operation Desert Shield, but has not seen combat.

VAQ-141 'Shadowhawks'

Callsign DESPERADO. Covered rescue of USAF pilot Scott O'Grady in Bosnia 8 June 1995. In 1996, shore-based at Aviano. Recently deployed with CVW-8 ('AJ' tailcode) on USS John F. Kennedy (CV-67). Saw action in Desert Storm and Deliberate Force (Bosnia).

VAQ-142 'Grim Watchdogs'

Callsign WHISKEY, but likely to be changed. Was a short-lived Prowler squadron that made one cruise before evolving into VAQ-35. Designated as the third expeditionary squadron, the 'Grim Watchdogs' stood up on 4 April 1997.

VAQ-209 'Star Warriors'

Naval Air Reserve squadron, established 1 October 1977, at NAF Washington (Andrews AFB, Maryland). The squadron's insignia is a likeness of Star Wars' Darth Vader. Deployed to Bosnia during 1995.

VMAQ-1 'Banshees' or 'Screaming Banshees'

Callsign BANSHEE; 'CB' tailcode. Saw action in Bosnia.

VMAQ-2 'Panthers'

Ex-'Playboys', callsign EASY. Participated in El Dorado Canyon (1986). Fought in Desert Storm (1991). Dropped former nickname 'Playboys' after members alleged to be in Tailhook scandal (1991). 'Panther' nickname honours North Carolina football team.

VMAQ-3 'Moondogs'

Callsign DOG, 'AB' tailcode, changed to 'MD'. Participated in combat in Bosnia.

VMAQ-4 'Seahawks'

Callsign HAWK, 'RM' tailcode. Established Whidbey, activated in 1991 during Desert Storm and transitioned to Prowlers. Moved to Cherry Point as a regular Marine unit in September 1992.

VX-5 'Vampires'

'XE' tailcode. Established 18 June 1957, was a key US Navy operational test and evaluation squadron, located at NWTC China Lake, California. Its mission was to test and evaluate Navy weapons and weapons systems. The squadron flew most Navy aircraft including the EA-6B. VX-4 at Point Mugu and VX-5 at China Lake, both in California, were disestablished on 29 April 1994 and merged the following day into VX-9, headquartered at China Lake.

VX-9 'Evaluators'

Established on 30 April 1994 at Point Mugu from the former VX-5, combined with VX-4. The squadron had at least one EA-6B Prowler on charge until 1995.

No Prowler has ever been lost in combat, but over the type's career 40 EA-6Bs have been claimed in mishaps, or 17 per cent of those built. Thirty-nine men have died in Prowler accidents, not including 14 flight-deck crew on USS Nimitz (CVN-68) who were killed on 26 May 1981 when a VMAQ-2 aircraft crashed on landing in the worst carrier accident since the Vietnam War. Although the Prowler is not a difficult aircraft to fly, most have been lost due to crew error, with fires leading the cause of mechanical failures (with the result that 'safety of flight' features are emphasised in the near-future Block 89A). Five of those losses were due to carrier launch/landing failures (soft 'cat shots' or arresting gear failures) and had nothing to do with the aircraft or crew. The most recent tragedy was the 23 August 1996 loss of a Block 82 aircraft (BuNo. 160435) belonging to VMAQ-1 at the Barry M. Goldwater training range 40 miles (65 km) east of Yuma, Arizona, which killed all four aboard, including the squadron's commander and executive officer (both ECMOs).

VAQ-209's aircraft proudly wear a badge depicting Star Wars' Darth Vader, the Empire's Dark Lord of the Sith and leading practitioner of the dark side of the Force. A Navy Reserve unit based at NAF Washington, DC (Andrews AFB), VAQ-209 holds the distinction of landing the first Prowler on the Navy's newest carrier, the USS John C. Stennis (CVN 74), during 1996.

Desert Storm experience showed that both tactics have their place, and the genius was having both capabilities inherent in the HARM design." Experts killed plans in the early 1980s for different variants of the HARM missiles tailored to Navy tactics and Air Force tactics.

During Desert Storm, in addition to employing EA-6Bs, the Navy dedicated a number of sorties each day to SEAD as the primary mission using A-7, F/A-18 and A-6 aircraft typically loaded with two HARMs in addition to other ordnance (Rockeye, AIM-9, AIM-7 and 20-mm). A-7s in particular proved to be valuable HARM shooters for long-range strikes near Baghdad for which other aircraft carried strike ordnance. Once the SEAD portion of the mission was completed, or if other missions emerged as priorities, the assets could be used in other ways (for rescue combat air patrol, armed reconnaissance or CAS).

With retirement of the F-4G Advanced Wild Weasel, the USAF developed the F-16 HTS pylon mounted in the HARM launcher. This was necessary because the F-16 did not have room for a command launch computer to support the onboard processing that was done in A-7, A-6 and F/A-18 Navy HARM implementation schemes. The EA-6B uses ALQ-99F system to programme HARM much like the F-4G implementation with the APR-38 and subsequent systems. Upgraded F-16 HTS provides limited bearing information using HARM's direction-finding capability. If the threat emitter is within HARM range, its bearing is all the missile needs. With that information it will then know the direction to turn, acquire the designated threat signal and make its own range calculations. In terms of maximising engagement range, this is not the optimum way to 'fly' HARM, since the missile uses energy and wastes some time in the boost phase to determine where it is going, but it is an effective way to work with a limited launch platform.

Prowler combat mission

Not blessed with excessive fuel capacity, the Prowler carries 15,400 lb (6990 kg) of JP fuel internally and about 2,000 lb (910 kg) in each external tank. (The US Navy is currently transitioning from JP-5 and JP-8 fuel.) Typically, the Prowler launches with full fuel capacity (except on a car-qual training sortie or a short-cycle maintenance flight), refuels from a tanker, and accompanies a strike force 600 miles (965 km) to cross into an opponent's territory. Mission

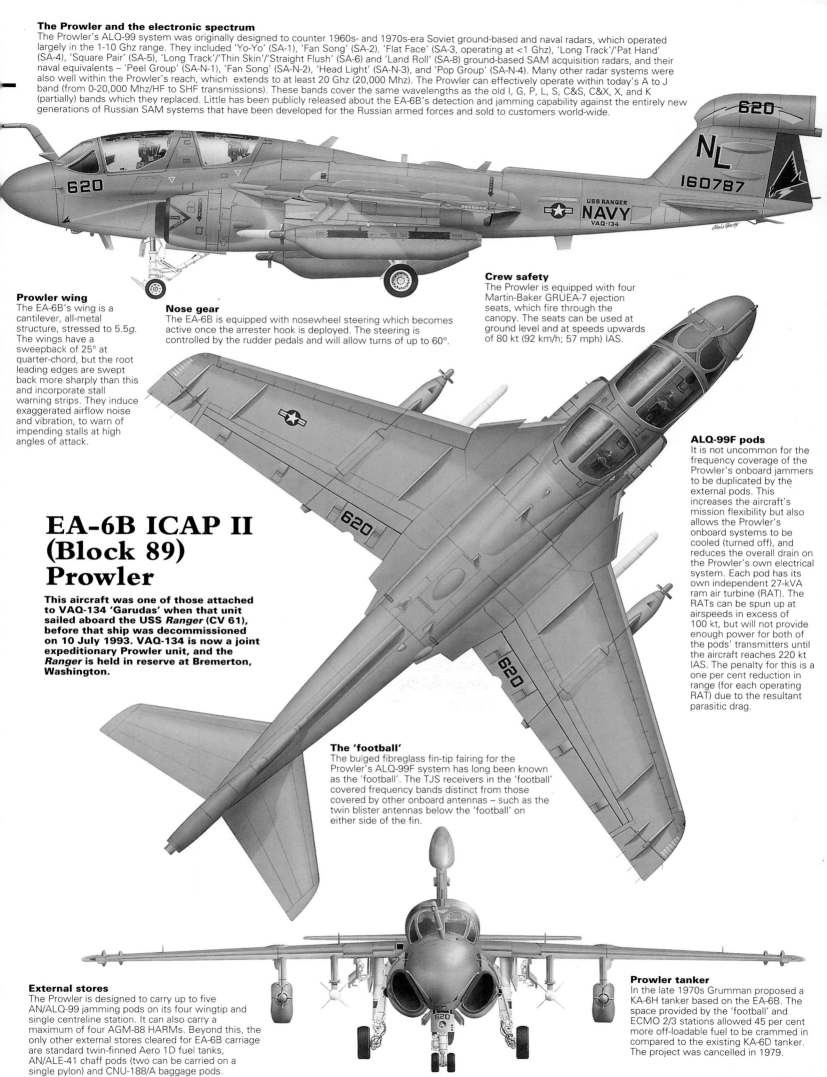

The Prowler and the electronic spectrum

The Prowler's ALQ-99 system was originally designed to counter 1960s- and 1970s-era Soviet ground-based and naval radars, which operated largely in the 1-10 Ghz range. They included 'Yo-Yo' (SA-1), 'Fan Song' (SA-2), 'Flat Face' (SA-3, operating at <1 Ghz), 'Long Track'/'Pat Hand' (SA-4), 'Square Pair' (SA-5), 'Long Track'/'Thin Skin'/'Straight Flush' (SA-6) and 'Land Roll' (SA-8) ground-based SAM acquisition radars, and their naval equivalents – 'Peel Group' (SA-N-1), 'Fan Song' (SA-N-2), 'Head Light' (SA-N-3), and 'Pop Group' (SA-N-4). Many other radar systems were also well within the Prowler's reach, which extends to at least 20 Ghz (20,000 Mhz). The Prowler can effectively operate within today's A to J band (from 0-20,000 Mhz/HF to SHF transmissions). These bands cover the same wavelengths as the old I, G, P, L, S, C&S, C&X, X, and K (partially) bands which they replaced. Little has been publicly released about the EA-6's detection and jamming capability against the entirely new generations of Russian SAM systems that have been developed for the Russian armed forces and sold to customers world-wide.

Prowler wing

The EA-6B's wing is a cantilever, all-metal structure, stressed to 5.5*g*. The wings have a sweepback of 25° at quarter-chord, but the root leading edges are swept back more sharply than this and incorporate stall warning strips. They induce exaggerated airflow noise and vibration, to warn of impending stalls at high angles of attack.

Nose gear

The EA-6B is equipped with nosewheel steering which becomes active once the arrester hook is deployed. The steering is controlled by the rudder pedals and will allow turns of up to 60°.

Crew safety

The Prowler is equipped with four Martin-Baker GRUEA-7 ejection seats, which fire through the canopy. The seats can be used at ground level and at speeds upwards of 80 kt (92 km/h; 57 mph) IAS.

EA-6B ICAP II (Block 89) Prowler

This aircraft was one of those attached to VAQ-134 'Garudas' when that unit sailed aboard the USS *Ranger* (CV 61), before that ship was decommissioned on 10 July 1993. VAQ-134 is now a joint expeditionary Prowler unit, and the *Ranger* is held in reserve at Bremerton, Washington.

ALQ-99F pods

It is not uncommon for the frequency coverage of the Prowler's onboard jammers to be duplicated by the external pods. This increases the aircraft's mission flexibility but also allows the Prowler's onboard systems to be cooled (turned off), and reduces the overall drain on the Prowler's own electrical system. Each pod has its own independent 27-kVA ram air turbine (RAT). The RATs can be spun up at airspeeds in excess of 100 kt, but will not provide enough power for both of the pods' transmitters until the aircraft reaches 220 kt IAS. The penalty for this is a one per cent reduction in range (for each operating RAT) due to the resultant parasitic drag.

The 'football'

The bulged fibreglass fin-tip fairing for the Prowler's ALQ-99F system has long been known as the 'football'. The TJS receivers in the 'football' covered frequency bands distinct from those covered by other onboard antennas – such as the twin blister antennas below the 'football' on either side of the fin.

External stores

The Prowler is designed to carry up to five AN/ALQ-99 jamming pods on its four wingtip and single centreline station. It can also carry a maximum of four AGM-88 HARMs. Beyond this, the only other external stores cleared for EA-6B carriage are standard twin-finned Aero 1D fuel tanks, AN/ALE-41 chaff pods (two can be carried on a single pylon) and CNU-188/A baggage pods.

Prowler tanker

In the late 1970s Grumman proposed a KA-6H tanker based on the EA-6B. The space provided by the 'football' and ECMO 2/3 stations allowed 45 per cent more off-loadable fuel to be crammed in compared to the existing KA-6D tanker. The project was cancelled in 1979.

Above: *Part of the Block 86 upgrade to the EA-6B removed the 15° off-boresight restriction that had previously hampered the Prowler as a HARM shooter. Prowlers can now fire HARMs at any target, without changing course. It also allowed EA-6B crews to reprogramme the missiles in flight for new threat signals. By 1996 all Block 86 aircraft had been upgraded to Block 89 standard.*

Left and below: *From a shore base at Aviano AFB, in north-eastern Italy, USN and USMC Prowlers became instrumental in the NATO air campaign over Bosnia. The aircraft seen here, armed and ready, are from VAQ-130 (left) and VMAQ-3.*

commander aboard the aircraft often is not the pilot but one of the ECMOs (as explained earlier, the senior ECMO is not necessarily the occupant of the ECMO 1 crew position). At low altitude, the EA-6B has no difficulty maintaining a cruising speed of around 500 kt (575 mph; 925 km/h), which is similar to the speed at which an F/A-18E/F Super Hornet fully laden with bombs can conveniently cruise. As one ECMO describes it, "At low altitude [10,000 ft/6096 m], the EA-6B can stay with just about any bomb dropper, and I have run Jaguars, Tornados, F-16s, F-14s and F/A-18s out of gas down real low, maintaining 500 kt indicated. The problem is, since the EA carries its external stores home with it, they usually can run away on the way home." When it entered service, the Prowler needed only to keep up with A-6s and A-7s, and "chasing pointy-nosed bomb-droppers at high altitude was never a design requirement."

Action in Bosnia

The Prowler played a central role in the nearly 1,000-day Operation Deny Flight, conducted from 12 April 1993 to 20 December 1995 in Bosnia-Herzegovina. Following the 8 June 1995 rescue of a US Air Force F-16C pilot shot down (on 2 June) by a SAM in Bosnia, in early August 1995, four NATO aircraft attacked two Serbian surface-to-air missile radar sites, in Croatia, using HARMs. Two US Navy EA-6Bs (they usually operated in pairs in Bosnia) and two F/A-18Cs struck sites near Knin and

Udbina in self-defence after the aircraft were targeted by SAM-associated radars. During the subsequent brief period of strike operations against the Bosnian Serbs (subtitled Operation Deliberate Force), Navy Prowlers fired 13 HARMs; at best, only one of the HARMs was a kill, confirmed ironically not by US intelligence but by a Bosnian Serb officer interviewed on the Cable News Network.

This flurry of fighting, when naval aviators made logbook entries in green ink (signifying combat), is recalled by an ECMO in these words: "VAQ-141 had deployed with Carrier Air Wing Eight aboard the USS *Theodore Roosevelt* (CVN-71) with an 'augment' of two

aircraft from reserve squadron VAQ-209. Once in the Adriatic, they were constantly tasked for operations 'over the beach'. Whenever the 'TR' went into port, 141 was off-loaded to Aviano where they worked with the USAF and USMC units based there. It's important to note that the EA-6Bs were the only portion of CVW-8 that NATO commanders wouldn't allow out of the area. While the rest of CVW-8 was in port on liberty in Haifa or Rhodes, VAQ-141 was in Aviano flying peacekeeping missions. In addition, VAQ-130 deployed to Aviano directly from Whidbey for Deliberate Force and joined 141 to make up a 10-aircraft squadron under 141 control."

Another ECMO, Lieutenant Commander Tom Burke of VAQ-209, remembers that, "we would fly with jammers off, waiting for the SA-6, which was the main threat [the 3M9 Cub SAM, NATO name 'Gainful', is a self-propelled mobile system]. Upon picking up signals, depending on the rules of engagement, we could fire. When the raids started, the ROE were relaxed. The raids were 'joint', with the Air Force and NATO allies, and required air-to-air refuelling. We took off from Aviano, flew down over the Adriatic, and caught the tankers, which could be British TriStars, Spanish C-130s, or US Air Force KC-135s. Then we would go 'in country', fly around for an hour and a half, go out, refuel, and pop back in. We flew with two drop tanks, two pods, and one HARM."

These Navy Prowlers were replaced by two Marine Corps units. One of these, VMAQ-1, fired HARMs during Bosnia operations. Since then the Marine Corps has held the Aviano commitment while Navy squadrons remain on carriers in the area.

EA-6B operations

The Marine Corps' EA-6B force is located at MCAS Cherry Point near Havelock, North Carolina. The US Navy's entire EA-6B force (except reserve squadron VAQ-209) is garrisoned at Whidbey Island, in the Puget Sound near Seattle, Washington. VAQ-209 is at Andrews AFB near Washington, DC. Whidbey is made up of two bases – Ault Field on the windward (western) side in a portion called Clover Valley, and the Seaplane Base on the leeward side (east) of the island. The town of Oak Harbor is in between. The Seaplane Base is still used for base housing and Navy Exchange (the converted PBY hangar), and is also the home for 'Dolly', the EW signal simulator the EA-6Bs use while airborne.

'Detachments' of Prowlers are described going aboard a carrier as part of the ship's air wing, but routine procedure is for an entire squadron of four or five EA-6Bs to go to sea for

a cruise, typically lasting four to six months. Deployment to 'concrete' locations – such as Iwakuni, Japan to support the US commitment in Korea or Aviano, Italy, to bolster operations in Bosnia – are usually for six months.

When planning for a mission, commanders and EA-6B crews know that they have the flexibility afforded by an aircraft that is both a shooter and a jammer, replacing other aircraft such as the F-4G and EF-111A which are either shooters or jammers. This is consistent with the Pentagon's overall plan to shift from one-mission aircraft to multi-mission aircraft. The F/A-18E/F Super Hornet replacing the F-14A/B/D and A-6E is another example of this emphasis.

To the theatre commander (as well as in Navy doctrine), the dual-role, shooter-jammer EA-6B Prowler represents a dramatic change that began with the installation of HARM in 1986. Until then, Air Force SEAD doctrine was to 'prosecute to destruction' (F-4G with HARM missile) whereas Navy doctrine was to 'prosecute to suppression' (EA-6B without HARM). The Air Force method was to use a SEAD aircraft to clear a pathway for the strike package by destroying air defence radars in a

selected corridor, whereas the Navy approach was to jam everything in the region. Now that the Navy EA-6B Prowler seeks not merely to disrupt and denigrate, but also to destroy, it becomes a more versatile weapon, a more 'joint' asset, and a prime candidate for the joint Navy-Air Force squadrons taking shape today.

The Prowler mission

The job assigned to the EA-6B is determined by the JFAC's operations staff when making up the daily Air Tasking Order (ATO). Fortunately, the Navy has improved the 'jointness' of its communications which hampered delivery of the ATO during the Gulf War. When the ATO is received at the airfield or carrier, mission planners slot the EA-6B into a take-off time and position based on the competing priorities of the other strike aircraft (the Air Force always preferred to use the EF-111A in pairs, but the EA-6B frequently operates as a one-ship element). At the tactical level, ECMOs make use of a computer system, the PRB Associates AN/TSQ-142 Tactical EA-6B Mission Support (TEAMS) System, to create the electronic order of battle. Each squadron has a TEAMS machine made up of two consoles, which aircrew (almost

Prowlers over Bosnia

The Grumman EA-6B Prowler made its combat debut in the Bosnian theatre of operations in November 1994 after Serb forces besieging the Bihac pocket activated their integrated air defence network containing scores of V-75 Dvina (SA-2 'Guideline') and 3M9 Kub (SA-6 'Gainful') SAM batteries. For months the Serbs had been building up their air defences to stop Bosnian and Croat resupply aircraft getting into the pocket, claiming an Antonov An-32 shot down on 1 August. By mid-November NATO's 5th Allied Tactical Air Force (5 ATAF) was gearing up to mount strikes against the Serb air base at Udbina inside Croatia, to deter the Serb air force conducting air strikes against Bihac in contravention of the United Nations' 'No-Fly Zone'.

VMAQ-4 'Seahawks' was ordered to deploy to NAS Sigonella, Sicily, on 19 November 1994 to provide 5 ATAF with specialised SEAD capability. Refuelling by USAF KC-10A tankers, the Marine Prowlers made an 11-hour non-stop transatlantic ferry flight from their home at Cherry Point, NC on 21 November, just prior to a major NATO air strike against Udbina. Within hours of being on the ground the squadron's six aircraft began flying operational sorties over Bosnia. NATO air commanders were becoming increasingly concerned about the Serb SAM threat to their aircraft, and the firing of two SA-2s against Royal Navy Sea Harriers flying near Bihac on 22 November forced them to change tactics.

On the morning of 23 November 1994, 5 ATAF launched a major strike package to protect eight British, Dutch and French reconnaissance aircraft that were to pin-point the location of the SAMs around Bihac. Flying 'shot gun' on the Jaguars, Mirages and F-16s was a SEAD package centred around the VMAQ-4 Prowlers, which were armed with AGM-88s. This package was put together very quickly as events unfolded, with the Prowlers being diverted from another mission, to the USAF base at Aviano, to receive briefings from senior NATO commanders.

As the package skirted the southeast edge of the Bihac pocket, a Serb SA-2 battery at Otoka illuminated the aircraft with its fire control radar, so the Prowlers fired two HARMs. Minutes later another SAM site came on line at Dvor, and another HARM was fired at it. The Prowler crews, using information from RC-135 'Rivet Joint' aircraft and previous photo-missions, had a good idea of the SAM positions and

manoeuvred themselves carefully to get the best shots at the radars guiding the hostile missiles. Serb missile crews were highly skilled at using long-range surveillance radars when given notice of NATO air patrols, and tended only to switch on radars for very short periods to prevent them being targeted by HARMs. The results of the first HARM strikes were decidedly mixed, so NATO and UN commanders agreed that a further combined armed reconnaissance package was authorised for later in the afternoon. F-15Es led the package, dropping two LGBs on the Otoka site and destroying SA-2 launchers. To protect the Strike Eagles, Prowlers fired three more HARMs when the SA-2s' and SA-6s' radars came up.

The VMAQ-4 Prowlers stayed in Italy for two months to support continued NATO air operations over Bosnia, flying 220 combat missions. The squadron was based mainly at Sigonella but regularly detached aircraft to Aviano to be closer to the action.

With the return of a US Navy aircraft-carrier to the Adriatic at the end of January 1995, VAQ-130 'Zappers' took over duty as 5 ATAF's specialist SEAD unit. At times when the USS *Eisenhower* was away from the Adriatic, VAQ-130 would disembark five aircraft to Aviano to provide SEAD coverage over Bosnia for up to 10 days at a time.

In May 1995 the USS *Theodore Roosevelt* arrived in-theatre and its embarked Prowlers, from the active-duty VAQ-141 'Shadowhawks' augmented by reservists from VAQ-209 'Star Warriors', assumed 5 ATAF's SEAD role. Prowlers and other HARM-armed aircraft now had to be present in Bosnian airspace to 'open the SEAD window' before other allied aircraft could follow them into the area of operations.

The *Roosevelt*'s Prowlers remained on patrol over Bosnia for the next six months, with detachments being sent to Aviano when the carrier was not in the Adriatic. On 8 June they provided SEAD support for the rescue of downed USAF pilot Captain Scott O'Grady from northwest Bosnia. As the rescue force was passing over the Serb-held Krajina region of Croatia, it was illuminated by SAM radars; VAQ-141/209 Prowlers detected the radars but NATO commanders refused to give authorisation for them to engage because the Serbs were then holding hostage hundreds of UN peacekeepers. Prowlers had not been in the air at the time the hapless USAF pilot

was shot down. Early in July the Prowlers were called to protect NATO fighters deep in Bosnian airspace as they flew close air support for UN troops trapped in the Srebrenica enclave. On 7 August two EA-6Bs and two F/A-18Cs from the *Roosevelt* took part in a HARM attack on Serb SAM radars at Knin, in the Krajina, after they were called to provide air protection for UN troops caught in the Croatian Operation Storm offensive.

By August 1995 the UN and NATO had finally lost patience with the Bosnian Serbs' policy of attacking so-called 'safe areas', and plans were formed for an air campaign to punish further provocation. First, the Serbs' integrated air defence system had to be neutralised. US Navy officers from VAQ-141 'Shadowhawks' and -209 'Star Warriors', plus other SEAD specialists on the USS *Theodore Roosevelt*, developed a plan to accomplish this, under the codename Dead Eye.

NATO was given the go-ahead to launch Operation Deliberate Force after 38 civilians were killed in a mortar attack in Sarajevo on 28 August. 5 ATAF had to be ready to attack in the early hours of 30 August. The first strike package, codenamed Dead Eye South East, was made up of EA-6Bs and F/A-18Cs from the *Roosevelt*, supported by F-16Cs equipped with the HARM Targeting System (HTS) and armed with AGM-88s. Its task was to take out the Serb air defences around Sarajevo, which it did with great determination, firing HARMs to put early warning radars out of action and dropping LGBs on the Serb SA-6 battery deployed near the Bosnian capital.

As the bombing offensive unfolded, 5 ATAF took no chances in case the Serbs covertly moved any of their mobile SA-6s to threaten NATO aircraft, so a SEAD package had to be in the air to 'open the SEAD window' before strike aircraft were allowed to go 'feet wet' over Bosnia. SEAD packages were built up from pairs of HARM shooters and jamming aircraft. Prowlers were teamed in pairs with other EA-6Bs, Hornets with HTS-equipped F-16s. They would enter Bosnian airspace and fly in racetrack patterns to protect the strike aircraft as they made their bombing runs. If Prowlers were not in the air then the strike aircraft entered holding patterns outside Bosnia until the SEAD aircraft were ready to lead the way. USAF EF-111A and EC-130H 'Compass Call' jamming aircraft closely co-ordinated their operations with the Prowlers to ensure maximum SEAD protection for NATO aircraft.

On 5 September 5 ATAF expanded its operations to hit at the Serb IADS targets in northwest Bosnia, striking first with stand-off missile to neutralise key air defence sites. Again the Prowlers from the *Roosevelt* were in the forefront of the offensive, using HARMs against early warning radars.

SEAD coverage continued around the clock through Operation Deliberate Force, with Prowlers being in the air almost continuously. The brunt of this effort fell on the six EA-6Bs of VAQ-141 and those from the reserve unit VAQ-209, with aircraft split between the *Roosevelt* and ashore at Aviano in northern Italy. By 5 September the intensity of SEAD operations meant two more aircraft from VAQ-130 'Zappers' were deployed to Aviano to help in the non-stop effort to defeat the Serb SAMs. During 10-12 September the *Roosevelt* handed over to the USS *America* and its embarked Prowlers from VMAQ-4 'Seahawks'. Additional support was provided by four more EA-6Bs of VMAQ-1 'Screaming Banshees', which relieved the Prowlers at Aviano towards the end of September.

During Deliberate Force a total of 56 HARMs was fired, with 10 being launched from VAQ-141's Prowlers alone. The squadron was airborne for 603 hours during 137 combat sorties in Deliberate Force.

In the weeks after Operation Deliberate Force, 5 ATAF maintained the intensity of its air activity over Bosnia to protect UN peacekeepers and keep the pressure on the Serbs. In an attempt to turn back the Croat and Bosnian offensive towards Banja Luka, the Bosnian Serb air force took to the air in early October, so NATO fighters began patrols to stop them breaching the UN 'No-Fly Zone'. Prowlers had to accompany the fighter sweeps into the SAM-infested areas of northwest Bosnia. On 4 October VMAQ-1 Prowlers were illuminated three times by Serb SAM radars, and on each occasion they launched a HARM.

During September and October 1995, the US Navy and Marine Corps Prowlers maintained a high level of SEAD protection in the face of the Serb IADS, and not a single NATO aircraft was shot down by a radar-guided SAM. The only aircraft lost during Operation Deliberate Force was the victim of a heat-seeking SAM at low level. In the words of VMAQ-4 executive officer, Major 'Muddy' Waters, "We were a success - no one was shot down on our watch." **Tim Ripley**

Above: This VMAQ-1 EA-6B refuels from a USAF KC-10A before attacking Serbian SAM sites on 4 October 1996.

Below: This VF-141 Prowler is being armed in preparation for the Operation Deliberate Force strikes in August 1995.

Above: This VAQ-132 'Scorpions' EA-6B (attached to CVW-17 onboard the USS Enterprise) is seen on a jamming sortie over the Adriatic. The aircraft is carrying an operational load of three ALQ-99F pods plus two 300-US gal (1136-litre) Aero 1D external fuel tanks. The EA-6B already has a usable internal fuel load of 2268 US gal (8585 litres).

VAQ-137 is dubbed the 'Rooks', and the unit's badge comprises a stylised North American Indian bird.

always ECMOs) use to plan their mission. The TEAMS develops information on navigation track, fuel consumption, jamming, and HARM plans. The entire mission is dropped to a tape drive which is loaded into the aircraft from the back seat. The results can then be manually adjusted or overridden during flight. The system was introduced concurrent with ICAP II and is now in its third version as it keeps up with airframe developments. Prior to its introduction, ECMOs were required to manually enter all mission data by keypad, a long, laborious process which is little missed (although the EF-111A still uses it). The aircraft also has a recorder system that records the actual mission for debriefing purposes.

Navy-Air Force operations

Pivotal to the future of the Prowler is an agreement (technically a memorandum of agreement, or MOA) between the Air Force and Navy which was three-fifths of the way towards full implementation in March 1997 but had not been signed. It is stalled in part over a sensitive issue: the Navy is reluctant to give Air Force officers full authority to command a VAQ squadron. Under the terms of the MOA, the Navy is tasked to establish five 'expeditionary' EA-6B Prowler squadrons to provide 'joint' electronic combat support for Department of Defense land-based units as the US Air Force EF-111A is phased out of service. The Air Force has cancelled an upgrade programme for the EF-111A and is expected to retire the last of 24 aircraft by 1 October 1998. The expeditionary squadrons are to be ready to deploy to land bases or operational carriers, whenever directed. As of early 1997, two of the five squadrons were working up (VAQ-133, VAQ-134) and the Navy was being criticised for moving slowly with an arrangement about which it had never been enthusiastic. The Air

Force had essentially created and carved out the agreement from its strong desire – hasty, in the view of critics – to retire the EF-111A.

Rear Admiral Dennis V. McGinn, the Navy's Director of Air Warfare, described the agreement in testimony before the US Congress's Subcommittee on Airland Forces on 15 March 1996, as part of the service's Aircraft Procurement, Navy (APN) plan. "Our nation's tactical jamming asset, the EA-6B, remains the premier tactical electronic warfare platform in the world. Projected to be in inventory until 2015, ICAP II (Block 89A) will require an upgrade planned to begin in 1998. Based on the Lower Cost Alternative to ADVCAP Study, planned modifications will address aircraft structure and supportability, as well as enhanced

warfighting capabilities, including a receiver upgrade. Beginning this year [1996], the EA-6B will assume the role of stand-off jammer for the Air Force, as well as for the Navy and Marine Corps, totally replacing the EF-111A by the end of FY 1998."

A year after the testimony by the Pentagon's McGinn (an attack pilot who flew A-7 Corsair IIs and F/A-18 Hornets), the USAF is pressing the Navy to fund all 104 deployable EA-6Bs covered by the agreement. The Navy's 1998 budget request includes 99 deployable EA-6Bs.

As conceived, the plan called for 'concrete' squadrons with no seagoing capability that would have operated solely from shore bases – meaning Iwakuni, Japan, where the commitment has traditionally but not always been handled by

The EA-6B does not have fuselage airbrakes (only the EA-6A had them). Instead, it uses wingtip airbrakes which deploy to 120°. The individual panels are approximately 2 ft x 4 ft (0.6 m x 1.2 m) – giving a total braking area of 32 sq ft (2.97 m²).

While the training for Air Force Prowler
crews progresses, operational problems remain
as the two services merge separate practices. For
example, compared with the Air Force, Navy
squadrons do not practise rapid deployments as
often, do not deploy with extensive spare parts
packages and support equipment on extended
deployments, and use different chemical warfare
gear. To iron out these differences, the two
existing joint-service squadrons are scheduled to
fly in Red Flag exercises at Nellis AFB, Nevada,
in an operational readiness inspection at Shaw
AFB, SC, in a composite wing exercise at
Mountain Home Air AFB in Idaho, in NATO
air operations over Bosnia, and in support of
UN air operations over southern Iraq.

Son of Prowler

Looking beyond the Prowler, whose career
seems assured through 2015, McDonnell
Douglas and Northrop Grumman announced
on 7 August 1995 that they agreed to jointly
develop a derivative of the F/A-18E/F Super
Hornet as an EW aircraft. The variant, called
the F/A-18 C^{2}W (Command and Control
Warfare) version, is intended as a possible
replacement for the EA-6B after the turn of the
century. Most scenarios for EA-6B missions tie
up fighters used as HVUCAP (high value unit
combat air patrol), and the F/A-18 C^{2}W offers
the advantage of being able to protect itself
against opposing fighters. The F/A-18 C^{2}W
will further aid planners by allowing them to

the Marines, and Aviano, Italy, from which
flying operations over Bosnia are mounted.
Once the joint squadrons were up and running,
the Prowler was expected to take over land-
based EF-111A commitments to the US
European Command at Incirlik, Turkey and to
the US Central Command, recently moved to
Al Kharj ("Al's Garage"), Saudi Arabia. The
agreement to keep the joint Prowler squadrons
land-based did not last long, however. Although
it received much from the deal – the Air Force
transferred $500 million in electronic warfare
funds that it otherwise would have spent on the
EF-111A – the Navy reneged on the plan to
keep the joint units land-based.

The plan created personnel problems for the
Navy since it meant that a new naval aviator in
an EA-6B squadron would be treated differently
than the equivalent person in another squadron:

junior officers receiving first-tour orders to a
concrete squadron would have to wait for a
second tour with a CV squadron to gain fleet
experience. The deal met the Air Force's needs
but not the Navy's, so the Navy proposed an
addendum that these squadrons must always be
able to deploy on short notice wherever needed
(including a boat). Therefore, USAF pilots in
these squadrons would be required to maintain
carrier quals.

On 1 July 1996, a three-man, all-Air Force
crew headed by pilot Lieutenant Colonel
Ronald Rivard landed an EA-6B Prowler on
USS Constellation (CV-64) in the Pacific. This
first all-Air Force achievement came just after
the first USAF flyers graduated from EA-6B
training the previous month. Rivard had been a
Navy pilot for seven years and had logged more
than 100 carrier landings in Vikings 15 years ago.

Tanking with drogue-equipped USAF aircraft, such as this KC-135R, has become routine for Prowler crews. However, they must now adapt to a new era of completely integrated operations.

utilise similar flight profiles, increasing fuel efficiency. The makers claim that automation will enable the F/A-18 C²W to do the Prowler's job with only two crew members. Work is underway to create a new pod which would allow the F/A-18 C²W to cover the same frequencies as does the EA-6B with four pods – leaving the Hornet able to serve as a strike platform with a combination of jammers, fuel tanks, air-to-air and air-to-ground weapons.

ICAP III, the uncertain future

In the near term, the Prowler will eventually be upgraded to a new ICAP III configuration. A competition to choose an ICAP III contractor is imminent. The first machines to be converted will be the oldest (all current Block 82s).

ICAP III is yet to be defined, but, with no change to the structure of the aircraft, will probably focus on three key goals: (1) replacing the ALQ-99 with improved TJS receivers that advance the system from a pre-emptive jammer to a selectively reactive jammer; (2) putting a fully integrated communication jamming systems into the TJS rather than retaining the USQ-113 as a separate, stand-alone system; (3) achieving 'connectivity' which will allow the EA-6B to meld what it sees with its new reactive system with what it sees from offboard sources. ICAP III will enable the Prowler to react to advanced radars associated with 'modded double-digit SAMs' (SA-10, SA-11, SA-12 and SA-17), and proponents say it is ideally suited to a world in which air defence radar acquisition systems have become more complex and more difficult to defeat, installations are far more numerous and varied than in the past, and EW aircraft must be able to distinguish friend from foe even when both have the same radars.

ICAP III, in a revealing glimpse at diminished expectations, is sometimes called 'ADVCAP Lite'. No longer part of the Navy's planning is the advanced Prowler version known as ADVCAP, flown in prototype form and

The EA-6B's future is secure, and there are now more deployed squadrons than at any time in the aircraft's history. What remains uncertain is how the Prowler will be able to serve two, or more, masters, while also dealing effectively with an ever-increasing SAM and radar threat.

planned for production in the late 1980s. This costly 'Cadillac of Prowler variants' was once the Great White Hope of the fleet but today is, much like generous defence spending, merely a memory of other times. When ICAP III emerges early in the next century, it will be a 'poor man's substitute' for the version that might have been. Alone among updates, ADVCAP would have been a remanufacturing programme rather than merely an improvement.

Among other things, ADVCAP would have increased the Prowler's carrying stations from five to seven. Every Prowler ever built has two additional wing stations (called station A and B, outside the wing fold) but no pylons were ever hung from them.

An internal Navy document says of ICAP III: "Delivery around 2005, if ordered, will have most of the advanced receiver capability of the cancelled ADVCAP at a fraction of the weight, so it will not need the engine and mods previously proposed. This will be the first major weapon system update since the introduction of HARM in 1986, although there have been a series of

small changes along the way, like the UEU (Universal Exciter Upgrade) and USQ-113 comm jammer." Any future upgrade programme for the Prowler would take place at Grumman's St Augustine, Florida facility.

Whether ICAP III will ever come is, in the end, one of those questions for the 21st century, when resources will be fewer and military challenges less predictable. Although the men and women of Prowler squadrons love their aircraft and would not trade it, most acknowledge that today's EA-6B - and tomorrow's, if there is one – is necessarily a compromise. The EA-6B is not as good a HARM shooter as the F-4G and in some circumstances not as good a jammer as the EF-111A, but it performs both jobs when neither of the others do. The US Air Force became a partner in EA-6B operations for the wrong reason – to achieve cost saving – by retiring the EF-111A Raven, and the US Navy got into the lethal, missile-shooting SEAD business very late in the game. The EA-6B does an excellent job, but it is also important because it is now the only game in town.　**Robert F. Dorr**

EA-6B Prowler current inventory

BuNo.	Block														
		161881	82	163031	82	163401	89	158040	82	159584	82	160707	82	163527	89
161119	89	161882	82	163032	82	163402	89	158540	82	159585	82	160709	82	163528	89
161120	89	161883	82	163033	82	163403	89	158544	82	159586	82	160786	82	163529	89
161242	89	161884	82	163034	82	163404	89	158649	89	159587	82	160787	89	163530	89
161243	89	161885	82	163035	82	163406	89	158650	82	159907	82	160788	82	163884	89
161244	89	162224	82	163045	82	163520	89	158800	82	159908	82	160791	89	163885	89
161245	82	162225	82	163046	82	163521	89	158801	82	159909	82	161115	89	163886	89
161347	89	162227	82	163047	82	156481	82	158802	82	159911	89	161116	89	163887	89
161348	82	162228	82	163048	82	158029	89	158804	82	159912	82	161118	89	163888	89
161349	82	162230	82	163049	89	158030	82	158805	82	160432	82	161119	89	163889	89
161350	89	162934	82	163395	89	158032	82	158807	82	160433	89	161120	89	163890	89
161352	89	162935	82	163396	89	158033	82	158810	82	160434	89	163522	89	163891	89
161774	89	162936	82	163397	82	158034	82	158811	82	160436	82	163523	89	163892	89
161775	89	162938	82	163398	89	158035	82	158815	82	160437	82	163524	89	164401	89
161779	82	162939	82	163399	89	158036	82	158816	89	160609	82	163525	89	164402	89
161880	82	163030	82	163400	89	158039	89	159583	82	160706	82	163526	89	164403	89

Royal Australian Air Force and Republic of Singapore Air Force
Joint Flying Training

A photo-feature by Peter Steinemann

The Republic of Singapore has a potent and expanding air force, whose training needs have outgrown the limited airspace of its small island home. In a unique agreement, Singapore has transferred its Flying Training School (with aircraft) to Australia, where it operates alongside the Royal Australian Air Force's own No. 2 FTS, at RAAF Pearce, on Australia's southwestern coast.

Top left: Singapore established its Flying Training School in August 1969. The unit comprises Nos 130 and 131 Sqns. Singapore became the first export customer for the Italian-designed SIAI-Marchetti (now Agusta) S.211 jet trainer in 1986, when the first of 30 aircraft were delivered.

Left: Australia's No. 2 FTS can trace its history back to the Australian Military Flying School which was established just after the outbreak of World War I. No. 2 FTS is today part of the RAAF's Training Command. The Pilatus PC-9A was introduced in 1989, and the bulk of the 64 aircraft acquired were assembled/built locally by Hawker de Havilland.

Left and above right: The S.211 replaced the T-33 and the Strikemaster in Singaporean service. An initial batch of 10 was ordered in 1983/84, and 20 additional options were taken up in 1986. The S.211 has had an unspectacular sales career and is in service with only Singapore and the Philippines (some were delivered to Haiti, but are no longer in use).

Right: The basic training units share Pearce air base with the Aermacchi MB-326Hs (licence-built as Commonwealth CA-30s) of the RAAF's No. 25 Sqn. They are in use as tactical trainers.

Above and left: Australia took delivery of a total of 97 fully weapons-capable Aermacchi MB-326Hs (87 for the Royal Australian Air Force and 10 for the Royal Australian Navy). Deliveries took place between 1967 and 1972, but the navy aircraft were absorbed by the air force in 1983. Today, slightly less than 50 'Macchis' survive in RAAF service with No. 25 Sqn, seen here, and No. 76 Sqn, based at Williamtown, NSW. The latter unit provides lead-in fighter training for the F/A-18 force, and also operates PC-9As in the FAC training role. No. 25 Sqn is a direct reporting element of the RAAF's Tactical Fighter Group and undertakes basic weapons and tactical training for pilots who complete the basic flying training course with No. 2 FTS. All Australian fast-jet pilots graduate from an initial course on the MB-326H. The black swan badge of No. 25 Sqn is echoed by the similar unit markings carried by the PC-9As of No. 2 FTS.

Right: In the early 1980s a RAAF specification (AFST 5045) was issued for a replacement for the MB-326, by the 1990s. A parallel requirement (AFST 5044) was issued for a CT-4 Airtrainer replacement. While the jet trainer was shelved, a CT-4 replacement was found in the shape of the EFIS-equipped Pilatus PC-9A. The acquisition of the PC-9s allowed a revision of the training syllabus that cut back the utilisation of the MB-326s for basic flying training. This extended their overall service lives accordingly. The MB-326H will now serve until the RAAF's new BAe Hawk 100 trainers are delivered. The first of them is due in 1999.

Left: By 1985 all the RAAF's remaining MB-326Hs had undergone a life extension programme at the hands of the Commonwealth Aircraft Corporation. Each aircraft was refitted with upgraded avionics and a revised cockpit layout, while wings, fuselages and fins were all completely overhauled. Today the MB-326Hs in service with No. 25 Sqn wear a mix of old- and new-style camouflage with high- and low-visibility unit markings. The aircraft seen here are lined up under mobile protective canopies to safeguard pilots and ground crews from the fierce heat of Australia's Indian Ocean coast.

Above: Singaporean pilots undertake their elementary flying training course at Seletar, in Singapore, with No. 150 Squadron. This unit is equipped with a mix of SIAI-Marchetti SF-260MS and SF-260W trainers.

Right: Australian student pilots undertake an 'all PC-9' course. The last 'Macchi' departed No. 2 FTS in December 1991 and in December 1992 the CT-4As of No. 1 FTS were retired, when that squadron was disbanded.

Below: Search and rescue coverage for Pearce air base is provided by a civilian contractor, Lloyd Helicopters, which operates a large fleet of Bell JetRangers and LongRangers, Sikorsky S-76s, Bell 412s and Eurocopter Super Pumas. An S-76A is permanently attached to RAAF Pearce.

Sukhoi 'Frogfoot'
Su-25, Su-28 and Su-39

Sukhoi's Jet Shturmovik

The concept of the *Shturmovik* is a uniquely Russian one, born even before the dark days of the Great Patriotic War. The *Bronironanyi Shturmovik* – literally an armoured attacker – was intended to support the troops on the ground from the air, yet survive punishing ground fire itself. In the years that followed the end of the war in Europe, several jet *Shturmovik* designs evolved. After bitter battles between rival design bureaux, Sukhoi's Su-25 won through. Inspired by experiences in Vietnam and the Middle East, and blooded in Afghanistan, the unflatteringly named 'Frogfoot' is now a proven combat aircraft – one which the Sukhoi bureau still hopes to improve.

P. Sukhoi   Design   Bureau

Su 25

Sukhoi Su-25, Su-28 and Su-39 'Frogfoot'

This sharkmouthed Slovak air force Su-25K is one of the 11 'Frogfoots' acquired by the newly-established Slovak Republic in 1993. Czechoslovakia had been the first export customer for the Su-25, and it was from Czech sources that the West received its first clear public views of the Su-25. Even before the partition of the two countries, the Su-25 force had a reputation for decorative unit markings. Sharkmouths were seen on several aircraft of the former Ceskoslovenske Letectvo and this tradition was carried on in Slovakia.

The Su-25 has often been assumed to be a Soviet clone of the USAF's AX COIN aircraft, based on the losing Northrop A-9 (rather than the winning A-10), and less agile and less armoured more as a result of Soviet incompetence than by deliberate design. The USAF's Vietnam War-inspired AX requirement was for the close air support of troops in contact and for counter-insurgency, which assumed a degree of air superiority or at least a low level of air and SAM threats. By contrast, the Russian aircraft was designed to meet a slightly later and very different requirement which stressed anti-armour and fighter-bomber capabilities over the modern battlefield. Combat proven in Afghan skies, the Su-25 is considerably more versatile than were its American counterparts, and is a remarkably efficient and cost-effective fighter-bomber.

Its export success has been limited by its lack of air-to-air fighter capability and by its lack of supersonic performance, since prejudice against the very idea of a subsonic combat aircraft remains strong. This can be gauged by the fact that even in the former USSR the aircraft was never procured in large numbers, while arguably less effective fighter-bombers (like the early Su-17s and MiG-27s) poured off the production lines in huge numbers. Overseas, sales of the Su-25 were further diminished by the ready availability of cheaper alternatives, many of which are retired and reroled fighters. Those customers willing to overlook the aircraft's

lack of speed have found it to be a remarkably potent weapon – perhaps unsuitable for independence day parades, but remarkably useful in its intended role once the bullets start flying. Combat experience pointed the way towards some obvious improvements and refinements, many of which were incorporated during production; more major changes resulted in an extensive redesign to produce a second-generation 'Frogfoot'. This aircraft emerged as the Cold War was ending, and it has proved almost impossible to win orders for the new variant either at home or overseas.

Shturmovik origins

During the Great Patriotic War (the approved Soviet term for the struggle against German invaders, which began in 1941) Russia pursued the design, manufacture and tactical use of dedicated ground attack and close support aircraft known generically as *Shturmoviks*, following the German lead set with aircraft like the Henschel Hs 123 and Hs 129. Britain and America preferred to use aircraft retired or switched from fighter or bomber duties (like the countless Spitfires, Hurricanes and Thunderbolts), or aircraft which had proved unsuitable for their design role (like the Hawker Typhoon). This Western approach set the pattern for the post-war world, with redundant or second-best jet fighters being hastily armed with bombs and rockets and pressed into service in the ground attack role.

Having successfully built up a family of dedicated ground attack and close support aircraft during the war, the USSR threw away its lead and followed Western practice afterwards. Successive generations of MiG-15s, MiG-17s and MiG-19s were pressed into service as fighter-bombers as soon as they were replaced in the fighter and interceptor roles.

The Ilyushin Design Bureau, previously responsible for the Il-2 and Il-10, attempted to produce a jet-powered *Shturmovik* in the shape of its Il-40, responding to a 1948 order. The aircraft was a jet *Shturmovik*, powered by twin AM-9 engines. It had a rear gunner and internal bomb bays in the wings, although it also drew heavily on the OKB's Il-28 twin-jet bomber. The Il-40 featured a quadruple package of NR-23 23-mm cannon, which could be traversed from the horizontal almost down to the vertical. It was also planned to use the new 'Groza' missile system. The prototype made its maiden flight on 7 March 1953 and the type was recommended for production in March 1954,

although it had problems with gun gas ingestion. A modified second prototype flew in October 1955 and passed its state acceptance tests in March 1956. This had extended air intakes stretching forward to the nose, which were inevitably nicknamed 'nostrils'. Three sub-variants were planned: the basic cannon-armed Ilyushin Il-40P, the Il-40R (Il-40ARK) reconnaissance and fire correction platform, and the Il-40UT trainer. The project was cancelled soon afterwards on 18 April 1956, apparently at the personal orders of Nikita Krushchev, who felt that it was an unnecessary diversion from the serious business of missile procurement. Records relating to the decision have reportedly disappeared from the official archives (see *World Air Power Journal* Volume 17 for more information on the Il-40 and Ilyushin's revived Il-102 design).

Five completed airframes at Rostov were destroyed, as well as one of the prototypes and the production tooling. This effectively killed off the concept of a jet *Shturmovik* until well into the 1960s, when USAF experience in Vietnam seemed to point out the weaknesses and inadequacies of the converted jet fighters used in the ground attack role, and the usefulness of ageing and slow propeller-driven strike aircraft like the Douglas Skyraider.

Revival of the concept

The USAF launched its own AX requirement with a request for proposals on 6 March 1967. This step, and those leading to it, were studied with great interest in the USSR. Existing fighter-bombers were studied with particular interest during the Warsaw Pact's major Dniepr '67 exercise: to everyone's surprise, the elderly MiG-17s and MiG-15s proved more effective than the faster but less agile MiG-21s and Su-7s. During the Six Day War, the devastating effectiveness of 30-mm cannon-equipped Israeli fighters (including obsolete Ouregans and Mystères) against ground targets (including tanks) provided further food for thought, and prompted Colonel General M. N. Mishuk to call for immediate production of the ancient Il-40. General I. P. Pavlovskii, commander of the Red Army, strongly supported those of his officers who argued for a new ground attack aircraft, and momentum began to build.

Deputy commander of the VVS, General Alexander Yefimov, was another powerful supporter, seeing a need for an aircraft like the Il-2s which he had flown during the Great Patriotic War.

While the Ministries of Defence and of the Aviation Industry considered the evidence and requests which were steadily accumulating, Sukhoi took matters into its own hands and in March 1968 began the design of a jet-engined *Shturmovik*. Ilyushin dusted off its drawings of the old Il-40 and revised it to become the Il-42.

Sukhoi's *Shturmovik* was designed by a loose group of senior personnel, including Oleg Samolovich, D. N. Gorbachev, Y. V. Ivashetchkin, V. M. Lebedyev and A. Monachev, who based the design on a configuration produced by I. V. Savchenko, commander of the air force air academy. It was known as the SPB project. The aircraft was designed around a pair of 17.2-kN (3,865-lb st) Ivchenko/Lotarev AI-25T engines. It was estimated that these would give the aircraft (which had an MTOW of 8000 kg/17,635 lb) a maximum speed of between 920 and

Above: This is a later mock-up of the T8 design than that seen on the page opposite. Note the changes that have been made to the cockpit and the three widely-spaced underwing pylons. Even at this early stage the outermost pylon was reserved for AAM carriage; however, the Su-25 was never fitted with such extravagant triple racks.

Top: In recent years Czech and Slovak Su-25s have appeared in increasingly outrageous colour schemes. The most extreme of these was undoubtedly this 'Frogfoot'-inspired monster.

Sukhoi Su-25, Su-28 and Su-39 'Frogfoot'

Above, from left to right: These very basic models of the Mikoyan MiG-21Sh, MiG-27Sh and MiG-27II illustrate some of the completely different, almost random, approaches made by the Russian design bureaux to the 1969 LSSh 'Shturmovik' requirement.

Right: This early, and rare, photograph of the T8-1 prototype in flight (taken in 1975) clearly shows some of the important differences between it and subsequent aircraft. They included its ventral gun pack, smaller rudder and wing and lack of wingtip pods.

Ilyushin's contribution to the history of the jet Shturmovik is substantial. Ilyushin had already turned the Shturmovik concept into reality, in the shape of the piston-engined Il-2 and Il-10. On 7 March 1953 Ilyushin flew the prototype of its Il-40 'Brawny' (Il-40-I) design, powered by two small AM-5F axial turbojets. The Il-40-I (below right) inherited its tail section from the Il-28 'Beagle' bomber and its rear gunner's position (equipped with twin NR-23 cannon) from its wartime experience. Political antagonism and military antipathy meant that the Il-40-I never really passed beyond its prototype stage. However, before Krushchev cancelled the programme, some or all of a five-ship pre-production batch were completed; the first of them, the Il-40-II, is seen here (far right). Problems with the first prototype, most notably gun gas ingestion, led to the radical modification of the Il-40-II's engine intakes – though from the wing leading-edge backwards it was essentially the same aircraft. It is unclear if Ilyushin secretly saved one of the Il-40s it was ordered to destroy, from which the Il-42/-102 may have been built.

1,475 kt (500 and 800 km/h; 310 and 500 mph) and a range of 1,390 nm (750 km; 465 miles) with its 2500-kg (5,510-lb) warload, which included an internal cannon. Sukhoi stressed 'closer, lower and quieter' as its key words, rather than the contemporary VVS slogan of 'higher, faster, further'. Programme goals were to design an aircraft with very high battle damage resistance and tolerance, which would be economic and simple to produce, operate and maintain, which would have unmatched performance and agility at very low level, and which could operate fully laden from a semi-prepared 120-m (390-ft) airstrip. Officialdom caught up with the two bureaux in March 1969, when an official LSSh 'Shturmovik' request for proposals was issued by the Ministry of the Aircraft Industry.

The launch of the competition did not represent a complete change of heart, however, since development of the swing-wing Su-17 and ground attack variants of the new MiG-23 continued apace. There was no guarantee that any design produced as a result of the competition would ever enter production, and if an aircraft type were to be manufactured it seemed likely that it would be in only small numbers, for further evaluation of the concept.

The jet *Shturmovik* competitors

Nevertheless, the new requirement was important enough for four experimental design bureaux to work on competing designs. Sukhoi continued with its T8, while Ilyushin continued with the Il-42. Yakovlev designed a version of its Yak-28 'Brewer' bomber as the Yak-25LSh, and Mikoyan worked on a pair of designs under the provisional designation MiG-27, although neither bore any

resemblance to the MiG-27 we know today. The MiG-27Sh was based on the MiG-21 airframe, but with side-mounted intakes and a broad-chord, modestly swept wing like that fitted to the Hawker Hunter and a heavily framed canopy incorporating great slabs of armoured glass. The cockpit was moved forward. The MiG-27II was more revolutionary, a supersonic *Shturmovik* with a similar armoured cockpit and canopy and with similar fuselage and intakes, but with the ogival delta wing of the A-144 Analog. The aircraft was powered by a pair of unspecified engines installed side-by-side in the rear fuselage, and was intended to carry a warload of up to 3000 kg (6,610 lb). A rewinged MiG-21LSh design was considered, but most of the attention was focused on the MiG-27 derivatives.

The Sukhoi T8 was redesigned under the guidance of bureau chief P. O. Sukhoi before it was formally submitted in response to the LSSh requirement. The most important of the changes suggested by Sukhoi was the addition of a pair of 29.5-kN (6,630-lb) (or 27 kN/6,070 lb, according to some sources) Mikulin RD-9B engines, non-afterburning versions of the MiG-19's turbojet powerplant.

Sukhoi takes the day

These changes were enough to allow the Ministry of the Aviation Industry to select the Sukhoi design as the winner of the competition, much to the annoyance of the Ilyushin OKB, which felt that their aircraft was superior and that their history and experience made them the natural choice to design a jet *Shturmovik*. They suspected that their aircraft had been rejected for the wrong reasons, conjecturing that the motive for selecting the T8 could be found in its single-

seat configuration, which did not require the training of a new generation of dedicated gunners. To Ilyushin this was an expensive heresy, for they believed that operational experience had shown that a rear gunner was absolutely essential in a slow-moving *Shturmovik*. They were also amazed that their turbofan-engined aircraft (powered by a pair of non-afterburning derivatives of the MiG-29's RD-33) had been beaten by an aircraft powered by thirsty and old-fashioned turbojets, which necessitated the carriage of a larger explosive and inflammable fuel load, and which the OKB also believed were more prone to battle damage.

The Ilyushin Design Bureau was now officially out of the picture, but it continued work on its aircraft privately, describing it as an aerodynamic research aircraft and later moving the prototype to a Byelorussian airfield to avoid attention. Much later, following criticism of the Su-25 after its initial combat experience in Afghanistan, the Ilyushin aircraft re-entered the 'Frogfoot' story, as will be described.

With the T8 declared as the winner of the design competition, approval was given for further development. Prototype drawings, and production tools and jigs were prepared at Factory No. 153 at Novosibirsk, a plant traditionally associated with Sukhoi aircraft. Production of the first prototype was scheduled to begin in June 1970, but was delayed until August 1971 when air force officers increased the required warload to 4000 kg (6,435 lb), and tried to force an increase in low-level maximum speed to 1200 km/h (745 mph). Sukhoi argued strongly that supersonic speed was unnecessary and would impose unacceptable penalties, but some air force officers, conditioned by their experience with Su-7s and MiG-21s, simply could not conceive that any aircraft could survive without supersonic capability. Sukhoi compromised on Mach 0.82 (having originally favoured Mach 0.7). The aircraft was redesigned to meet the amended requirement (becoming the LVSSh) with larger fuel tanks, bigger overall dimensions and a revised MTOW of 10530 kg (6,540 lb).

The T8 team

Mikhail Simonov was appointed as project manager, with Oleg Samolovich remaining as chief designer on the aircraft from August 1972 until 9 October 1974, when he moved to the T10 (Su-27) and Y. V. Ivashetchkin took over. This was one month before the redesign was complete, in September 1972. Ivashetchkin had been Samolovich's deputy from 25 December 1972. Under Ivashetchkin was Vladimir Babak, who supervised a design team consisting of Yuri Rybishkin (detail airframe design), Alexander Blinov (durability), Pietr Lyrshchikov (combat

survivability) and Alexei Ryzhov (engine integration). The production supervisor was Valerii Nikolskii, and the chief of testing was Colonel Stanislav Nazarenko.

At around this time, the Sukhoi designers got their first glimpse of the US Fairchild A-10, and this caused something of a crisis. Several members of the team were keen to follow the US example of mounting the engines in pods above the fuselage, but this was felt to impose an unacceptable drag penalty; anyway, it was already too late for such a fundamental change.

The T8 mock-up was presented to the authorities at Khodinka, near Moscow, but an official order for prototypes was not placed. Two prototypes (T8-1 and T8-2) were in fact already under construction, Sukhoi having authorised the start of work after approving the preliminary design on 6 June 1972. The reason that the prototypes were not officially ordered became clear at a meeting between the OKB and the Minister of the Aviation

Top: Despite the problems that affected the T8, and the bitter combat experience of early-model Su-25s after they entered service, the Su-25 ultimately became a formidable attack aircraft.

Above centre: Another view of the T8-1 prototype.

Above: The Il-40 'Brawny' design reappeared – astonishingly, but once more unsuccessfully – in the early 1990s, in the shape of the Il-102. The Il-102, originally designated Il-42, might even be a rebuilt Il-40.

55

Sukhoi Su-25, Su-28 and Su-39 'Frogfoot'

Right: Sukhoi rebuilt the T8-1 to become the T8-1D. This aircraft was re-engined with R-95Sh turbojets and also gained the revised engine nacelles and inlets, armoured cockpit, larger wing (with leading-edge slats), larger fin and rudder, and the extended nose and tail adopted for production-standard Su-25s. The T8-1D first flew on 21 July 1978.

Below: Sukhoi used the T8-3 airframe for damage resistance testing. Sections of the cockpit were specially armoured and then fired at, from close range.

Below: T8-4 was the second production-standard aircraft and is seen here at the Tbilisi plant – the badge on the nose is believed to be the factory emblem. This aircraft is carrying FAB-250 bombs and B-8M1 rocket pods. T8-4 made its maiden flight in September 1979. By then the Sukhoi design had already been catalogued as 'Ram-J' by Western intelligence agencies.

Industry, P. V. Dementiev, when the aircraft's MTOW was again revised upwards, to 12220 kg (5,540 lb), and warload was increased to 5000 kg (3,110 lb) (although this was later relaxed back to 4000 kg/2,485 lb). A maximum *g* limit of 6.5 was specified, and the important systems were to be protected against damage by shells of up to 20-mm calibre.

P. O. Sukhoi lived long enough to see the mock-up of the aircraft for which he had fought, but died in 1973 before the prototypes were formally commissioned. The order to complete two T8 prototypes (one, T8-0, to be a static test airframe) was finally issued on 6 May 1974. This order was a tactical-technical requirement, which funded prototype aircraft and a limited flight test programme, but

held out no promise of production funding. Sukhoi realised that the aircraft would have to be produced on a shoestring budget, and that existing equipment, avionics and systems would have to be used wherever practical.

The T8-0 was delivered for static testing on 12 September 1974. The T8-1 prototype was completed with a modified version of the nav/attack suite fitted to the Su-17M2 'Fitter' and had a modified version of the SPPU-22 cannon pod mounted internally as the VPU-22 gun station. This contained a GSh-23 twin-barrelled 23-mm cannon with barrels which could be depressed for strafing. It was almost certainly only ever intended as an interim gun for the Su-25, whose concept had stressed the advantages of heavier calibre 30-mm weapons. The aircraft's avionics included the FON-1400 laser rangefinder, DISS-7 Doppler, and KN-23 navigation computer (designed for the MiG-23B series fighter-bombers). The flying prototype was delivered to the LII Gromov Flight Research Centre's Zhukhovskii airfield for testing in early December 1974. The Sukhoi bureau's chief test pilot, General Vladimir Ilyushin, was nominated as the initial project pilot and made the first high-speed taxi runs on 25 December 1975. The first taxi runs with the nosewheel raised off the runway took place on 3 January 1975. On 11 January, two days before the scheduled date for the maiden flight, one of the RD-9 engines (which had actually been scavenged from a redundant MiG-19, according to legend) suffered a turbine bearing failure, and several blades separated, causing major damage. The first flight was finally made on 22 February 1975.

Engine shortfalls

These problems with the RD-9 engine represented a particularly bitter pill for Sukhoi to swallow, since it had already been decided that a more powerful engine would be needed to cope with the aircraft's planned increased weight, and since the Minister for Aircraft Production, P. V. Dementiev, had already refused to authorise production of the Su-25 with the 'obsolete' RD-9. This was found in the shape of the Tumanskii R-95Sh, which was essentially the MiG-21's R-13F-300 with its afterburner removed. The new engine was again based on an afterburning turbojet, and not on a more modern, more suitable, and more economical turbofan. For the rest of its life, the Su-25 was handicapped by its primitive powerplant, and from time to time proposals were made that the aircraft should be re-engined with RD-33s (without afterburners). The answer was always the same: the necessary structural changes were too extensive to make re-engining worthwhile.

Although it was undeniably primitive, the R-95Sh was extremely robust and reliable. The powerplant was a twin-spool turbojet, with an axial compressor, a three-stage low-pressure section and a five-stage high-pressure section. The axial turbine was of two stages. The engine also had a

10-chamber annular combustor, with twin igniters. Auxiliary gearboxes were mounted on the bottom of each engine, driving the DC starter and generator, the AC generator, and the hydraulic, fuel and oil pumps. The R-95Sh was also designed to be able to run using different fuels, although this was only possible for four hours when using non-standard fuels such as vehicle diesel fuel. While the new engine was being developed, the aircraft continued to fly, and continued to experience difficulties. The aileron control system proved to have inadequate power, and eventually (from about 1984) BU-45 hydraulic boosters had to be fitted.

Despite the problems, the aircraft was transferred to Akhtubinsk in June 1975, where it undertook a variety of live weapons firing trials. These were concluded in August, military pilots noting that the aircraft's control forces were unacceptably high (even by Soviet standards, where higher stick forces are accepted as the norm), and that the cockpit was inadequately ventilated. The RD-9 engine had also proved prone to stalling when the cannon or rockets were fired, and was considered to be deficient in thrust.

In its original configuration, the first T8 looked quite different to all subsequent Su-25s. It had a shorter fin, with a small, single-piece rudder, and the wing was of shorter span and lacked the later Su-25's distinctive wingtip airbrake pods. The wings may have been slightly more swept, but this cannot be confirmed. The VPU-22 gun station took the form of a streamlined constant-section tube semi-submerged into the lower forward fuselage, with a fore-and-aft aperture in the front for the depressing gun barrels. The nosewheel was mounted 210 mm (8.3 in) to the left of the centreline.

The 'all new' T8D

The problems suffered by the first T8 prompted the eventual decision to entirely rebuild the aircraft with a host of modifications and improvements, completely changing its appearance and capabilities. It was rolled out after a two-year lay-up on 26 April 1978, just in time to take part in the state acceptance trials which began on 21 July 1978, for which the aircraft flew under the revised designation T8D (D for *Dvigyatel*, or engine). The second prototype had already joined the flight test programme, making its maiden flight on 26 December 1975. This aircraft was the first with a production-representative titanium cockpit bathtub, the first aircraft having had steel armour of the same weight. The T8-2 was also the first prototype which actually looked like a real Su-25, with long-span wings and a tall tailfin. The long-span wings included longer span (and thus increased area) ailerons, servotabs and a leading-edge dogtooth discontinuity. The aircraft was re-engined with R95Sh engines to become the T8-2D in March 1976 (before the first prototype was re-engined). The new engines had a new thrust line, and the tailplanes were modified in consequence, going from 5° anhedral to 5° dihedral. This was achieved by simply swapping the tailplanes from one side to the other and turning them upside down.

When it emerged from its rebuild, the T8D closely resembled the second aircraft in appearance, with a dihedral tailplane, taller fin, long-span wings and ailerons, and wingtip pods. The wingtip pods first fitted to the T8-2 contained a retractable landing light forward, and had a horizontally split rear section, with upper and lower halves which split apart to act as airbrakes. It was originally intended that the split airbrakes could be operated together to act as speedbrakes, or individually (in conjunction with appropriate rudder input) to generate side force. This capability was found not to be tactically significant, and the physiological effects on pilots were unpleasant. The T8-1 was originally built without airbrakes at all, and before it gained its wingtip pods the T8-2 had petal-type airbrakes mounted on the back of the engine nacelle sides.

'Ram-J' is revealed

The original VPU-22 gun station had been removed and replaced by an AO-17 30-mm twin-barrelled cannon mounted in the lower port forward fuselage. This necessitated moving the nosewheel again, to a position to the right

Top: This view of T8-2 shows the aircraft after it had been rebuilt as the T8-2D, in 1976. T8-2 was the first of the two initial prototypes to be re-engined and rebuilt (T8-1 followed in 1977/78).

Above: T8-5 is seen here at Kubinka air base, where much of the trials programme was hosted. T8-5 was lost in a crash in June 1980, soon after its maiden flight.

Below: With surprising speed – almost as soon as T8 development gave way to Su-25 production – export 'Frogfoots' were delivered to Czechoslovakia.

Right: This view of T8-9 shows the aircraft fitted with the TL-70 Kometa podded winch and towed target system. In fact, T8-9 was revised, rebuilt and repainted to serve as the Su-25BM (Bukshir Mishenyei) prototype – a dedicated target-tug variant. Work on the Su-25BM project began in 1986 and aerial trials commenced in 1989. A total of 50 Su-25BMs was eventually built for the VVS. Operationally, a single pod was always carried on the centre wing pylon, counterbalanced by another store (such as the FAB-500 bomb seen here) on the opposite wing.

Above: T8-12 rapidly drew attention to itself when it appeared on public display. It had been modified – reportedly for radar cross-section reduction – with what appeared to be radar-absorbent material on the nose and a faired-over gun port. However, as its air data probes, IFF antenna and other protuberances had not been removed, the true purpose of the changes to this Su-25 remain a mystery.

Below: This Su-25 is seen at Akhtubinsk in CFE verification photo-calibration markings.

of the aircraft's centreline. The change of cannon finally fulfilled Soviet air staff demands for a larger calibre gun packing a heavier punch. The T8 was eventually 'spotted' at Zhukhovskii by a Western intelligence satellite during 1977, and the aircraft was allocated the provisional Ramenskoye-series (the nearest town to the then anonymous test and trials airfield) reporting name 'Ram-J'.

Avionics improvements

Underneath the skin, even more important changes had been made. The navigation and attack suite of the Su-17M-2 was replaced by the upgraded and enhanced avionics of the Su-17M-3. The Fone laser rangefinder was replaced by a Klen-PS laser ranging unit, while the aircraft also received a KN-23 navigation computer, a DISS-7 Doppler, an RV-5M radar altimeter and an ASP-17BC-8 gunsight. This equipment suite was fitted to the T8-3 and subsequent pre-production aircraft from the start. The net effect of the many equipment changes was to enhance the accuracy of both navigation and weapon aiming. The KN-23 navigation

computer, the DISS-7 Doppler, and the ASP-17BC-8 gunsight were retained in the production avionics suite.

So little priority was accorded to the T8 that production of the aircraft had to be moved from Novosibirsk after the construction of only the first two prototypes to make way for more important work on the Su-24 'Fencer' and Su-27 'Flanker'. Even the factories at Smolensk and Irkutsk were busy with Su-24 and Su-27 work, and Sukhoi was forced to look elsewhere. Licence-production in Poland was seriously considered, before the OKB eventually took the project to the under-utilised Factory No. 31 at Tbilisi in Georgia. The T8-3 and T8-4 were built at Tbilisi to the revised configuration, making their maiden flights on 18 June 1979 and during September 1979, respectively.

T8 trials in Afghanistan

The Su-25 has been associated with the Soviet intervention in Afghanistan since the start of its career. From 16 April until 5 June 1980 (50 days), the first and third T8 prototypes were sent to Afghanistan to participate in a portion of the state acceptance trials which were to be 'conducted under as near real battlefield conditions as possible'. These trials, undertaken under the codename Romb-1, were not operational trials, although the pilots were warned that they might be asked to undertake missions by local divisional commanders. The two aircraft operated from a semi-prepared strip at an Afghan tank base near Shindand. They made 100 combat sorties in Afghanistan, 30 of which counted towards the state acceptance trials. They flew real missions, tasked by ground force commanders, who quickly found the agile T8s especially well-suited for attacking inaccessible targets in ravines and steep valleys. A pair of AV-MF Yak-38s participated in Romb-1 in Afghanistan at much the same time. The Su-25s were seen and photographed by Western journalists accompanying Mujahideen guerrillas, and though taken from very long range the photos were distinct enough to allow Western intelligence officers to see that the aircraft they knew as 'Ram-J' was flying operations. The full ASCC reporting name 'Frogfoot' was allocated soon afterwards.

The fourth Su-25 prototype (T8-4) was left to complete state acceptance tests at Mary in Turkmenistan until March 1981, when production was finally recommended. One of the loudest voices arguing in favour of this step was that of General Alexander Yefimov, deputy commander of the VVS and himself a distinguished former *Shturmovik* pilot during the Great Patriotic War. While this marked a successful step in the T8's career, the step forward was accompanied by two steps back. The test fleet was already depleted by the planned use of the T8-3 for battle damage resistance tests, in which weapons of increasing calibre and

velocity were fired at the airframe, but was due to be further reduced. The fifth T8 prototype (T8-5, which had joined the test programme during early 1980) had already been destroyed on 23 June 1980. It disintegrated at only 7.5 *g*, killing the test pilot, Y. A. Yegerov, and in January 1981 the Afghan veteran T8-1 disintegrated in a dive from which A. Ivanov ejected safely.

T8 trials developments

Additional T8 airframes soon joined the flight test programme. The T8-6 was used for gun-firing trials, while the T8-9 was used for aerodynamic and spinning trials. Rough field and external warload trials were undertaken by T8-10, including trials of backward-firing rocket projectiles from a heavily modified B8M pod (which still appeared to face forward). The T8-11 was the first aircraft with boosted ailerons. It later tested the new W-section four-part airbrakes. The next prototype finished its test-flying life trialling a special radar-absorbent ('stealthy') skin, and reportedly undertook compatibility trials with at least one type of tactical nuclear weapon. This laid the groundwork for the Su-25's later secondary (and little known) nuclear role. Su-25s have been associated with the IAB-500 'shape' that is believed to be the training weapon associated with the RN-61 nuclear bomb carried by various Frontal Aviation fighter-bomber types. With its 'stealthy' coating, the T8-12 had its laser window and gun port covered over, and at the end of these trials was retired to the museum at

Khodinka. This was an accidental breach of the security surrounding the new coating (which may have been under test for a more advanced aircraft type, possibly the MiG 1-42) and, when it was noticed, the aircraft was quickly withdrawn and replaced by a less sensitive Su-25. The aircraft is now believed to be in the Central Museum of the Great Patriotic War in Bralev Fonchenkou in Moscow.

The T10-14 and T10-15 were eventually used as R-195 engine testbeds, after extensive service as development mules. The T10-15's career included combat service in Afghanistan. The T8-7, T8-8 and T8-13 designations were not used by flying prototypes, and may have been static test and battle damage airframes, or may have become the Su-25UB and Su-25T prototypes.

Su-25 into production and for export

The first production Su-25s rolled off the line at Tbilisi and were delivered to the 200th OShAE at Sital Chai in Azerbaijan during April 1981. Universal export success was destined to elude the Su-25 – only two of Russia's Warsaw Pact allies ever bought the aircraft – but the type was exported (albeit in modest numbers) from quite an early stage in its career. The export version of the little fighter-bomber was designated as the Su-25K, and was externally identical to the version delivered to Frontal Aviation *Shturmovik* regiments. The first Su-25Ks were delivered to Czechoslovakia in April 1984, and the first good quality photos of the Su-25 started to appear in Czech aviation

T8-15 had an important early career as an engine testbed, trialling the R-195 engine. The extended (IR-suppressant) jetpipes and extra air cooling scoops (above the rear cowling) required by the new engine are obvious in this view. This aircraft has also been fitted with an additional bank of ASO-2V chaff/flare dispensers above the engine. The R-195 was an improved version of the R-95Sh, but it was never fitted to many aircraft and the Su-25 remained hampered by its ancient engine technology. The R-195 did find an application in the improved T8M (Su-25T) series, however. Remarkably, T8-15 is alleged to have gone on to see combat service in Afghanistan. Following this, the same aircraft was given a new identity, as 'Blue 301', and appeared at the Paris air show in 1991.

This anonymous Su-25 is wearing the original dark camouflage scheme tested on the Su-25, but soon abandoned. Throughout their entire service history Soviet/Russian Su-25s have worn a single camouflage scheme of two-tone brown and green, with light grey undersides.

Above: Two-seat Su-25UBs operated alongside the front-line Su-25Ks in the East Germany-based units. This is one of the 'Frogfoot-Bs' attached to the 368th OShAP, formerly based at Demmin-Tütow.

Below: This is the T8UB-1 prototype, the first Su-25UB. Consideration was given to training Su-25 pilots on existing types, such as the MiG-15UTI but, wisely, the decision was made to develop a two-seater.

magazines the following year. The deliveries to Czechoslovakia took place early in the Su-25's career, even before the type had reached the Group of Soviet Forces in Germany, and while only one of the 60th OShAP's squadrons was available for combat in Afghanistan. The Su-25Ks delivered to Czechoslovakia and Bulgaria differed little from the aircraft used by Soviet regiments during the same period, although they almost certainly had slightly downgraded defensive avionics equipment and were not compatible with nuclear weapons. Identically designated Su-25Ks delivered to other customers (e.g., North Korea and Iraq) were probably even more downgraded, although they displayed few external differences to the Soviet Su-25s.

Shopping for an Su-25

The costs of military aircraft are seldom revealed. Even when one is, it is hardly clear what level of spares support, ammunition, and ground support equipment has been included. Furthermore, prices actually differ according to political circumstances, the customer's 'status' (in relation to the supplier), and the extent to which the deal is being financed by the home government (as aid, as a genuine commercial deal, or in exchange for some commodity). Today, Russian aircraft manufacturers often find themselves supplying their aircraft as part of debt repayment packages. Prices can also differ according to whether the deal involves offsets, or according to the currency in which the customer will be paying. Finally, the exact specification of the aircraft being delivered will have an impact on price, as will the inclusion of any training within the USSR.

For all of these reasons, it is unusual for the price of a military aircraft to be openly released. The price offered to a long-standing customer or a close ally, paying with gold (or $US) and not demanding complex offsets, will be very different to the price offered to a customer paying in palm oil and unlikely to make even those payments on time or in full. Surprisingly, quite detailed prices for the Su-25K emerged during the early 1990s. They gave an indication of the amount of equipment and weaponry supplied in a standard package (to equip a single squadron).

Twelve Su-25Ks, with a set of tools, spares and ground maintenance aids, were quoted at $132 million ($11 million each), plus two Su-25UBKs cost an additional $23.8 million ($11.9 million each) with the same tools, spares and equipment. Each aircraft was supplied with two SPPU-22-01 gun pods, eight BD-3-25 pylons, two PD-62-8 pylons, two APU-68-85E launchers, two APU-60-1MD launchers and three empty B8M rocket pods, while two BD-3-25AKU pylons and their associate two AKU-58E launchers were supplied with each group of four aircraft. These allowed the aircraft to carry the Kh-58 (AS-11 'Kilter') anti-radiation missile. A conversion training course was costed at $1.596 million, and a KTS-18 simulator at $5.35 million. Four spare R-195 engines were priced at $4.72 million ($1.18 million each).

Weapons which could be supplied included 3,360 S-8KM unguided rockets (at $1,607 each), 840 S-13T rockets (at $5,110 each) and 840 S-13OF rockets (at $4,450 each). The larger S-24B (retailing at $5,210 apiece) were supplied in batches of 336, and 84 S-25-OFM-PUs were offered at $14,167 each.

For the built-in 30-mm cannon, 5,000 rounds of OFZ shells were offered at $26,364 per thousand, while similar OFZ shells for underwing 23-mm cannon retailed at $7,460 per thousand and were supplied in batches of 30,000. The 23-mm BZT round (supplied in the same quantity) cost $5,653 per thousand.

Missiles available included the Kh-25ML (168 of which constituted a standard batch, at $103,643 each) and the Kh-29L (84 for $175,241 each). Inert captive acquisition training rounds for both missiles were available in pairs, at $77,734 and $131,433 each, respectively.

Most types of bomb were supplied in quantities of 336, and unit prices included $1,445 for a FAB-250-270 fire bomb, $1,956 for a FAB-250M62, $8,705 for a BETAB-500, $10,195 for a FAB-500SHL, $12,054 for an ODAB-500PM, $13,728 for an RBK-500 AO-2 cluster bomb and $20,538 for a BETAB-500SHP. The RBK-500 PTAB-1 was the most expensive bomb offered, at $21,021 each. Smaller bombs were generally delivered in bigger batches, with the bargain basement $859 OFAB-100-120 coming in batches of 1,344 bombs. A handful of specialist stores were supplied in smaller quantities. A batch of 20 FOTAB-250T photoflashes retailed at $5,060 each, while 100 SAB-250-200 illuminators cost $4,821 each.

Technical description

The Su-25K's service life was given as 1,500 flying hours before a major overhaul, and the service interval as 700 hours. They obviously did not expect high utilisation, since the 700-hour interval was also given as a seven- to eight-year gap. The first production Su-25 hardly differed from the later prototypes, and a technical description of one would apply just as well to the other. In fact, all Su-25s up until the Su-25T/TM were structurally similar, with much the same systems. Only a handful of changes were made as a result of later combat experience in Afghanistan, and they were limited in scope, despite their impact and significance.

The Su-25 was of conventional configuration and construction, apart from the extensive use of armour plate. The aircraft was an all-metal monoplane with a high-set, high aspect-ratio wing which was modestly tapered and slightly swept on the leading edge, but not on the trailing edge. The wing incorporated 2°30' of anhedral. Engines were mounted to the fuselage sides in semi-conformal nacelles. Sixty per cent of the aircraft's structure was of

The Su-25UB retains all the combat capability of the single-seat Su-25. This aircraft is unlikely ever to see any dangerous action, however, as it is the sole Su-25UB in the possession of the Slovak air force. The Czech air force also operates a single Su-25UB. All Slovak 'Frogfoots' are based at Malacky-Kuchyna air base, north of the capital city of Bratislava. Interestingly, Slovak Su-25s have retained the original white horse badge – the Ostrava coat of arms – which was worn by the aircraft when they were all in Czechoslovakian service, and is still worn by Su-25s in today's independent Czech air force.

The Su-28 trainer began life as the Su-25UT and made its maiden flight in 1987. The aircraft was closely based on the combat-capable Su-25UB and the prototype, seen here, was built from the T8UB-1 prototype. In the Su-28, Sukhoi hoped to produce a combined basic/advanced jet trainer that had all the strengths of the Su-25 (rough field capability and tough landing gear, good mission endurance and a wide range of fuel compatibilities) without any of the mission equipment or armour that weighed down the front-line aircraft.

The similarities and differences between the Su-25UB and Su-28 are clear when one compares this aircraft with the Su-28 above. The most obvious change is the elimination of the pylons.

conventional Duralumin construction, with 13.5 per cent titanium alloys, 19 per cent steel, 2 per cent magnesium alloys and 5.5 per cent fibre-glass and other materials. Virtually no use was made of carbon-fibre composites or advanced aluminium lithium alloys.

Electrical power was supplied by a single 28.5-volt DC circuit, and by three 36-volt/400-Hz and one 115-volt/400-Hz AC circuits. The DC circuit consisted of a transformer, voltage regulator, and circuit breakers. Power was generated by a pair of engine-driven GSR-ST-12/400 generators, with two 25 Aph NiCad batteries available as an emergency power source.

Fuel system

The Su-25's fuel system delivers fuel to the engines from four pressurised main tanks, and from any external tanks (up to four of which can be carried underwing). The system incorporated DCN-44S-DT supply pumps, ECN-91B centrifugal delivery pumps and SN-6 ejector pumps, together with an NR-54 regulator, filters, cleaners, and dump valves, and with flow-meters, pressure and contents sensors. The internal tanks are pressurised using bleed air from the compressor's eighth stage. The No. 1 and No. 2 tanks are located in the fuselage, with the No. 2 (rear) tank sub-divided into two and acting as a collector tank. The fuselage tanks contained a total of 2386 litres (525 Imp gal) and had armoured bottoms and sides, beside

being self-sealing and lined with reticulated foam. The wing tanks contained a total of 1274 litres (280 Imp gal). The tanks could be filled manually, through gravity filler caps, or using a single pressure-refuelling point in the No. 1 tank. The engines can run using five types of aviation kerosene (PL-4, PL-6, T-1, TS-1 and RT) or in emergency can run for a limited time on diesel.

The Su-25 has independent twin hydraulic systems, each powered by an engine-driven NP-34-1M supply pump and each using 18 litres (4 Imp gal) of AMG-10 hydraulic fluid, pressurised to between 20 and 23 MPa using nitrogen. The port engine drove the system designated as the primary hydraulic system (PGS), which powered the nosewheel steering unit, the initial chambers of the aileron boosters, the airbrakes, the slats, the flaps and the tailplane, and could be used for emergency undercarriage extension. The starboard engine drove the secondary (VGS) system, which was used for undercarriage extension and retraction, mainwheel braking, and the yaw damper, and for the second chambers of the aileron boosters.

The semi-monocoque fuselage consisted of four sections (nose, forward fuselage, centre section and rear fuselage) and was built up around 35 bulkheads, longerons, auxiliary bulkheads, stringers and a stressed skin. The foremost nose section extended from the first to the fourth bulkhead, to which were attached the twin air data booms with their pitot-static sensors. The nose incorporated a downward-

opening forward fairing, whose chiselled front edge included the Klen PS laser rangefinder window, and which swung down to give access to the Klen equipment. The unpressurised navigation and auxiliary avionics bay behind this incorporated four upward-opening access doors.

The nosewheel bay contained the rearward-retracting nose oleo, which incorporated a twin-chamber hydro-pneumatic shock absorber (containing nitrogen and AMG-10 hydraulic fluid) with a maximum stroke of 340 mm (13.4 in). The nosewheel was hydraulically steerable through 60°, and was covered by a large mudguard/debris deflector. The nosewheel bay was covered by tandem twin doors, the long, thin rear door closing again after undercarriage extension. The undercarriage doors were linked to the oleo by rods. Retraction and extension was controlled hydraulically, usually by the secondary hydraulic system, but by the primary system in emergency.

Armour plated

A key feature in ensuring survivability over the battle-field was the provision of an armoured cockpit to protect the aircraft's most vulnerable component: the pilot. This took up most of the forward fuselage section, back to Bulk-head No. 11, together with the nosewheel bay, the gun bay and the main avionics bay. The cannon bay lay between bulkheads 4 and 7 in the lower left 'corner' of the fuselage and accommodated a single AO-17A twin-barrelled 30-mm cannon (also known as the GSh-30-2, or as the 9A623) with its 250-round ammunition box. This weapon had a rate of fire of 3,000 rpm and a muzzle velocity of 870 m (2,855 ft) per second.

The Sukhoi OKB originally planned a steel-armoured cockpit 'bathtub' that would come up to the pilot's shoulders. It was designed to use two layers of hard and soft

steel. Welding such a structure meant losing some of the armoured properties, but using rivets or bolts risked these fasteners becoming secondary projectiles when hit. It was finally decided that the pilot's cockpit 'bathtub' would be of welded titanium plates, each between 10 and 24 mm (0.4 and 0.9 in) thick. This was an expensive but highly efficient solution to the problem, and resulted in the pilot sitting in a box of armour which was reportedly capable of withstanding hits by up to 50 20-mm or 23-mm rounds. The titanium cockpit was not ready for installation in the first prototype, so steel plates machined to be the same weight as the 24-mm titanium sheets were used.

Protecting the pilot

The pilot sat as low as possible in the cockpit, and, because this restricted his ability to maintain a good all-round lookout, he was provided with a rear-facing periscope set into the top of the canopy, and with rear-view mirrors mounted on the windscreen arch. By necessity, the pilot's head projected a certain amount above the cockpit rails where it was vulnerable to ground fire. To protect his head, the pilot looked out through a windscreen of armoured glass, and a massive plate of armour sat above the ejection seat headrest, protecting the pilot from rounds coming from above and behind.

It was not only the pilot that was protected by armour. Virtually all vital systems and components were protected by armour, or duplicated, or both. The main engine oil tank, housed in the starboard nacelle, was protected by armour plate, and the main fuel lines leading from the main fuel tank to the engines were armoured and routed so that they could not spray fuel onto the engines if severed. The fuel tanks themselves were self-sealing and filled with reticulated foam to prevent explosions if breached.

The single Su-28 (which has also been referred to as the Su-25M or Su-25UT) was painted in a red, white and blue display scheme and wore DOSAAF titles on the tail. The paramilitary DOSAAF was the 'private flying' organisation of the former Soviet Union that provided basic flying training for students – most of whom would end up in the armed forces or other state aviation bodies. The Su-28 was mooted as a replacement for the DOSAAF's huge number of Czech-built Aero L-29 and L-39 jet trainers which were becoming increasingly difficult to support, even before the fall of the Warsaw Pact. In truth, the ungainly Su-28 was ill-suited to such a task, but it did make a few brief appearances at Western air shows in this guise. After a Paris debut in 1989, it travelled to Dubai (as seen here, in 1991) and later to the Philippines.

Sukhoi Su-25, Su-28 and Su-39 'Frogfoot'

The control surfaces were actuated via titanium control rods each 40 mm (1.5 in) thick, proved against damage by small-calibre (up to 12.7-mm) machine-gun fire. Unlike cables, these could be distorted or nicked and still continue to function. The elevator control rods were duplicated. It has been suggested that pitch controls were better protected than roll and yaw controls so that the pilot would have the maximum chance of being able to pull up to eject if he suffered catastrophic damage while at low level.

Cockpit systems

The pilot sat on a Severin K-36L ejection seat. The K-36L was a simplified version of the K-36D or K-36DM used by aircraft like the MiG-29 and Su-27. Surprisingly, the seat was not capable of zero-zero operation; instead, it was cleared for operation at ground level, at speeds of over 55 kt (100 km/h; 65 mph). The seat was able to cope with inverted ejections at heights of 150 m (490 ft) or above, and 90° ejections from heights of 50 m (165 ft) and above. The cockpit also incorporated an air conditioning system, though this was intended more to maintain a degree of overpressure (between 3 and 5 kPa) in the cockpit, to prevent NBC contamination, than to maintain pilot comfort. The air conditioning system also supplied air to the pilot's anti-*g* suit and ventilated the windscreen and canopy, while also providing cooling air for the avionics compartments. Air for the system was bled from the eighth (final) compressor stage, and then passed through two heat exchangers and a turbocooler.

The separate oxygen system supplied a mix of air and pure oxygen to the pilot at altitudes in excess of 2000 m (6,560 ft), with pure oxygen above 7000 m (23,000 ft). The oxygen/air mix was produced in a KP-52M mixer unit. The oxygen was drawn from four 5-litre (15-MPa) bottles housed in the nosewheel bay. A BKO-3VZ emergency oxygen system was housed in the ejection seat, primarily for use during an ejection at high altitude, and gave a three-minute supply.

The cockpit was as conventional in layout as the aircraft was conventional in configuration: ergonomically laid out, but with rows of conventional analog instruments, switches and selectors, and without any electronic 'glass' display screens. The overall effect was old-fashioned and cramped, and the layout would have felt familiar to a late-generation MiG-21 pilot, or to pilots accustomed to the MiG-23 or Su-17. The panel was painted in a blue-grey colour slightly less vivid than the near-turquoise once used in Soviet combat. The cockpit incorporated many typically Soviet features, from the painted white vertical line on the lower

Above: 'Blue 08' was the prototype Su-25UTG carrier trainer and made its first landing aboard the carrier Tbilisi (which became the Admiral Kuznetsov) in November 1989. The Su-25UTG was intended to train Soviet/Russian pilots in basic carrier operations, but they were never conducted at a proper operational tempo. The Soviets' headlong rush into carrierborne aviation was defeated by lack of funding, before the terrible problems caused by moving straight into full-blown fast-jet operations at sea became manifest.

Above right: The prototype Su-28 (T8UTG-1) is seen here making its first ski-jump at the Saki naval training airfield.

Right: 'Blue 08', and the production UTGs, have a modified rear fuselage structure to cope with the loads imposed by arrested landings. The Su-25UTG has an (arrested) landing distance of 90 m (295 ft) and is stressed for a load of 5g on landing.

panel which showed the pilot the stick central position (useful when recovering from a spin or departure) to the rail-mounted throttles and chunky-topped control column.

The throttles were mounted on a pair of parallel rods on the port cockpit wall, below the canopy rail. The port console mounted external stores, weapons selectors and jettison controls, as well as trimmers, drag chute, oxygen and air conditioning controls. The starboard side console and cockpit wall contained navigation system, radio, transponder, lighting and chaff/flare dispenser controls, plus the engine start panel and generator controls.

The rear cockpit of the two-seat Su-25UB was broadly similar to the single-seat or front cockpit. It lacked the gunsight and instead had a control panel for a system which allowed the instructor to simulate emergencies in the front cockpit, or to generate synthetic symbology in the front-seat sight. Full dual controls were fitted.

Su-25 avionics

The Su-25 was well equipped, with superb equipment and aids for precise navigation, accurate weapons delivery and self-defence. Even before details of the exact equipment fit became known, Western analysts were able to make some fairly accurate estimates of what types of equipment were fitted from the plethora of antennas, fairings, bumps and protrusions which littered the airframe from nose to tail. The nose culminated in an angular 'chisel', whose sloping face was transparent, behind which was the Klen-PS laser rangefinder. Immediately above the tip of the nose was a pair of parallel instrumentation booms, serving as pitot-static sources for the instruments and the weapons aiming system. The main (port) PVD-18G-3M probe is always thought to have carried sideslip and AoA sensor vanes, and a cruciform RSBN-6S antenna, whereas the tandem cruci-form finlets all seem to have been fixed antennas for the RSBN, and not pivoting vanes. The starboard (secondary) PVD-7 probe is a simple pitot. The RSBN-6 system is used in conjunction with RSBN-2N or RSBN-4N ground beacons for navigation, or with PRMG-4 for instrument

landing approaches. This allows approaches down to 60 m (200 ft) above the runway. The DUA-3 AoA vanes were actually mounted low on the forward fuselage sides, roughly in line with the forward edge of the windscreen. A single DUA-3M yaw vane was mounted below the nose, on the centreline, just ahead of the gun muzzle. The nose

Ukraine's Su-25UTGs were obtained from former Soviet forces, left behind when Ukraine split from the USSR/CIS. The aircraft adopted Ukrainian markings (left) over their existing camouflage and squadron badges. Today, some if not all of Ukraine's Su-25UTGs are operated by the International Fighter Pilot's Academy (above), which flies from Kirovskye air force base in the Crimea.

After the Kuznetsov made its IFOR deployment to the Adriatic in 1996, it made a port visit to Malta with this Su-25UTG on board.

These photographs illustrate the two T8M prototypes. The top photograph shows T8M-1, the first Su-25T, which made its maiden flight in 1984. The second aircraft (above) is the T8M-2 posing at Akhtubinsk. This aircraft was later lost during flight testing.

This aircraft is the T8M-1, repainted, as displayed at the MAKS '95 air show held at Zhukhovskii in 1995.

ejection seat survival pack. The wingtip pods mounted dielectric leading edges which covered SPO-15 (L-006LE) Sirena RHAWS antennas, and some later Su-25 variants had a square antenna projecting from the side of the pod. This served the Gardeniya active jammer.

Under the rear fuselage were a short 'towel rail'-type antenna serving the R-828 'Eucalyptus' radio. The 20-W R-828 radio is used for communicating with army units on the ground. Further aft on the rear fuselage was a blade antenna for the MRP-56P radio beacon receiver, and a flush disc-shaped antenna serving the RV-15 (A-031) radio altimeter. Further aft (behind the towel-rail), there was sometimes a tripole antenna below the rear fuselage, similar to that above the nose, this serving the SRZ/SRO IFF system. The sharp spike-like fairing projecting aft above the tailcone housed an RSBN antenna in the tip, with scabbed-on SRZ/SRO antennas on the sides.

The pilot entered the cockpit using a three-rung retractable boarding ladder, which is telescopic and which then folds upwards into a well incorporating two footholds. From the top foothold, the pilot steps across forward to a fold-down step, from which he can reach the cockpit itself. Grab handles are mounted behind the canopy and further aft on the side of the spine. The two-seater was fitted with a simpler entry ladder, which consisted of a simple telescopic pole to which were attached folding footsteps. This freed the pilot from reliance on ground support equipment ladders. Surprisingly, in view of this advantage, many late Su-25UBs seem to have been built without an integral boarding ladder.

Internal fuel tankage

The centre fuselage incorporates the wing centre-section and two integral fuel tanks, and runs between bulkheads 11B and 21. The No. 1 fuel tank (between bulkheads 11B and 28) contained 1128 litres (250 Imp gal), and the No. 2 tank (between bulkheads 18 and 21) contained an additional 1250 litres (275 Imp gal). The top of the centre fuselage section contained a duct through which ran the control rods, fuel lines and other hydraulic, air conditioning and wiring runs. In the bottom of the centre fuselage, between bulkheads 12 and 18, were the mainwheel bays. The main oleos, which incorporated 400-mm (16-in) stroke twin-chamber hydro-pneumatic shock absorbers, retracted forwards. The mainwheels braked automatically during retraction, and were each covered by tandem doors. The forward doors were hinged outboard, and closed inward again after undercarriage extension.

The engine nacelles and intake ducts were attached to

contours were broadly similar to those of the similarly equipped MiG-23B and MiG-27 fighter-bombers.

Below the 'roots' of the instrumentation booms, well in front of the AoA vanes, were two small spherical antennas serving the SRO RWR, and two broadly rectangular dielectric fairings which covered the SO-69 transponder. Under the nose, just behind the yaw vane, was a small blade antenna which served the SO-69 transponder.

Further aft, the tandem antennas for the DISS-7 Doppler were housed under a flush dielectric panel immediately ahead of the gun bay access door. A similar panel on the fuselage spine covers the ARK-15M radio compass, while a slightly-swept T antenna further forward serves the R-862 radio. The 30-W R-862 VHF/UHF radio is used for routine air-to-air and air-to-ground communications in the 100-149.975 MHz and 220-399.975 MHz ranges. A 10-W R-855 emergency radio (20-59.975 MHz) is housed in the

the sides of the centre fuselage. They were constructed from bulkheads, longerons and double skin, and stood 60 mm (2.4 in) from the fuselage sides, leaving a slot for the extraction of boundary layer air. The intake lips were raked forward by 7°, giving slightly better air flow at higher angles of attack.

Rear fuselage assembly

The rear fuselage ran back from bulkhead 21, and incorporated the engine mounts (at auxiliary bulkheads 20 and 27) and the tailplane attachment points. The brake chute compartment and its upwards-hinging cover were mounted on the last bulkhead, No. 35. The compartment contained a pair of cruciform PTK-25 brake chutes, each of 25 m² (270 sq ft) area, which were deployed using springs and small drogue chutes. The three-spar fixed tailfin was attached to three points above the rear fuselage, and incorporated a cooling inlet at the root for the electrical generator.

A Tester UZ flight recorder was buried inside the fin structure, which also served as the mounting point for the antenna (below a dielectric fin cap), and for SPO-15 RHAWS and R-862 UHF/VHF radio antennas on the trailing edge. The trailing-edge rudder was divided into upper and lower sections, with the upper section independently controlled through the SBU-8 oscillation damper and an RM-130 hydraulic actuator.

Above the brake chute compartment, behind the fin leading edge, four upward-firing chaff/flare dispensers were recessed into the top of the rear fuselage decking, each containing 32 cartridges. Between the side-by-side pairs of chaff/flare dispensers on each side of the centreline was a slender tubular fairing projecting aft and culminating in a sharp dielectric spike. This housed an antenna for the RSBN TACAN, and had antennas for the SRO IFF system scabbed onto its sides.

The horizontal tailplane had a swept leading edge

This view of an Su-25T shows the redesigned chaff/flare housing above the brake chute fairing. For the 'Super Frogfoot', Sukhoi expanded even more on the Su-25's already substantial self-defence fit. The Su-25T's UV-26 countermeasures dispenser can carry a mixture of 192 PPI-26 IR decoys and PPR-26 chaff cartridges.

The Su-25TK is the export-dedicated version of the Su-25T – though whether its equipment fit is equivalent to the Su-25T or Su25TM remains unclear. Any actual systems fit can probably be dictated by the customer, but this confusion is a reflection of the lack of information about the Su-25T/Su-25TM family in general. For example, this is the aircraft displayed at the Farnborough air show of 1992 as an Su-25TK, yet 'Blue 10' was probably built to Su-25TM standard, from a converted Su-25T. Russian sources have labelled this aircraft as the T8M-10, Su-25T and Su-25TK.

Above: The second Su-25T prototype is seen here carrying pairs of R-60 (AA-8 'Aphid') AAMs, B-13L 122-mm rocket pods, FAB-500M-62 HE bombs, 9M120M Vikhr anti-tank missiles (16), one KAB-500L LGB and one Kh-29T (AS-14 'Kedge') TV-guided missile.

Below: A detailed view shows the seeker heads of the Kh-29T and the semi-active laser-homing Vikhr M missiles.

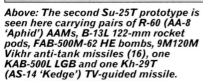

This Su-25K (above) has the late-model single-piece muzzle for its GSh-2-30 30-mm cannon. On the Su-25T (left) and Su-25TM the same gun has been moved to a ventral housing (designated NPPU-8M). Below can be seen the sideways feeding ammunition train for the GSh-2-30's VPU gun assembly. Up to 250 30-mm rounds can be carried.

Below: Seen here under the wing of an Su-25T is a (red-nosed) Kh-25ML (AS-10 'Karen') semi-active laser-guided missile. Kh-25ML has a range of 20 km (12.5 miles) and a 90-kg (198-lb) warhead. Beside it is a B-13L 122-mm rocket pod. The B-13L is a five-round pod that can fire rockets with a range of warheads. A dummy R-60 is also carried.

Right: This Su-25TM is carrying a grey MPS-410 Omul ECM pod alongside an (extremely fanciful) Vympel R-77 (AA-12 'Adder') medium-range AAM – the so-called 'AMRAAMski'. No Su-25 yet has the capability to use such a weapon.

Below: This eight FAB-100s bombload on this Guards Regiment Su-25 is more representative of the capabilities of the 'Frogfoot' than some of the other loadouts seen here. The Su-25 excels as a 'bombtruck', as proved in Afghanistan and other more recent conflicts.

Below right: The greatest lesson learned by the Soviets in Afghanistan was the need for much improved self-defence measures. Twin banks of ASO-2V dispensers are now fitted to the Su-25.

Sukhoi Su-25 'Frogfoot'
378 OShAP/378 OSAP
VVS-SSR

This 'Frogfoot', 'Red 29', was one of those based at Bagram in Afghanistan during the late 1980s, and is seen here in the markings it wore in 1988. It was during this period that Soviet operations in Afghanistan were at their peak – a fact reflected by the number of incursions made by VVS combat aircraft over the Pakistani border. In August 1988 an Su-25 was shot down by a Pakistani air force F-16. This particular aircraft is carrying an unusually heavy warload for an Afghan combatant. Standard loadouts usually comprised a small number of very large calibre rockets.

The grach
It was in Afghanistan that the grach (rook) marking, which has become synonymous with the Su-25 in Soviet (and Russian) service, first appeared. The origins of the cartoon bird are unclear, but it was soon worn by virtually all of the aircraft that served in Afghanistan. When some of these units returned to their bases in East Germany the black grach artwork returned with them.

Sukhoi Su-25 specification
Dimensions: fuselage length including probe 15.530 m (50 ft 11½ in) (15.36 m/50 ft 5 in for Su-25UB); fuselage length excluding probe 14.59 m (47 ft 10½ in); span 14.36 m (47 ft 1 in); area 30.1 m² (324 sq ft); tailplane span 4.65 m (15 ft 3 in); tailplane area 6.47 m² (69.7 sq ft); overall height 4.8 m (15 ft 9 in) (5.2 m/17 ft 1 in for Su-25UB); wheel track 2.5 m (8 ft 2 in); wheelbase 3.58 m (11 ft 9 in)
Powerplant: two Soyuz/Gavrilov R-95Sh turbojets each rated at 40.21 kN (9,039 lb st) thrust
Weights: empty operating weight 9185 kg (20,250 lb); normal take-off weight (early aircraft) 14250 kg (31,415 lb); normal take-off weight (late aircraft, after 1984) 14530 kg (32,025 lb); maximum take-off weight (early aircraft) 17350 kg (38,250 lb); maximum take-off weight (late aircraft, after 1984) 17530 kg (38,645 lb); normal landing weight 10800 kg (23,810 lb); maximum landing weight 13300 kg (29,320 lb)
Fuel and load: internal fuel 3000 kg (6,614 lb) or 3600 litres (790 Imp gal); normal weapon load 1340 kg (2,954 lb); maximum weapon load 4340 kg (9,568 lb)
g limits: +6.5 to -3 at basic design gross weight
Performance: maximum level speed 'clean' at sea level 1000 km/h (620 mph); limiting Mach No. 0.71 (early aircraft) or 0.82 (late aircraft, after 1984); service ceiling 7000 m (22,950 ft); range with underwing tanks 1950 km (1,053 nm; 1,212 miles) (1850 km/999 nm/1,450 miles for early aircraft, manufactured before 1984); range with 3000 kg (6,615 lb) of fuel 500 km (270 nm; 310 miles); take-off run 500-900 m (1,640-2,953 ft); landing roll 600-800 m (1,969-2,625 ft); take-off speed 240-270 km/h (130-135 kt; 149-155 mph); landing speed 225-260 km/h (121-124 kt; 225-230mph)

Sukhoi Su-25TK specification
Dimensions: fuselage length including probe 15.33 m (50 ft 4 in); span 14.52 m (47 ft 8 in); overall height 5.2 m (17 ft 1 in)
Powerplant: two Soyuz R-195 turbojets each rated at 44.13 kN (9,921 lb st) thrust
Weights: maximum take-off weight 19500 kg (42,990 lb)
Fuel and load: internal fuel 3840 kg (8,465 lb); normal weapon load up to 4360 kg (9,610 lb) air-to-ground
g limits: + 6.5 at maximum design gross weight
Performance: maximum level speed 950 km/h (513 kt; 590 mph); limiting Mach No. 0.82; service ceiling 10000 m (32,810 ft); ferry range 2500 km (1,350 nm; 1,550 miles); low-level radius of action 400 km (215 nm; 250 miles) with 2000 kg (4,410 lb) of weapons; high-level radius of action 700 km (380 nm; 435 miles) with 2000 kg (4,410 lb) of weapons

Wingtip airbrakes
Early-production Su-25s had a straightforward two-section, clamshell airbrake. It was subsequently modified and two smaller 'petals' added, resulting in an enlarged, four-section, staggered, articulated airbrake.

The Ulan-Ude bear
While Su-25s have adopted the 'unofficial' rook badge, two-seat Su-25UBs all wear the factory badge of their home, the Ulan-Ude Aviation Plant (Joint-Stock Company), situated in the Buryat Republic.

Warload
This aircraft is seen carrying a load of four FAB-250-270 250-kg bombs and four UV-32M rocket pods. FAB- (fugasnaya avia-bomba/'aerial demolition bomb') series bombs have been in production since the 1950s and are unsophisticated high-drag weapons, filled with high explosive. The Su-25 can carry a maximum load of eight FAB-250s – the outermost pylons on each wing are not stressed to carry that weight. The UV-32 rocket pod can carry up to 32 S-5KP 57-mm rockets. The Su-25 can carry a maximum load of eight pods. Aircraft serving in Afghanistan often carried a lighter load of two or four S-24 240-mm rockets on the outer pylons, with (small) bombs inboard.

Undercarriage
The nose gear of the Su-25 is offset to port and fitted with a mudguard, to lessen the risk of debris ingestion to the engines. The main undercarriage uses levered suspension legs, an oleo-pneumatic shock absorber and low-pressure tyres to enhance rough-field performance.

Cockpit

The Su-25TM's retention of the Su-25UB airframe gives it a uniquely hump-backed profile, with what was once the rear cockpit fixed in place and 'skinned over'. The canopy, based as it is on the front canopy of the two-seater, is longer than that fitted to the baseline Su-25, and more heavily framed. Unlike the basic single-seat model, the Su-25TM's canopy incorporates no overhead rear-view mirror, instead having provision for rear-view mirrors around the canopy arch. Inside the cockpit, there is little change from the instrument layout of the original Su-25, though a CRT screen is provided for the display of LLTV or FLIR imagery. The aircraft also features a new head-up display, which looks similar to that fitted to the MiG-29, in place of the original Su-25's simple gunsight. Production versions of the Su-25TM might incorporate new cockpit displays, perhaps similar to those flying in the Su-27M.

Powerplant

The Su-25T and Su-25TM are powered by the 44.1-kN (9,913-lb) R-195 engines u by late-series Su-25s and Su-25Ks, rather than the original 40.2-kN (9,036-lb) R-95 engines fitted to early aircraft. The newer, higher-thrust engine can be distinguish externally, even installed in its nacelle, by the unorthodox mixer tube which proje from the centre of the jet pipe, and which mixes bypass and core efflux to reduce signature. Both the R-95 and the R-195 are non-afterburning derivatives of the Tumanskii R-13F-300, and are of broadly similar configuration and layout. The eng has a twin-spool, axial-flow compressor, with a three-stage LP compressor, five-stage HP compressor and a two-stage turbine. The annular combustor consists o chambers, with two igniters.

Underfuselage pods

Although the space once occupied by the rear cockpit provided additional internal volume for avionics and increased fuel capacity, the Su-25TM was always intended to carry some of its mission-specific sensors in external pods, on the centreline. Pods available include the Merkuriy (Mercury) LLTV (Low-Light TV), the Khod FLIR (Forward-Looking Infra-Red), and podded versions of the Khinzhal MMW radar or the Kopyo radar. The Khod and Khinzhal pods are understood to use a common airframe, shown in this view of the T8-M10. When carrying Khod, the front of the pod incorporates a sensor window, protected by articulated upward/downward-opening doors. Khod and Merkuriy are both primarily intended as aids to low-level navigation at night, the Shkval LLTV in the aircraft nose being for weapons guidance. The LLTV or FLIR picture may be displayed on a small CRT display high on the right-hand side of the panel, next to the HUD's up-front controller. This screen may also be used to show the Shkval picture. It is not known whether the HUD itself can display a FLIR (or LLTV) picture. The Khinzhal millimetre wave radar is associated with guidance of the Vikhr ATGM. Kopyo is a pulse-Doppler radar (also used in a number of MiG-21 upgrade applications) and is a more versatile multi-mode radar with attack, mapping and other modes. The Kopyo radar pod would be especially useful in the carrierborne, maritime attack Su-25TP. The Su-25TM's centreline pylon may be able to carry a number of weapons instead of the sensor pods listed above, though such loads have never been photographed. There have been suggestions that SPPU-22-01 gun pods, Kh-35, Kh-31, or Kh-58 ASMs may have been cleared for carriage on the centreline.

Su-25TM (T8-M10)
Sukhoi OKB Flight Test Department
Detached to GLITS (State Flight Test Centre)
Akhtubinsk, Russia

Akhtubinsk houses the front-line fast-jet and offensive elements of the Air Forces' Scientific and Technical Institute (NII-VVS). Primarily responsible for service clearance and acceptance of new aircraft types, systems and weapons, the centre is also used for trials by some of the aircraft design and production companies, who use the base's infrastructure and the adjacent ranges. No Russian air forces order has been placed for the Su-25T or TM but the type has been evaluated and tested at Akhtubinsk, although the aircraft operate primarily from the Sukhoi facility within the LII airfield at Zhukhovskii. 'Blue 10' was probably the 10th T8-M, and probably the third Su-25TM (T8-TM). The aircraft was also almost certainly the first built to Su-25TM standards from the start. It has been used for demonstration flights overseas, and as such has sometimes been referred to as an Su-25K. It has led a busy life as a weapons/weapons system workhorse, testing different elements of the Su-25TM's weapons system, including both Mercury LLTV and Khod FLIR pods. The aircraft wears the standard Su-25 brown and green camouflage, unlike some Su-25TM and Su-25Ts which were painted in experimental grey/blue colour schemes. Some reports suggest that the aircraft was converted to serve as the carrier-capable Su-25TP prototype, but this cannot be confirmed. In the austere funding environment following the end of the Cold War, the advanced Su-25TM has so far been unable to win a vital launch order, though there have been reports of orders from Slovakia, Georgia, Bulgaria and a number of other customers, most of whom were already operators of the baseline Su-25.

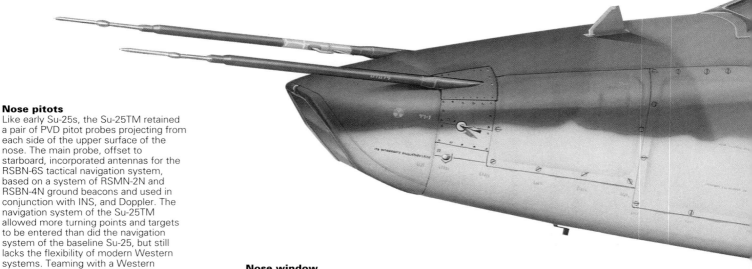

Nose pitots
Like early Su-25s, the Su-25TM retained a pair of PVD pitot probes projecting from each side of the upper surface of the nose. The main probe, offset to starboard, incorporated antennas for the RSBN-6S tactical navigation system, based on a system of RSMN-2N and RSBN-4N ground beacons and used in conjunction with INS, and Doppler. The navigation system of the Su-25TM allowed more turning points and targets to be entered than did the navigation system of the baseline Su-25, but still lacks the flexibility of modern Western systems. Teaming with a Western avionics manufacturer might give the aircraft a great deal more appeal to potential customers.

Nose window
The Su-25T and Su-25TM had a recontoured nose with an enlarged hexagonal forward oblique window covering the collimated optics for the Prichal laser rangefinder and target designator, and for the I-251 Shkval LLTV missile guidance system. Shkval is not used as a low-level night flying aid, for which a Mercury LLTV pod can be carried.

Cannon
In the second-generation Su-25T and Su-25TM, the original GSh-30-2 (AO-17A/(A623) cannon in its internal VPU-17A carriage was originally to have been replaced by an internally-mounted elevating 45-mm cannon, but this weapon was abandoned before development was complete, and the original cannon bay was soon filled with avionics modules for the Shkval (Squall) system. With the new variant's night-attack capabilities and increasingly sophisticated PGM capability, some consideration was reportedly given to dropping the cannon altogether, marking a complete shift from CAS to BAI duties, but this met fierce resistance. When the GSh-30-2 cannon was reinstated it was fitted in an externally mounted, partially-faired NPPU-8M gun carriage, mounted further aft and offset 270 mm (10.7 in) to starboard. The nosewheel and nosewheel bay had to be relocated 220 mm (8.6 in) to port to compensate. Ammunition capacity was reduced from 250 to 200 rounds.

Structure and construction
The Su-25TM was based on the airframe of the basic Su-25UB trainer, with no real change in construction techniques or materials, and with no appreciable increase in the use of new materials or advanced alloys. Thus the airframe remains primarily of Duralumin (60%), with significant amounts of steel (19 per cent) and titanium alloys (13 per cent), and comparatively little use of magnesium alloys (2 per cent) composites and plastics (5.5 per cent). This makes manufacture fairly simple and economical, and gives scope for licence assembly or component manufacture if required. The relatively extensive use of steel and titanium bestows good battle damage tolerance and considerable airframe strength. The fuselage is a conventional semi-monocoque, constructed from bulkheads, longerons, stringers and a stressed skin. Unusual features include the welded titanium cockpit 'bathtub', and the huge 'keel' between the two engines. Simple, double-skinned, oval-shaped fixed intakes are attached to the fuselage sides extending back into the engine nacelles and jetpipes. The engines drop down for removal or replacement, and are covered by massive doors. Access for routine servicing is superb. The fuselage incorporates the centre-section of the wing, with two integral fuel tanks, to which the wings themselves are attached. The wings are constructed around a central box spar, to which the leading and trailing edges are attached. Generally the aircraft is simply designed and well engineered, useful virtues in an aircraft intended to operate from austere forward airfields and in the high-threat environment over the battlefield.

Variation on the *grach* badge

Brake chute
All (land-based) Su-25s have a pair of brake chutes housed in the extended tail fairing, hidden behind a neat 'flip-up' cover. The chutes themselves are cruciform PTK-25 brake chutes, each of 25 m² (270 sq ft) area, which are deployed on landing, using springs and smaller drogue chutes.

Armoured cockpit
The Su-25 pilots sits on a K-36L ejection seat surrounded by 24 mm (0.94 in) of welded titanium, under an armoured canopy – which opens to starboard. Above the canopy is a small mirror to compensate for the pronounced lack of rearward visibility. The canopy transparency is curved, apart from the reinforced (flat) front panel.

Su-25 antenna fit
The large blade aerial behind the cockpit of this Su-25 is the R-862 UHF/VHF radio aerial. Above the nose the three SRO-2 'Odd Rod' IFF aerials have been replaced by the single blade antenna of a newer system. The small dielectric panel on the side of the nose serves the SO-69 transponder. The small circular antennas for the SRO radar warning receiver were later added to the nose of Su-25s, in front of the SO-69 fairing. Jutting ahead of the nose are the main (starboard) and auxiliary pitot probes – the first of them also carries antennas for the RSBN navigation system. Inside its 'chisel' 'nose, the Su-25 carries the Klen-PS laser rangefinder and marked target seeker. Underneath the nose is a pitch vane, and some aircraft have an additional IFF antenna immediately behind this. On the side of the fuselage, below the cockpit, is the Su-25's angle-of-attack sensor. On the front of each of the wingtip fairings are antennas for the SPO-15 RHAW system. Formation lights and pop-out landing lights are located on the side of, and underneath, the tip fairings, respectively. Not visible here are the RV-15 radar altimeter and MRP-56P beacon tracking antennas, located between the engines on the underfuselage. Behind the engine outlets is a second RV-15 antenna and the large 'towel-rail' antenna for the R-828 radio. Another IFF aerial is located under the fin and on the extended tail 'sting', which itself is tipped by a second RSBN antenna.

Variations on the *grach* badge

Sukhoi Su-25 'Frogfoot-A'

1. Pitot head
2. Secondary dynamic pressure probe
3. RSBN ILS antennas
4. Klen-PS laser ranger and marked target seeker
5. Gun camera
6. SO-69 transponder antenna
7. SRO RWR antenna
8. Yaw vane
9. Cannon muzzle aperture
10. DISS-7 Doppler navigation antennas, offset to starboard
11. Nose avionics equipment bays, access port and starboard
12. SRZ IFF antenna
13. Armoured glass windscreen panels
14. ASP-17BC-8 weapons sight and recording camera
15. Instrument panel shroud
16. Control column
17. Rudder pedals
18. Ammunition magazine, 250 rounds
19. Cartridge case collector
20. Incidence transmitter
21. GSh 30-2 (AO-17A) twin-barrelled 30-mm cannon
22. Levered suspension nosewheel leg strut, hydraulically steerable
23. Single nosewheel with mudguard, aft-retracting
24. Nose undercarriage pivot mounting and hydraulic retraction jack
25. Fold-out cockpit step
26. Slide-mounted engine throttle levers
27. Pilot's K-36L ejection seat
28. Cockpit canopy, hinged to starboard
29. Rear view periscope mirror
30. Cockpit head armour
31. Welded titanium box structure armoured cockpit pressure section
32. Centre fuselage avionics equipment bay
33. Boarding steps
34. Nosewheel housing, hinged for avionics bay access
35. 5-litre oxygen bottles (4)
36. Telescopic boarding ladder
37. Port engine air intake
38. No. 1 forward fuselage fuel tank, armoured and filled with fire-suppressant foam; total internal fuel capacity, 3660 litres (805 Imp gal)
39. Control runs, damage-tolerant duplicated system
40. Dorsal avionics equipment compartment
41. Starboard engine intake duct
42. Fuselage tank gravity fuel filler
43. R-862 UHF/VHF antenna
44. Starboard wing integral fuel tank
45. Wing tank fuel filler
46. Leading-edge slat guide rails and operating linkage
47. Stores pylons, five per side
48. 1150-litre (252-Imp gal) ferry tank, maximum of four
49. S-250FM unguided rockets
50. Outboard pylon with R-60M (AA-8 'Aphid') air-to-air self-defence missile
51. Starboard five-segment leading-edge slats
52. Landing light glare shield
53. Retractable landing light
54. Forward and starboard oblique SPO-15 RHAW antenna
55. Starboard navigation light
56. Starboard 'crocodile' airbrake, open
57. Starboard aileron
58. Aileron geared tab
59. Trim tab, starboard only
60. Aileron hinge control linkage
61. Starboard two-segment double-slotted flap
62. Ferry tank tail fins
63. Exhaust duct cooling air intake
64. ARK-19 DF antenna
65. ASO-2V 32-round chaff/flare launchers (8)
66. Dual generator cooling air intake
67. Rudder control linkage
68. Starboard trimming tailplane
69. Yaw damping upper rudder segment hydraulic actuator
70. Fin-tip VHF antenna
71. Rear SPO-15 RHAW receiving antenna
72. Tail navigation light
73. Upper rudder segment
74. Manually operated lower rudder segment
75. Rudder geared tab
76. Trim tab
77. Rear chaff/flare launchers
78. Rear SRO RWR antennas, port and starboard
79. Rear RSBN ILS antenna
80. Parachute door
81. Dual brake parachute stowage
82. Elevator geared tab, additional trim tab to starboard
83. Port manually operated elevator
84. Port trimming tailplane
85. Lower SRZ IFF antenna
86. Three-position trimming tailplane hydraulic actuator
87. Tailplane hinge mounting
88. R-828 HF antenna
89. RV-15 (A-031) radar altimeter antenna
90. Port engine duct chaff/flare launchers
91. Exhaust stream cooling air injector plug (infra-red suppression)

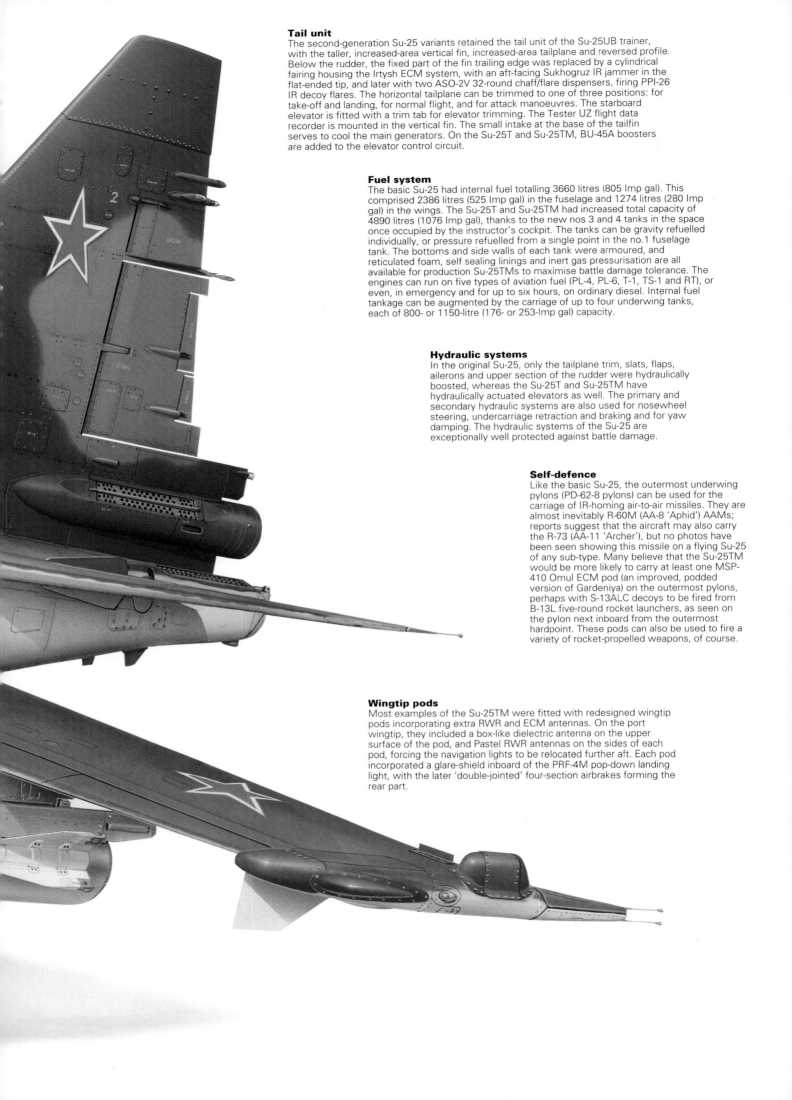

Tail unit
The second-generation Su-25 variants retained the tail unit of the Su-25UB trainer, with the taller, increased-area vertical fin, increased-area tailplane and reversed profile. Below the rudder, the fixed part of the fin trailing edge was replaced by a cylindrical fairing housing the Irtysh ECM system, with an aft-facing Sukhogruz IR jammer in the flat-ended tip, and later with two ASO-2V 32-round chaff/flare dispensers, firing PPI-26 IR decoy flares. The horizontal tailplane can be trimmed to one of three positions: for take-off and landing, for normal flight, and for attack manoeuvres. The starboard elevator is fitted with a trim tab for elevator trimming. The Tester UZ flight data recorder is mounted in the vertical fin. The small intake at the base of the tailfin serves to cool the main generators. On the Su-25T and Su-25TM, BU-45A boosters are added to the elevator control circuit.

Fuel system
The basic Su-25 had internal fuel totalling 3660 litres (805 Imp gal). This comprised 2386 litres (525 Imp gal) in the fuselage and 1274 litres (280 Imp gal) in the wings. The Su-25T and Su-25TM had increased total capacity of 4890 litres (1076 Imp gal), thanks to the new nos 3 and 4 tanks in the space once occupied by the instructor's cockpit. The tanks can be gravity refuelled individually, or pressure refuelled from a single point in the no.1 fuselage tank. The bottoms and side walls of each tank were armoured, and reticulated foam, self sealing linings and inert gas pressurisation are all available for production Su-25TMs to maximise battle damage tolerance. The engines can run on five types of aviation fuel (PL-4, PL-6, T-1, TS-1 and RT), or even, in emergency and for up to six hours, on ordinary diesel. Internal fuel tankage can be augmented by the carriage of up to four underwing tanks, each of 800- or 1150-litre (176- or 253-Imp gal) capacity.

Hydraulic systems
In the original Su-25, only the tailplane trim, slats, flaps, ailerons and upper section of the rudder were hydraulically boosted, whereas the Su-25T and Su-25TM have hydraulically actuated elevators as well. The primary and secondary hydraulic systems are also used for nosewheel steering, undercarriage retraction and braking and for yaw damping. The hydraulic systems of the Su-25 are exceptionally well protected against battle damage.

Self-defence
Like the basic Su-25, the outermost underwing pylons (PD-62-8 pylons) can be used for the carriage of IR-homing air-to-air missiles. They are almost inevitably R-60M (AA-8 'Aphid') AAMs; reports suggest that the aircraft may also carry the R-73 (AA-11 'Archer'), but no photos have been seen showing this missile on a flying Su-25 of any sub-type. Many believe that the Su-25TM would be more likely to carry at least one MSP-410 Omul ECM pod (an improved, podded version of Gardeniya) on the outermost pylons, perhaps with S-13ALC decoys to be fired from B-13L five-round rocket launchers, as seen on the pylon next inboard from the outermost hardpoint. These pods can also be used to fire a variety of rocket-propelled weapons, of course.

Wingtip pods
Most examples of the Su-25TM were fitted with redesigned wingtip pods incorporating extra RWR and ECM antennas. On the port wingtip, they included a box-like dielectric antenna on the upper surface of the pod, and Pastel RWR antennas on the sides of each pod, forcing the navigation lights to be relocated further aft. Each pod incorporated a glare-shield inboard of the PRF-4M pop-down landing light, with the later 'double-jointed' four-section airbrakes forming the rear part.

Underwing hardpoints

Apart from the lightly-stressed PD-62-8 pylons furthest outboard, all of the pylons fitted to the Su-25 are of the heavy-duty universal BD3-25 type, with the inboard and centre pylons being 'plumbed' for the carriage of external fuel tanks. Two types of fuel tank are available: the 800-litre (175-Imp gal) PTB-800 and the lengthened PTB-1150, which holds up to 1150 litres (252 Imp gal). The BD3-25 pylon can accommodate any current Russian air-to-ground bomb up to a maximum weight of 500 kg (1,102 lb), and with adaptor rails to allow the carriage of a wide range of air-to-air and air-to-ground missiles. The centre pylons on each side are wired to allow the carriage of SPS-141MVG-E Gvozdika ECM jammer pods. This aircraft carries an atypical 'air show'-type loadout, with a Kh-29T (AS-14 'Kedge') TV-guided ASM just launched from the innermost pylon; eight 9M120 Vikhr ATGMs next; an S-25L laser-guided high-calibre (250-mm) tube-launched rocket next; and a B-13L pod on the outermost BD3-25.

Wing

The wing of the Su-25TM incorporates 2° 30' of anhedral (negative dihedral or droop) with modest sweep on the leading edge and a straight trailing edge. The wing box spars are built up around top and bottom flanges, with front and rear walls and a network of ribs and stringers. The area between the first and 10th ribs is sealed to form an integral fuel tank. The leading edge is built up around ribs and a skin, and incorporates the aileron control rods, wiring for the lighting, wingtip antennas and pylons. They also mount the five-section leading-edge slats, each section of which is connected to the leading edge using two hinges. The slats extend to 12° for take-off and landing and to 6° for combat manoeuvring. There is a dogtooth leading-edge discontinuity at the root of the third slat section, reducing induced drag by generating a powerful vortex across the wing. The trailing edge of the wing incorporates a two-section flap inboard, with ailerons outboard. The flaps deploy to 20° for combat manoeuvring and differentially (35° inboard and 40° outboard) for take off and landing. The boosted ailerons (deflecting to ±18°) are actuated via a BU-45A booster unit.

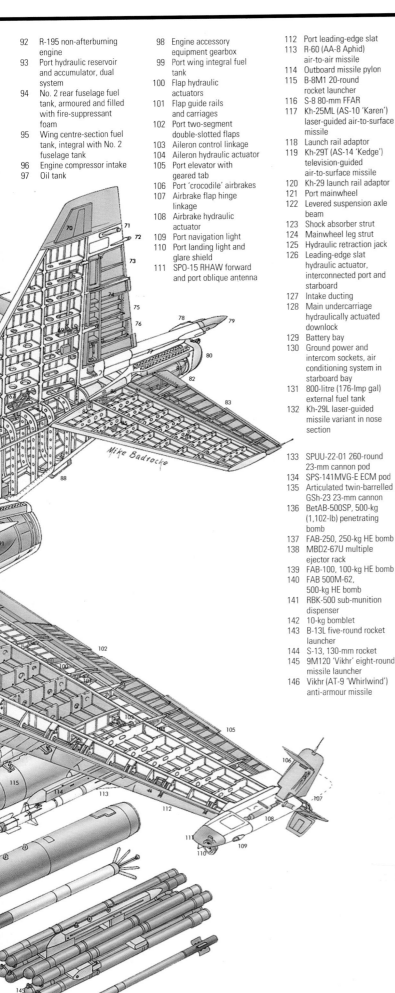

92 R-195 non-afterburning engine
93 Port hydraulic reservoir and accumulator, dual system
94 No. 2 rear fuselage fuel tank, armoured and filled with fire-suppressant foam
95 Wing centre-section fuel tank, integral with No. 2 fuselage tank
96 Engine compressor intake
97 Oil tank
98 Engine accessory equipment gearbox
99 Port wing integral fuel tank
100 Flap hydraulic actuators
101 Flap guide rails and carriages
102 Port two-segment double-slotted flaps
103 Aileron control linkage
104 Aileron hydraulic actuator
105 Port elevator with geared tab
106 Port 'crocodile' airbrakes
107 Airbrake flap hinge linkage
108 Airbrake hydraulic actuator
109 Port navigation light
110 Port landing light and glare shield
111 SPO-15 RHAW forward and port oblique antenna

112 Port leading-edge slat
113 R-60 (AA-8 Aphid) air-to-air missile
114 Outboard missile pylon
115 B-8M1 20-round rocket launcher
116 S-8 80-mm FFAR
117 Kh-25ML (AS-10 'Karen') laser-guided air-to-surface missile
118 Launch rail adaptor
119 Kh-29T (AS-14 'Kedge') television-guided air-to-surface missile
120 Kh-29 launch rail adaptor
121 Port mainwheel
122 Levered suspension axle beam
123 Shock absorber strut
124 Mainwheel leg strut
125 Hydraulic retraction jack
126 Leading-edge slat hydraulic actuator, interconnected port and starboard
127 Intake ducting
128 Main undercarriage hydraulically actuated downlock
129 Battery bay
130 Ground power and intercom sockets, air conditioning system in starboard bay
131 800-litre (176-Imp gal) external fuel tank
132 Kh-29L laser-guided missile variant in nose section

133 SPUU-22-01 260-round 23-mm cannon pod
134 SPS-141MVG-E ECM pod
135 Articulated twin-barrelled GSh-23 23-mm cannon
136 BetAB-500SP, 500-kg (1,102-lb) penetrating bomb
137 FAB-250, 250-kg HE bomb
138 MBD2-67U multiple ejector rack
139 FAB-100, 100-kg HE bomb
140 FAB 500M-62, 500-kg HE bomb
141 RBK-500 sub-munition dispenser
142 10-kg bomblet
143 B-13L five-round rocket launcher
144 S-13, 130-mm rocket
145 9M120 'Vikhr' eight-round missile launcher
146 Vikhr (AT-9 'Whirlwind') anti-armour missile

Above and below: In the cockpit of the Su-25, primary flight instruments (KUS-2 airspeed indicator, UV-75-15-PV altimeter, A-031-4 radar altimeter, PPD-2 VOR/DME, KPP-K1 artificial horizon, NPP-MK navigation/heading indicator, DA-200P VSI and turn gauge, clock, fuel gauges and other systems gauges) are flanked to the left by the main weapons panel, and to the right by the SPO-15 RHAW display, master warning lights, RHAW controls, brake and hydraulic controls. The left side-panel houses jettison switches, radios, drag-chute release, environmental and oxygen controls. The POM throttle assembly is mounted above this panel. The right side-panel (below) contains the RSBN and ARK-2 controls, transponder and radio switches, interior lighting, engine start switches and chaff/flare panel.

Left: The Su-25 has nothing as sophisticated as a HUD in the cockpit. Instead, the main instrument panel is dominated by the ASP-17 BC-8 electro-optical weapons sight. The black pipe-shaped object mounted in front of the sight's reflecting flat glass panel is the AKS-5-75os 'gun camera', which films directly through the sight.

Left and below: The nose avionics bay of the Su-25UB and Su-25 (below) are similar, despite the lack of the Klen-PS system in the former. Visible here are the modules for the RSBN-6 beacon tracking system. Weapons-related systems are housed to port.

Left: The Su-25 has a neat integral access ladder, while the Su-25UB has a less heavily framed design.

Right: This is the housing for the Su-25's twin drag chutes. Both chutes are held in a single tidy package until required. Above the chute housing is an RSBN antenna.

Above and below: The front cockpit of the Su-25UB (or UBK) trainer is largely identical to that of the Su-25, but the rear cockpit has the weapons sight replaced by an additional stores control panel, which replicates the functions of the same panel in the front seat. The heavy framing around the second cockpit substantially limits the vision of its occupant, to an even greater degree than that of the frontseater.

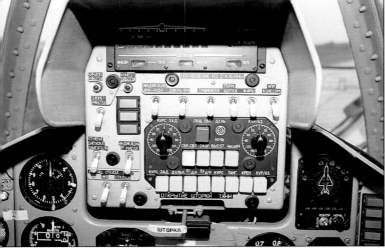

Above: The Su-25 (seen here) has a Klen-PS laser rangefinder, while the Su-25TM is fitted with the advanced Prichal system. The aircraft's nosecone hinges down for access.

Below: The Su-25 has five underwing pylons, on each wing. The four inner pylons are stressed to carry up to 500 kg (1,102 lb). The outer pylon is reserved for lightweight AAMs only.

Right: Like most front-line Russian-built combat aircraft, the Su-25 is fitted with the extremely reliable Zvezda K-36L zero/zero ejection seat. The firing handles for the seat are between the pilot's legs. This view of a K-36L shows the 'windshield' fitted above the seat (in the 'Frogfoot') and the two tubular housings for the seat's unique stabilising drogue parachutes.

77

Top: Until the arrival of the Su-25T the only 'Frogfoots' to be fitted with uprated engines were the handful of Su-25BM target-tugs. Their improved R-195 engines fit neatly into the existing engine bays and only small clues betray their presence. Chief among them are the extended jet-pipes that protrude from the engine efflux cowlings. If the Su-25BM were not carrying the TL-70 target-towing system, it could still be identified by the missing intake at the base of the fin.

Above: Experience in Chechnya, when bad weather grounded the VVS Su-25 force, underlined the need for the all-weather Su-25T/TM. This Su-25TM is seen at Zhukhovskii carrying the Kopyo-25 radar pod.

(slightly more swept than the wing) and a forward-swept trailing edge. It was built around two spars in two halves, and was then joined by a centre-section which ran through the rear fuselage. The tailplanes incorporated some dihedral to keep them clear of the jet wash from the engines, and to keep them out of the turbulent air coming off the wing. The tailplane was hydraulically adjustable to any one of three positions, one used for take-off and landing, one for normal flight, and one for dive attacks. The elevators were joined to the trailing edge of each tailplane by three hinges and were aerodynamically and mass balanced. They could deflect to 14° upward and to 23° downward. An elevator trim tab was fitted to the starboard elevator.

Wing design

The wing, like the tailplane, was built in two halves, and each section was constructed around a central box-section spar with ribs, longerons and stringers. The area between the first and 10th ribs on each side was sealed to form an integral 637-litre (140-Imp gal) fuel tank. Control rods (including those for the aileron) and wiring was buried in the leading edge, with slat actuator hinges mounted on load-bearing ribs. The trailing-edge section contained fuel and hydraulic lines, and mounted the flap and aileron hinges and boosters.

Moving control surfaces extended across virtually the entire span of the leading and trailing edge. Two-section double-slotted flaps occupied the inboard part of the trailing edge, with conventional ailerons outboard. The flaps could be extended to 20° for manoeuvring, or to 35° (inboard sections) and to 40° (outboard sections) for take-off or landing. The ailerons deflected to 18° upward or 18° downward. The leading edge of each wing was occupied by an interconnected five-section slat (each section with two hinges). A leading-edge dogtooth discontinuity began at the root rib of the third flap section. The slats could be deployed through 6° for manoeuvring, or to 12° for take-off and landing.

Broad flat pods were attached to the wingtips. They consisted of a dielectric antenna for the SPO-15 RHAWS forward, with a pop-down PRF-4M landing light in the underside (usually with a fixed vertical anti-glare shield inboard), and with the appropriate red or green navigation light on the outboard edge. The trailing edge of each pod was split into upper and lower sections which opened as airbrakes. The wingtip pods also incorporated connectors for the SPU-9 pilot-to-ground crew intercom system.

Weapons hardpoints

The wing also served as the mounting point for the Su-25's external warload, which was carried on 10 underwing hardpoints. The four inboard hardpoints under each wing were fitted with universal BD3-25 pylons, and the outboard hardpoint a PD-62-8 pylon. The latter are believed to mount only APU-60-1MD missile launch rails, compatible with the R-60 or R-60M (AA-8 'Aphid') IR-homing dogfight missiles, carried for self-defence. There is no reason why the R-73 (AA-11 'Archer') AAM should not be carried with the appropriate pylon adaptor.

The inboard underwing pylons could be fitted with a range of adaptors, allowing the carriage of a wide variety of stores. The pylons closest to the wingroot, and next but one outboard, were 'plumbed' for the carriage of PTB-800 800-litre (175-Imp gal) or PTB-1150 1150-litre (253-Imp gal) external auxiliary fuel tanks. These outboard 'tank-capable' hardpoints (the middle station of the five under each wing) can also be used for the TL-70 Kometa target winch system on the Su-25BM, and for the carriage of an SPS-141MVG-E ECM pod on aircraft assigned to the anti-radar role. These hardpoints may be the ones used for

the carriage of nuclear weapons.

The BD3-25 pylons were stressed for the carriage of a wide variety of stores weighing up to 500 kg (1,100 lb) per pylon, up to the maximum load of 4340 kg (9,570 lb). The eight main pylons were seldom used simultaneously, for the Su-25 normally carries much smaller warloads on only a portion of its available hardpoints, since the carriage of a full load imposes range, performance, agility and take-off penalties.

The 'man pod'

Arguably the most unusual stores which can be carried underwing are the pods which constitute the AMK-8 mobile maintenance unit. The Su-25 is optimised for operation from primitive forward airstrips, and can ferry its own vital ground support equipment in underwing pods modelled on the airframe of the PTB-800 external fuel tank. There are four standard types of pod. The K-1E houses electrical power units, with a compressor and tools for maintenance and field repairs. The K-2D contains refuelling equipment (a pump and rubberised cells). The K-3SNO has maintenance tools and intake blanks, chocks, and camouflage netting, while the K4-KPA has diagnostic and checking equipment, and equipment for radio and avionics maintenance. A final, slightly reshaped AMK-8 pod is available (but is understood not to have been deployed at unit level). This is designed to transport a ground crew member, albeit in some discomfort.

The Su-25's orthodox and conventional configuration,

systems and construction were accompanied by predictable and benign handling characteristics. Transitioning to the Su-25 was thus not a major step for even fairly inexperienced pilots, since the aircraft enjoyed relatively simple and uncomplicated handling procedures. It was possible to conduct most training solo, with an instructor flying chase, and it was felt that the MiG-15UTI and Aero L-39 would be adequate for instrument training and check rides, although the air force did issue a draft requirement for an Su-25UB as early as 1975. The preliminary design for the two-seat Su-25 was completed in 1977, but the project was not accorded a high priority, since many felt that the

Above: The basic Su-25 still has an inventory of largely 'dumb' ordnance, such as the 57-mm FFAR rocket.

Top: 'Yellow 25' is now the dedicated Su-25TK demonstrator. The greatest sales effort for this version has been directed at Persian Gulf states and the Su-25TK has visited the IDEX show in Dubai.

Su-25 'Frogfoot' in Afghanistan

The USSR invaded Afghanistan in December 1979. The Su-25's involvement in that war was initiated with a combat trials deployment for the T8, but began in earnest when early-production Su-25s were delivered to Shindand in 1982. These photographs were largely taken around Bagram air base, near Kabul, in 1988, the last full year of Soviet involvement. By February 1989 Russian forces had left completely, after an unsuccessful 10-year war of attrition.

MiG-15UTI was adequate for the conversion and continuation training of Su-25 pilots.

The two-seat Su-25UB

Even after the decision was made to produce a two-seat trainer, the project was always subject to interruption, delay and the diversion of resources. The first export successes of the Su-25 in 1984 added impetus to the development of the trainer, and the first example of an Su-25 (designated T8UB-1 and coded 'Red 201'), finally made its maiden flight on 10 August 1985. An original Su-25UB prototype had been started in 1981, but the incomplete airframe, and two more, were actually completed as the T8M-1 and T8M-2 prototypes (and as the T8M-0 for static testing) of the advanced Su-25T. This variant of the aircraft is described in detail later. Work on the Su-25UB was delayed, and finally passed to the Production Plant No. 99 at Ulan-Ude, where a second, new T8UB-1 prototype was built, which had that plant's distinctive bear badge on its nose. The same insignia was worn by the second Su-25UB built at Ulan-Ude, 'Red 202', which acted as the second prototype. Further Su-25UBs had a similar bear, slightly smaller, on a tilted rectangular shield. The two-seater retains full combat capability and is said to be universally known as the 'Sparka' in Russian and Soviet air forces service.

In order to reduce development time to a minimum, airframe changes were avoided wherever possible. Instead of lengthening the fuselage to accommodate a second cockpit (which would have involved other airframe modifications simply to compensate), the instructor's cockpit replaced a fuselage fuel tank, with a new pair of heavily framed cockpit canopies fairing into a bulged spine. The second cockpit was raised by 0.44 m (1.44 ft), giving the instructor a 7° sight-line down over the nose. This gave the two-seater a considerable increase in keel area forward, and the tailfin was enlarged to compensate. The horizontal tail was increased in area, and was of revised profile. The Su-25's usual retractable folding ladder was replaced by a simpler telescopic tubular strut supporting three narrow footrests. The Su-25UB's heavily stepped cockpits gave the backseater a better view forward than was obtainable in most Soviet two-seat trainers, and this made provision of the almost-traditional periscope less essential. It was offered as a customer option on the Su-25UBK, the export version of the two-seater, but was seldom requested. The prototypes and early Su-25UBKs did not have the periscope fitted, but many Soviet UBs were so equipped.

Some reports suggest that Sukhoi made plans for a three-seat trainer (with all three cockpits 'in tandem') but the reasons for such an aircraft remain unclear, unless it was expected to serve as a high-speed liaison aircraft. Develop-

Above and below: Some Su-25s based in East Germany wore distinctive disruptive camouflage schemes that Western observers dubbed 'Afghanistan camouflage'. Two contradictory stories emerged from Soviet ground crew to explain the unusual paint schemes. Some said that the colours had been worn in-theatre in Afghanistan, and had been retained when the aircraft returned to Europe. Others said that the schemes had been painted on only in Germany, but as a direct result of their experience in Afghanistan, to better camouflage the aircraft in European conditions. To date no photographic evidence has emerged of aircraft in Afghanistan wearing anything other than the standard three-tone scheme.

Two VVS Su-25 units were based in East Germany as part of the 16th Air Army (Group of Soviet Forces in Germany). They were the 357th Otdelnyi Shturmovoi Aviatsionnaya Polk (OShAP/Independent Shturmovik Aviation Regiment) based at Brandis, and the 368th OShAP based at Demmin-Tütow. The 357th arrived with its aircraft in October 1985, while the 368th arrived in December 1988, directly from Afghanistan. Aircraft from the two regiments were largely indistinguishable as both used individual red codes with white outlines. This is an Su-25 of the 368th OShAP, seen landing at Tütow.

The other major European operator of the Su-25 was the Czechoslovak air force (the Su-25 is also in service in Bulgaria). Czechoslovakia was the first export customer for the 'Frogfoot', gaining its aircraft even in advance of Soviet units engaged in Afghanistan. Initial deliveries were made, by Soviet pilots, to Hradec Králové air base in April 1984 (by June, Czech pilots were undertaking these flights). These aircraft are seen at Pardubice, in 1993, following the split of the Czech and Slovak Republics. Czech aircraft were delivered with black, stencilled four-digit codes, which later became solid numerals with white outlines (mid-1980s) and finally all-white, by the early 1990s, as seen here.

ment was reportedly abandoned soon after it began in 1991. The aircraft was allegedly referred to within the OKB as the Su-25U3.

Trainer family

The Su-25UB combat trainer formed the basis of the stillborn Su-25UT (later redesignated Su-28). This aircraft was intended as a dedicated advanced trainer to replace the Aero L-29 and Aero L-39, both with the Soviet air forces and with the paramilitary DOSAAF. It was a simplified, unarmed two-seater, with no combat capability, no gunsight, no laser rangefinder, no RHAWS, no chaff/flare dispensers, and no internal cannon. Weight was reduced by 2000 kg (4,400 lb). Fuel tank linings were removed, and provision was made for just four underwing pylons, for the carriage of external fuel tanks only. The prototype was produced by conversion of the T8U-1, and first flew in its new guise on 6 August 1985. The Su-25UT introduced a revised wing leading-edge planform, with the dogtooth discontinuity between inboard and outboard leading-edge sections replaced by a short length of leading edge of reduced sweep, giving a gentle step in the leading-edge profile. The Su-25UT prototype was painted in a predominantly white colour scheme, with red and blue trim, and initially with DOSAAF tail markings and the code 'Red 07'. The aircraft took part in the 1988 DOSAAF aerobatic championships, and in the hands of Yevgeni Frolov seized a

creditable third place. It was later recoded with the Paris air show code 'Blue 302' for the 1989 Paris Air Salon, by which time it also wore the revised Su-28 designation on its intakes. Only a single prototype of the Su-25UT was completed, and no orders were forthcoming. Reports that the Su-25UT prototype was subsequently converted to become the Su-25UTG are entirely without foundation, and the aircraft remains in use with the OKB's test fleet at Zhukhovskii.

Su-25UTG for the navy

Another derivative of the Su-25UB was the navalised Su-25UTG. This had many of the same modifications as the Su-25UT/Su-28, but was especially strengthened to withstand the stresses of a carrier landing and was fitted with a retractable arrester hook, a revised undercarriage and a carrier landing system. The hook resulted in the new variant's change in designation (the Russian for hook being *Gak*). Sukhoi had hopes that a carrierborne single-seat Su-25 might be selected as a carrierborne attack aircraft for the *Tbilisi* (now *Kuznetsov*) and its sister ships (all later scrapped or cancelled). The T8-4 was tested on the dummy deck at Saki in 1984 at the same time as were the T10-24, T10-25 and the MiG-29KVP. The selection of the multi-role MiG-29K for the new carrier air wings led to these hopes being frustrated, although it was clear that the Su-25 could form the basis of a cheap and simple land-based but

carrier-capable trainer for teaching carrier landings. It was anticipated that the aircraft would primarily be used for teaching experienced MiG-29 and Su-27 pilots the rudiments of carrier landing, mainly using dummy carrier decks like the one at Saki. The majority of actual carrier landing training would be conducted after pilots had converted to their operational type (the Su-27K or MiG-29K), perhaps after a familiarisation flight or two in the Su-25UTG. Since the Su-25UTG would not actually be based aboard carriers, but would instead fly to and from a carrier from its shore base, it was decided that wing folding would not be required.

The varied career of the Su-25UTG

The Su-25UTG prototype (designated T8-UTG1 and coded 'Blue 08') made its maiden flight in September 1988. The aircraft was flown onto *Tbilisi* on 21 November 1989 by Sukhoi project pilot Igor Votintsev and LII pilot Alexander Krutov, landing after the Su-27K and MiG-29K. The Su-25UTG may have been converted from an Su-25UB in the OKB's own workshops. The aircraft certainly wore a Sukhoi logo on its nose, instead of the Ulan-Ude factory bear badge applied to most two-seaters (though, interestingly, never to export Su-25UBKs). The single prototype was followed by a batch of 10 new production Su-25UTGs. Five aircraft (coded 'Red 04', '06', '07', '10' and '11') were sent to Severomorsk, home to the Kuznetsov's air wing and to an AV-MF Su-25 regiment. Five more (coded 'Red 60', '61', '62', '63' and '64') were left behind at Saki where they became part of the Ukrainian

forces. 'Red 60' is believed to have been written off in an inadvertent wheels-up landing, while 'Red 07' suffered a fatal accident near Murmansk on 11 November 1992.

Even though only one carrier entered service, the four Su-25UTGs in service with the unit at Severomorsk were considered to be inadequate for the training task which faced them. Accordingly, Sukhoi was asked to produce 10 similar aircraft by conversion of existing Su-25UBs under the designation Su-25UBP. They were to have the same airframe strengthening and naval features as the Su-25UTG, but were also to be fitted with a retractable inflight-refuelling probe. There have been reports that the Su-25UBP programme has been halted, but it is unclear whether this situation is temporary. The Sukhoi OKB has not given up its quest to produce an operational carrier-borne Su-25 derivative, and reports suggest that the bureau may still be working on a single-seat, carrier-capable, probe-equipped Su-25TP based on the advanced Su-25T airframe, equipped with Kh-31 and Kh-35 ASMs.

The true combat debut

Following the successful combat evaluation of the Su-25 in Afghanistan, it became inevitable that production examples of the type would be used in the conflict when they became available. Twelve of the first Su-25s equipped the 200th Independent *Shturmovik* Squadron (often erroneously described as a Guards unit, and as being either a regiment, or alternatively a flight) at Shindand. This unit later transferred to Kabul (probably during 1982) and expanded to 24 aircraft (with 80 pilots) to become the 60th OShAP (some-

Czech Su-25s were briefly based at Hradec Králové, in Eastern Bohemia, between 1984 and 1985. Their unit, the 30th 'Ostravsky' Fighter-Bomber Air Regiment, then moved to Pardubice in June 1985, becoming the 30th Ground Attack Air Regiment later that year. The Communist party collapsed in Czechoslovakia in November/December 1989, following the 'peaceful Revolution', and occupying Russian forces were ordered to leave. The military structure of the Warsaw Pact was disbanded on 31 March 1991 and the last Russian forces departed in June 1991. Both Czech and Slovak Republics began to move towards independence in the early 1990s, and the armed forces were reorganised in anticipation. By 1992 the division of the Su-25 force into two had begun.

These aircraft and personnel of the 368th OShAP in Germany are seen preparing to depart for one of their final training missions, in 1993. By this time Russian forces were unwelcome guests who had outstayed their welcome in the reunited Germany. The 357th OShAP had already left Brandis in April 1992 and the 368th would follow in June 1993 – one of the last GSFG units to do so.

times described as the 80th OShAP). The regiment's commander was given special dispensation to conscript reinforcement aircraft and aircrew from Su-25 units in neighbouring republics, notably Turkmenistan. The 60th OShAP finally withdrew to Sital Chai in Azerbaijan in 1988.

Another long-term Su-25 unit in Afghanistan was the 378th OShAP, in action from 1984. A third Su-25 regiment served in Afghanistan between October 1986 and November 1987. This was the 368th OShAP, which transferred to Afghanistan from Uzbekistan, and moved to Demmin-Tütow in East Germany following its combat tour, during which it was based at Bagram and Kandahar. The unit may have been one of several which made brief deployments to Afghanistan.

While the Su-25 demonstrated great accuracy and good battle damage tolerance from the very start of its involvement in Afghanistan (especially by comparison with other aircraft in use in the theatre), it was equally clear that there was considerable scope for improvement. The threat posed by Blowpipe, Stinger and Redeye SAMs prompted the installation of four ASO-2V chaff/flare dispensers in the upper surfaces of the rear fuselage, on each side of the fin trailing edge. These usually contain up to 30 PPI-26 IR decoy flares, giving a total of 120 flares.

The effect of the Stinger

The advantage of having two engines was fully exploited in the Su-25, in which the powerplants are mounted so close together that damage to one engine could cause collateral damage to the other. This became abundantly clear following the 1984 introduction of the Redeye SAM by the Mujahideen, and by the October 1986 delivery of General Dynamics FIM-82A Stinger SAMs. The introduction of Redeye was followed by the loss of two Su-25s in very quick succession, these aircraft having proved unable to decoy the SAMs away using flares. Flare capacity was increased from 128 to 256, by the addition of four 32-round dispensers scabbed onto the top of the engine nacelles. When the Mujahideen started using Stinger, the effect was even more dramatic. Four Su-25s were destroyed in three days, with two pilots lost. The Stingers tended to detonate close to the engine exhaust nozzles, piercing the rear fuel tanks with shrapnel and causing fires which could burn through control runs, or causing damage to the far engine. In order to prevent damage to one engine from taking out the other, a 5-mm armour plate was added between the two engines (acting as a giant shield and firewall), about 1.5 m (5 ft) long.

A new inert gas (Freon) SSP-2I/UBSh-4-2 fire extinguisher system was provided. This consisted of six UTBG sensors in the engine nacelles, which were connected to cockpit displays. The pilot had four push-buttons to actuate the extinguisher's first and second stages for each section of the engine. The Freon was stored in spherical 4-litre (0.87-Imp gal) bottles, each containing 5.64 kg (12 lb) of gas pressurised at 6.9 to 14.2 MPa.

These modifications proved a great success, dramatically reducing the Su-25's loss rate. No Su-25 equipped with the inter-engine armour was lost to a Stinger, although many were hit. The modifications were quickly incorporated on the production line, and were retrofitted to existing Su-25s.

Additional improvements were added during the period in which Su-25s were fighting in Afghanistan. On aircraft from the 10th production series, for example, the aileron control rod was fully faired in and the aileron trim tab was deleted. Elevator pivots were more effectively faired. Tenth

Above and right: The GSFG Su-25 units each had Su-25UBs which routinely operated alongside their Su-25s. The 357th OShAP was allocated two two-seaters, and one of its aircraft is seen above. The 368th OShAP had five aircraft (right). Most front-line units in Germany operated two-seat versions of their aircraft, largely to make up for their lack of simulation facilities. This task was less important to the 'good weather only' Su-25 regiments, who had little need for instrument training. The Su-25UBs did, however, make excellent liaison aircraft and base 'hacks'.

series Su-25s also gained a second external APU/GPU socket. Other features appeared gradually, and cannot yet be pinpointed to a particular production series. The nose-wheel was changed, from one which accepted a tubeless KN-21-1 tyre to one which took a tubed K-2106 tyre. The single long fuel tank access panel on the top surface of each wing was replaced by three shorter access panels, side by side. Small fins were added to the inboard faces of the bottom of each wingtip fairing, acting as glare shields when the PRF-4M pop-down landing lights were deployed. At the trailing edge of these pods, the airbrakes themselves were modified. Previously simply splitting 50° up and 50° down to give a > shape with the point forwards, they gained auxiliary segments which hinged upwards through another 90° at their trailing edges to give a shape reminiscent of a W turned on its side, with the central point pointing forwards. During production of the ninth production series the cannon muzzle was redesigned, with the ends of the twin barrels covered by a single muzzle shield. Many late production Su-25s had their distinctive SRZ and SRO 'Odd Rod' antennas replaced by simple blade

antennas, similar to the SRO antennas fitted to later MiG-29s (which retained the traditional tripole SRZ antennas above their noses). The revised antennas may have combined interrogator and responder functions.

The 'Frogfoot' becomes the 'rook'

The Su-25 proved extraordinarily successful in Afghanistan, enjoying greater accuracy and a lower loss rate than the MiG-27s, MiG-21s, MiG-23s and Su-17s used there. The Mujahideen dubbed the Su-25 the 'German product', believing that its prowess and effectiveness marked it out from the other Soviet aircraft operating in-theatre, and indicating that it must have come from else-where. Combat experience in Afghanistan also generated a Russian nickname for the aircraft: 'Grach' (Rook). Publicists and official historians credit the nickname to ground troops, who reportedly appreciated the aircraft's close support capability which they likened to the mother rook's habit of covering her young with her wings when faced with danger. Other sources suggest that the 'Grach' nickname was first applied by the pilots of the 200th

The comparatively small number of Su-25s based in east Germany is somewhat surprising. It is a reflection of the fact that Soviet Shturmovik theory had largely been applied to the attack helicopter and that the Su-25 was a useful adjunct to this, instead of the primary exponent. There is little doubt, however, that the existing regiments would have been extensively reinforced in time of war. This aircraft is seen landing at Gross Dölln (Templin), north of Berlin, which was home to the Su-17M-4s of the 20th APIB. Like the Su-25, there were two 'Fitter' regiments based in East Germany.

Though unit markings and badges were not common throughout the GSFG, the Su-25 units were perhaps the least colourful of all. Only the grach badge, carried on some aircraft, broke the monotony of their camouflage. Soviet/ Russian military aviation units do have an intense pride in their history and traditions, but this is rarely expressed through special colour schemes or badges, as in the West. Most of the bases in East Germany had gate guards of historic aircraft, including Il-2s, which the units brought with them when they moved from the Soviet Union and took away again when they returned.

Sukhoi Su-25, Su-28 and Su-39 'Frogfoot'

This 368th OShAP Su-25 is armed with B-8M1 20-round rocket pods. Standard 'Frogfoot' loadouts with the B-8M1 seem to involve only two pods, whereas either four or eight UV-32-57 pods were often carried. The B-8M1 fires the 80-mm S-8 FFAR rocket. The B-8M1 is the streamlined 80-mm pod developed for use on fast jet aircraft (helicopters, for which the system was originally developed, use the B-8V20A pod). The S-8 rocket comes fitted with a HEAT anti-armour warhead, an 'anti-shelter' demolition warhead, a fuel/air explosive warhead or as a 2-million candlepower illumination round.

OShAE, many of whom were former MiG-21 pilots, who likened the slow and ungainly Su-25 to a rook, by comparison with their fast and graceful Falcons. Whoever invented the name, cartoon rook badges soon started to appear on Su-25s flown in Afghanistan. This rook badge has become a widely accepted insignia for Soviet Su-25s, and was applied to many of the aircraft used in East Germany. There have been unconfirmed suggestions that the badge is worn only by Su-25s that flew in Afghanistan.

Bringing back the pilots

The aircraft were often hit by ground fire and SAMs, habitually after they had overflown the target and were egressing. The damaged Su-25s usually limped home (even after a direct Stinger hit), often too badly damaged to fly again but generally saving the precious pilot. The aircraft were even sometimes repairable and were always at least a good source of spare parts. The Su-25 was effectively invulnerable to cannon fire; it took 80 20-mm hits to down an Su-25, compared with only 15 for a MiG-21 or Su-17.

Colonel Alexander Rutskoi, later briefly President of the Russian Federation, flew as an Su-25 pilot in Afghanistan while serving on the staff of the Commander of the 40th Air Army, and became the war's most highly decorated pilot. Some reports suggest that the T8-15 ('Blue 15') was one of the aircraft flown by Rutskoi in Afghanistan, and one which was severely damaged while being flown by him on two separate occasions, once by ground fire and once by two AIM-9s fired by a Pakistani F-16. Rutskoi was unluckier in April 1986 when he was downed by a SAM, ejecting inverted at only 100 m (330 ft) altitude. He was forced to eject again during his second tour of duty in Afghanistan, on 4 August 1988, when he was once more

engaged by a Pakistani F-16. Hit by an AIM-9, Rutskoi was forced to eject from his crippled aircraft ('Red 03') and was captured, being released after two weeks. The remains of his aircraft were put on display at Kamra. Some reports suggest that Rutskoi commanded a unit (perhaps an element of the 378th OShAP) which conducted sustained night operations before being disbanded and split up between other units in-theatre.

Afghanistan weapons

The Su-25 used a wide variety of weapons during the long involvement in Afghanistan. In order to maximise performance and agility, the Su-25s were seldom fully laden, often carrying weapons on only two or four underwing pylons. A common loadout was two or four S-24 240-mm unguided rockets, or a similar number of shaped-charge S-25 OFMs. Underwing fuel tanks were sometimes carried, either on the innermost hardpoints or on the third pylons out from the root. Various 250-kg or 500-kg (550-lb or 1,100-lb) bombs were also used in Afghanistan, and unguided small calibre rockets were carried in UB-32-57 (32 unguided 57-mm rockets per pod) or B8M (20 unguided 80-mm rockets per pod) pods. Towards the end of the Soviet involvement in Afghanistan, Su-25s started to be seen carrying guided weapons, including the S-25L laser-guided, tube-launched 250-mm rocket, the Kh-25ML and the Kh-29L laser-guided ASMs. According to the OKB, 139 laser-guided missiles were launched by Su-25s in Afghanistan, and 137 of them scored direct hits.

Another commonly seen Su-25 weapon which may have been used in Afghanistan is the SPPU-22-01 cannon pod. The Su-25 can carry up to four of these pods, usually on its innermost pylons. Each pod contains a single twin-barrelled

Most Soviet/Russian flying operations are routinely conducted in the open, from the flight line. Both Brandis and Tütow had a large number of revetments for their Su-25s, but no hardened shelters.

23-mm NR-23 cannon, with 260 rounds of ammunition, and with barrels which can be depressed through 30° up, allowing the aircraft to strafe a target simply by overflying it in level flight. This is especially effective against line targets (e.g., vehicles on a road). The pod may be mounted backwards, with the barrels elevated through 23° up, allowing the aircraft to fire backwards after overflying the target. It is common practice to pair a forward-firing and rearward-firing pod. Each pod had a rate of fire between 3,000 and 4,000 rounds per minute.

Afghanistan combat report

Twenty-three Su-25s were lost in action in Afghanistan; more were destroyed on the ground, including eight at Kabul in a single rocket attack on 23 June 1988. The aircraft shot down represented about 10 per cent of Soviet fixed-wing losses in Afghanistan, with a reported loss rate of one per 2,800 flying hours. The type made 60,000 operational sorties. Interestingly, the cockpit armour of the Su-25 proved particularly successful, and no Su-25 pilot was killed by projectiles or shrapnel. Several Su-25 pilots received the Soviet Union's highest honour, the Hero of the Soviet Union. Lieutenant Colonel Pietr V. Ruban was given a posthumous award, and a second was awarded to a Captain Dyakov. Other well known Hero of the Soviet Union awards were made to Captain Vladislav Gontcharienko, who flew 415 combat missions, and to Senior Lieutenant Konstantin G. Paliukov, who destroyed two Stingers launched against his formation leader, using gunfire and unguided rockets, during a December 1986 mission. He was killed on 21 January 1987, ejecting after being hit by another Stinger. He held off the Mujahideen for an hour before killing himself (and several of his tormentors) with a hand grenade.

According to official reports, only one type enjoyed a lower loss rate in Afghanistan than the Su-25, and that was the obsolete Il-28. Their tail gunners tended to discourage Mujahideen gunners from popping out of cover to fire as the ancient bombers egressed, and were also able to call out rear hemisphere threat warnings. Encouraged by this, Ilyushin again promoted its aircraft (as the Il-102) as an Su-25 replacement, but the aircraft was again rejected and the air force preferred to concentrate on Sukhoi's own extensively modified Su-25 derivative, the Su-25T.

War in the former republics

Afghanistan was not the only war from which the designers of the Su-25 could draw lessons based on real combat experience. Azeri forces used Su-25s in their war against Armenia during 1992, while from late 1992 the Georgians used Su-25s against Abkhazian forces fighting for independence, who were themselves supported by Russian forces, which included Su-25s. Among the earliest incidents of this brief but bloody conflict (which lasted until the end of 1993) was an engagement on 27 October 1992,

involving two Georgian Su-25s and two Russian Su-25s which were escorting Mi-8s delivering humanitarian relief. None of the aircraft were shot down. Six Georgian Su-25s (then virtually the entire Georgian Su-25 fleet) were shot down later in the war, together with a Russian Su-25 and one of the Su-25s handed over by Russia for operation by Abkhazian forces. Following the secession of Abkhazia, the last Georgian Su-25 was shot down on 5 November while conducting operations against rebel Zviadist forces who supported former President Zviad Gamsakhurdia. Georgian Su-25s wore standard Russian camouflage and red star markings, and this may have been the origin of the Russian tricolour tailfin badges applied to some Russian Su-25s.

While development of the extensively redesigned Su-25T progressed slowly, Sukhoi introduced some final improvements to the baseline single-seat Su-25 and

two-seat Su-25UB. The most important of these was the adoption of the R-195 engine, a derivative of the R-95 which offered increased thrust and a lower IR signature. The powerplant had been intended primarily for the heavy-weight Su-25T, but its availability came as a blessing to Sukhoi, which saw it as a welcome means of improving Su-25 and Su-25UBK performance, even though only a relatively small number of aircraft remained to be built. The new engine was first flown in the T8M-1 prototype, while the T8-14 and T8-15 were re-engined to enable the engine trials to be completed more swiftly.

The T8-15 (c/n 10192, already used for combat trials in Afghanistan, and badly damaged while being flown by Alexander Rutskoi) was used to make the Su-25's Western public debut at the 1989 Paris Air Salon at Le Bourget. Some sources suggest that the aircraft was again re-engined with its original R-95s to preserve secrecy, but this seems unlikely. It is more probable that the Sukhoi OKB merely failed to remark on the change of engine.

The installation of the new engine necessitated some changes to the engine nacelles and to the rear fuselage. Auxiliary intakes were added below the rear part of the nacelle, and additional auxiliary intakes were added above the nacelle. The small intake at the base of the tailfin was removed. A tubular pipe projected from the centre of the jet pipe of the R-195, mixing cool bypass air into the middle of the jet efflux to reduce the engine's IR signature. The R-195 had a designated service life of 1,500 flying hours or seven years, with a 500-hour TBO. Following its participation in the Paris Air Salon, the T8-15 was used for a variety of trials, including some maximum weight weapons tests. It was finally retired to the Central Air and Space Museum at Khodinka airfield on Leningradsky Prospekt in Moscow.

The Su-25BM target tug

There is some confusion regarding the designation of the R-195-powered single-seat Su-25s. Some have suggested that the only single-seaters powered by the new engine were the batch of 50 Su-25BM (*Bukshir Mishenyei*) dual-role fighter-bomber/target tugs. Others suggest that more Su-25s were built or retrofitted with the R-195 engine, and only a proportion of these should be referred to as Su-25BMs. Confusingly, some authorities have even suggested that certain Su-25BMs were powered by the R-95 engine. The re-engined aircraft does retain the same ASCC 'Frogfoot-A' reporting name.

Work on the Su-25 target tug began in 1986, and the OKB looked at the possibility of producing either a single-seat or two-seat version. As far as is known, a decision was made to concentrate on producing a target-towing derivative of the R-195-powered single-seater, under the designation Su-25BM. This was always intended to be a 'convertible' which could be reconfigured for full combat duties at squadron level. When operating in the target-towing role, the aircraft carried a TL-70 winch unit with a Kometa towed target below the port wing, and an inert FAB-250 or FAB-500 bomb below the starboard wing to counter the asymmetry in weight and drag. The TL-70 winch could wind out 2300-3000 m (7,545-9,845 ft) depending on the type of target. A new TL-70 target control unit panel replaced the gunsight and gunsight control panel, and an unidentified fairing, with a long, shallow knife-blade

antenna, was carried on the centreline. This may have served the Planyer-M system, which could detect target miss-distances and display them in the cockpit, and simultaneously transmit them to a suitably equipped ground station. As an alternative to towed targets, the Su-25BM could carry four rocket-powered free-flying PM-6 targets, or four M-6 parachute targets.

As far as can be ascertained, the R-195-engined Su-25BM has attachment points for the Vyuga datalink pod, used in conjunction with the Kh-58U/E (AS-11) anti-radiation missile. This latent capability may have been the reason for the reported transfer of Su-25BM target tugs from the 16th Air Army's target facilities unit at Damgarten to the 368th OShAP at Demmin-Tütow. Certainly, the 368th OShAP did include 12 R-195-engined aircraft, but it cannot be confirmed that they were the ex-Damgarten target tugs, nor that they were designated as Su-25BMs. Su-25BM target tugs probably equipped a number of squadron-sized specialised target-towing units, but were doubtless also attached to other units in ones and twos.

The Su-25BMK designation is theoretically applied to export versions of the Su-25BM, but, as far as is known, none have been delivered to any overseas customer, and the R-195 engine was once rumoured not to have been cleared for export.

Su-25T: the second generation

The main application of the R-195 engine was for the advanced 'Frogfoot' in all of its T8M forms – the Su-25T, Su-25TM, Su-34 and Su-39. These designations covered similar sub-variants of an advanced single-seat attack aircraft, based on the airframe of the two-seat Su-25UB, but with the former instructor's cockpit space occupied by advanced avionics and some restored internal fuel tankage in new No. 3 and 4 fuel tanks. Total internal fuel capacity increased to 3840 kg (8,466 lb) from the Su-25UB's 2725 kg (6,008 lb) and the original single-seater's 3000 kg (6,614 lb). The T8M retained the profile of the Su-25UB, but with metal skinning replacing the rear cockpit canopy. This gave the aircraft a distinctively humped appearance.

Bulgaria's Su-25Ks and Su-25UBKs are operated by the 22nd Iztrebitelno-Bombardirovachen Aviopolk/Fighter-Bomber Regiment (22 IBAP), based at Bezmer air base. The 'Frogfoots' are divided between two squadrons.

The Su-25K is just one element in the BVVS inventory of attack/strike aircraft. Bulgaria also operates Su-22M-4 'Fitter-Ks', MiG-23BN 'Flogger-Hs' and MiG-21MF 'Fishbed-Ks'. In addition, the BVVS has Mi-24D/V 'Hind-D/E' assault helicopters.

Sukhoi Su-25, Su-28 and Su-39 'Frogfoot'

This Czech Su-25K wears the white prancing horse badge that consistently remained as the emblem of the Czech Su-25 unit, despite the many changes that unit underwent. The Su-25s of the independent Czech air force are now based at Námest (33rd Tactical Air Force Base) as the 322nd Tactical Flight. Though the Czech air force has been cut back severely since independence (and even before), the Su-25 force has been retained while other more impressive assets, such as the MiG-29, have been withdrawn.

Work on a 'super Frogfoot' began in 1981, just as the results of the combat evaluation of the original T8 prototypes were being evaluated, and as recommendations were being made that this original aircraft should be put into production. The new variant would be a heavier aircraft, with even better resistance to ground fire and battle damage, and with more advanced sensors and systems optimised for the night and all-weather attack roles. Vladimir Babak was given leadership of the project, which was accorded a high priority.

T8M changes

Such was the importance attached to the new T8M that the partially complete T8U prototype airframes (and a T8U static test airframe) were taken over to form the basis of the new version. Work on these airframes began in 1983. Internal volume was exploited wherever possible, allowing the increased internal fuel already referred to, and making it possible to find space for many new avionics systems. These included a new Voskhod navigation system, with twin digital navigation computers. Armour was increased and improved, with the avionics bay, fuel feed tank and fuel pipes all gaining extra protection. Fuselage compartments adjacent to the fuel tanks were filled with a porous elastic filler, intended to prevent impulse splashing of the fuel if hit by a bullet or shrapnel fragment. The OKB estimated that survivability had been enhanced by a factor of between four and six.

In order to provide extra internal volume, the original cannon bay was deleted, and it was decided to carry the gun externally, below the belly. At first it was hoped that the T8M (soon given the air force designation Su-25T) would be armed with a new 45-mm cannon, with depressing barrels for ground strafing. In the event, the Su-25T used the same AO-17A (GSh-30-2, 9A623) 30-mm cannon as the basic Su-25, but carried below the fuselage as the NPPU-8M, offset to starboard by 270 mm (10.5 in). This necessitated moving the nosewheel another 220 mm (8.6 in) to port.

Improved sensor system

The nosecone was lengthened slightly, and tapered less sharply in plan view. The nose window was enlarged to allow it to serve the Krasnogorsk OMZ I-251 Shkval (squall) optical-TV system, which combined high-resolution television, a Prichal laser rangefinder and target designator, and a Vikhr laser guidance system. The Shkval could present a wide-angle (36° x 27°) picture for target search, or a 23-times magnified (1° x 0.7°) picture for tracking. The sight-line could be steered through 70° horizontally, and from 15° above the centreline to 80° below. A moving armoured target could be tracked to an accuracy of 0.6 m (2 ft) at ranges of up to 8 km (5 miles). The laser designator illuminated a 5 x 5-m (16.4 x 16.4-ft) box, and transmitted steering commands directly to the laser sensors mounted at the rear of the 9M120 Vikhr laser-guided tube-launched missiles. The system was essentially the same as that fitted to the Ka-50 'Hokum', and made the Su-25T fully compatible with a wide range of laser-/TV-guided bombs and missiles.

For night and all-weather missions, the Su-25T could carry a Mercury LLTV pod under the fuselage. The image from this conventional TV camera could be electronically enhanced, and offered an 18.2° x 13.7° field of view for search and a 7.3° x 5.5° field of view for tracking. This allowed a tracking range of 3 km (1.9 miles) for a tank-sized target. Narrow FoV pictures were displayed on a CRT display, while wide FoV imagery was displayed on the new wide-angle HUD. Surprisingly, this was one of the few new features within the cockpit, since, unlike second-generation versions of the MiG-29 and Su-27, the Su-25T's cockpit was not subjected to a major redesign or modernisation. A new IT-23 hooded display screen for the I-251 Shkval was added to the top part of the right-hand side of the panel, but there were no CRT or LCD display screens.

The Su-25T was given a much improved Irtysh ECM and defensive avionics system, with a Gardeniya active ECM jammer, an SPO-15 Beryoza RHAWS, and SPO-32

Above: Czech and Slovak air force aircraft have gained a reputation for increasingly bizarre 'special schemes'. This Czech aircraft, from the 30th GAR, first appeared in this basic blue and white scheme at the 1994 CzAF air show at Pilsen. The 'Lubrifilm' sponsorship titles were added in 1995.

Right: This Slovak Su-25K, from the 2nd Mixed Air Regiment, first appeared in this scheme at the SIAD '93 air show, in Kosice.

Pastel RWR. RHAWS coverage is through a full 360° in azimuth, and 30° in elevation, going from 1.2-18 GHz. The system can be used for cueing Kh-58 ARMs. From the third prototype an L-166S1 Sukogruz IR jammer (based on a powerful 6-kW Cesium lamp) was installed in a cylindrical fairing at the base of the tailfin, alongside the UV-26 chaff/flare dispensers flush-mounted in the rear fuselage. They contained a total of 192 PPI-26 IRCM or PPR-26 chaff cartridges. The airframe of the T8M was otherwise almost unchanged, although it gained BU-45A hydraulic boosters (as used by the MiG-21) for the elevator controls.

The T8M-1 prototype made its maiden flight at Zhukhovskii on 17 August 1984, in the hands of A. N. Isakov. This aircraft (apparently coded 'Red 02') had a glazed rear canopy painted onto the spine. Subsequent aircraft did not hide the fact that they merely had metal skinning which followed the same contours as the two-seater's cockpit. Two more prototypes joined the test

programme in 1985 and 1986, although A. Gontcharov was forced to eject from the T8M-2 during trials. Two more non-flying airframes were used for static (damage to airframe) and fatigue tests.

Su-25TK for export

The new variant was offered for export under the designation Su-25TK (with the T8M-3 serving as prototype/demonstrator, after slight changes to the avionics), until an entirely new designation was applied by the OKB. The Su-25TK was redesignated Su-34 in an effort to attract funding, and to give the impression that it was a new design. The designation was not recognised by the air force, and was eventually reassigned to the production version of the Su-27IB, although again it remained unrecognised by the air force. One of the Su-25Ts made its debut as the export Su-25TK demonstrator at Dubai in 1991. The aircraft was fitted with a BA-58 Vyuga datalink pod under

Slovak air force aircraft all wear the air force insignia of a shield bearing the Slovak cross (cross of Lorraine). This shield is also the centrepiece of the national flag. Slovakia gained its independence from its larger and better developed Czech neighbour in 1993 – though the move towards independence was politically inspired by the leaders of the day and was not a desire strongly shared by the bulk of the citizens. Assets of the Czechoslovakian air force were mostly split on a 2:1 basis and so 11 Su-25Ks and one Su-25UBK were handed over to the Slovak air force, from late 1992 onwards. These aircraft now make up the 3rd Flight of the 33rd Air Base, at Malacky-Kuchyna. They had previously been based at Piestany and Trencin air bases (as the 1st Flight of the 2nd Mixed Regiment).

This aircraft, from the 10th Su-25 production batch, is one of the 24 Su-25Ks that remain in service with the Czech air force. Sharkmouths have also been seen on some Russian Su-25s, noticeably on aircraft of the 186th (Instructors) ShAP, at Buturlinovka air base.

Above: Many Sukhoi aircraft (including Su-17Ms) attached to the 16th Air Army wore the design bureau's 'sniper' badge on their fins. This 357th OShAP Su-25 is seen being refuelled at Nöbitz air base (long known to Western observers as Altenburg), which was home to a MiG-29 regiment.

Right: This 'Frogfoot' is probably representative of the operational status of most of the Iraqi Su-25 inventory. At least two of Iraq's Su-25s were destroyed as air-to-air kills and and an unknown number were destroyed by LGB attacks on their hardened shelters. On first sight, this aircraft appears to have been hit during take-off or landing – its main gear has left substantial tracks in the desert and the drag chute has been deployed before it burned out and broke its back. However, it may equally have been towed away to a remote area of the airfield, in the hope of avoiding attack, and then been caught in the open.

Opposite page, top: Russia's 'Sky Hussars' team (sometimes referred to as the 'Celestial Hussars') has taken the unusual step of operating the Su-25 as a formation display aircraft.

the fuselage, for compatibility with the Kh-58 (AS-11 'Kilter'). The streamlined fairing at the base of the rudder was clearly empty on this aircraft, lacking the IR jammer in its trailing edge, and instead having flush-fitting twin chaff/flare dispensers let into the sides.

The end of the Su-25?

An initial production series of eight Su-25Ts was produced at Tbilisi, the first flying in July 1990. By then, work was already well advanced on the further improved T8TM, or Su-25TM, which combined radar and imaging infra-red sensors to maximise night/all-weather capability. Unfortunately, once Georgia gained its independence it was decided that all further Su-25 production would have to be undertaken at Ulan-Ude. This effectively brought production to a complete halt for months, or perhaps even years. The step was essential, however, since production of the baseline Su-25 in war-torn Georgia ground to a halt almost immediately, and has not recommenced. Any nation wishing to buy a new single-seat Su-25 or Su-25K would probably have to persuade the factory at Ulan-Ude to tool up for production of the type. This would be by no means straightforward, since the plant has hitherto built only Su-25 variants based on the hump-backed two-seat airframe. It is probably safe to say that the first-generation Su-25 is effectively dead in its single-seat form.

The Su-25TM differs very little from the Su-25T/TK in external appearance. Its principal advantage lies in its ability to carry new pods under the fuselage centreline. The first of these was the Kinzhal (Dagger) 8-mm MMW (Millimetre Wave) radar pod, and the second was the Khod (Motion) FLIR or IIR pod, which used virtually the same pod airframe. The Leninets Kinzhal pod was dropped after development problems, mainly because it had been sourced from the Ukraine, and the OKB understandably wanted all equipment to come from a single republic, after the difficulties it had experienced having a production plant in Georgia. Leninets is based in St Petersburg, and estimated that it would take at least two years to build a new version using Russian-supplied components. Babak himself estimated that four years would be required, including the writing of new software.

Kopyo-25 radar for the Su-25TM

The aircraft can also carry a centreline Kopyo-25 radar pod. The Phazotron Kopyo radar is a close relation to the same company's Zhuk, but with a somewhat smaller antenna. It has some air-to-ground radar modes but is usually thought of as an air-to-air radar, and was developed primarily for use in MiG-21 upgrades. Of four test sets produced, one was used for ground and airborne rig testing, two were provided to Mikoyan for the MiG-21-93, and one was podded for trials with the Su-25TM. To the Su-25TM, the Kopyo pod brought a degree of terrain-avoidance capability, as well as various types of Doppler beam sharpening, radar mapping, target designation and missile guidance function.

The Kopyo-25-equipped Su-25TM is described as being compatible with the BVR-capable R-27 (AA-10 'Alamo') and R-77 (AA-12 'Adder') air-to-air missiles. Such a capability did not come anywhere close to transforming the sluggish and slow Su-25TM into a fighter, but it did introduce some useful versatility, and a healthy self-defence proficiency. More importantly, the new radar allows the Su-25TM to carry weapons like the Kh-31A (AS-17 'Krypton') and Kh-35 (AS-X-20 'Kayak').

The first Su-25T prototype (T8M-1) served as the Su-25TM prototype, redesignated as the T8TM-1. It was followed by two more prototypes (T8TM-2 and T8TM-3, 'Blue 09' and 'Blue 10'), which may have been converted from Su-25Ts (perhaps T8M-9 and T8M-10), or which may have been newly built. The second Su-25TM made the type's public debut at the massive display mounted for CIS leaders at Minsk Maschulische in February 1992. The Su-25TM is designated Su-39 internally, by the OKB, but this designation remains entirely unofficial.

Development of a navalised version of the Su-25TM (known as the Su-25TP) – which combined features of the Su-25TM with the specific naval features of the Su-25UTG – may have been halted, suspended or abandoned. No prototype has yet been flown. During 1995 and 1996, the Sukhoi OKB appeared to have lost some of its political influence, and other aerospace organisations, including the MiG/MAPO/Kamov grouping, seemed to be winning back some of the influence they had lost. The fulfilment of Russian air forces' requirements became more open to competition, and Sukhoi could no longer expect orders for all of its products. In this new environment, the Su-25TM has failed to win a production order, and its future must be open to question. An offer of licence-production in Poland failed to generate an order from the Polish air force, and only the UAE and Bulgaria have seriously looked at the type. Bulgaria and Slovakia would reportedly be interested in acquiring a handful of Su-25TMs to act as pathfinders for their respective air forces' existing fleet of baseline Su-25s. Negotiations began in late 1993 and 1995 for the lease of small numbers of Su-25TMs to both nations.

An uncertain future

The Sukhoi Su-25 has proved the validity of its original concept, but has also demonstrated a need for more effective night-attack sensors and systems, and for improved armour and self-protection systems. Unfortunately for Sukhoi, just as these were finally developed for the advanced Su-25T and Su-25TM, the end of the Cold War resulted in a massive decrease in defence spending. The Su-25TM is probably still too revolutionary to be a core programme, and to attract a share of much more scarce funding. Money is far more likely to be allocated to advanced versions of the MiG-29 and Su-27, which have been designed to be compatible with advanced precision-guided air-to-surface weapons, and which offer greater versatility. In a time of economic cutbacks, such multi-role aircraft are almost

certainly more likely to prosper than less flexible single-role aircraft, even if the latter are superior. The future of the Su-25 and its advanced derivatives will depend on their ability to attract export orders. Unfortunately, overseas customers have so far proved to be no more far-sighted than the superpowers in being able to order such a specialised attack aircraft, and such a superficially unimpressive performer. America has allowed the A-10 to wither and die, and Russia looks set to do exactly the same with the Sukhoi Su-25. **Jon Lake**

An Su-25UTG lands on Kuznetsov, under the gaze of an Su-27K. Prestige projects such as the Su-27/35 'Flanker' have pushed the Su-25 into the background at Sukhoi and this, coupled with production and funding problems, may sharply curtail any plans for future 'Frogfoots'.

Sukhoi Su-25 Operators

Russia

About 700 Su-25s are believed to have been delivered to the VVS (Frontal Aviation) and the AV-MF. This is considerably more than was initially believed, with early estimates suggesting that the VVS only received about 300 aircraft. In fact, 350 Su-25s are understood to remain in service in Russia alone. About 250 single-seaters serve with Frontal Aviation, together with an estimated 27 two-seaters. The remainder serve with the AV-MF. A total of 10 regiments is known to have been fully equipped with the Su-25 (two of them under the command of the AV-MF) in Soviet times. Remarkably few Su-25 units ever reached the front-line air armies in Western Europe, with just two regiments in East Germany and none in Poland, Hungary or Czechoslovakia. In the event of a war, many of the Russia-based Su-25s would presumably have forward-deployed. The Su-25 force probably included many squadron-strength Su-25 elements at its peak, but details of these are not known. When the USSR finally split asunder, the air forces lost about five Su-25-equipped regiments to the air forces of the newly independent Belarus and Ukraine. Other aircraft (in smaller numbers) went to the air forces of other newly emerging republics.

The **60th OShAP** was formed from the **200th OShAE** in 1982 and spent the first years of its existence at Sital Chai, with one or two of its constituent squadrons always forward-deployed in Afghanistan. It finally

withdrew in 1988 to Sital Chai in Azerbaijan, an airfield designated for its planned disestablishment. During its period in Azerbaijan, the regiment lost one aircraft when an Azeri pilot defected to a rebel-held airfield. The regiment moved back to Russia in May 1992, without having disbanded. The unit's Su-25s wore red-outlined white codes and a white rim around the laser window after their return from Afghanistan, and probably wore white outline codes (and these may perhaps later have been 'filled in' in red) in Afghanistan.

The **186th OShA(T)P** is based at Buturlinovka, as part of the training centre at Borisoglebsk. During 1993, the instructors deployed with some of the aircraft to Kakaidy in Uzbekistan, to take part in bombing missions over Tajikstan. They had earlier participated in fighting in Georgia. The unit's aircraft wear red codes outlined in white. Some aircraft have been photographed with a large black and white sharkmouth on the nose (e.g., 'Red 27', '32').

The **206th OShAP** was based at Lida in what is now Belarus. The unit now forms part of the Belarus air force.

The **234th IAP** at Kubinka is a dedicated 'show unit' whose primary peacetime role is to display Frontal Aviation's aircraft and capabilities to visiting dignitaries, and to provide aircraft for display within and outside Russian borders. It maintains combat capabilities, and may have a tactical development and training role. The regiment is much larger than normal Russian regiment-sized units, and parents several single-type squadrons, each of which may

be close to a normal regiment in terms of size and aircraft establishment. Su-25s are operated by the regiment's third squadron. The front-line Su-25s, Su-25UBs and Su-25BMs wear white outline codes and white-outlined red codes. Some of these aircraft wear a red, blue and white Russian tricolour on the tailfin, although such designs are not standardised and some even incorporate the old double-headed Imperial Eagle of the Romanovs. The squadron includes the 'Sky Hussars' (perhaps more accurately translated as the 'Celestial Hussars') display team. The team's aircraft wear a colour scheme based on an old cavalry uniform, with predominantly red undersides and white 'piping' like that on a dress uniform jacket on the aircraft's belly.

The **357th OShAP** formed at Pruzhany, Belarus in October 1984, under the command of Alexander Rutskoi, and moved to Brandis in East Germany one year later to become the 16th Air Army's first Su-25 unit. The regiment's aircraft originally wore white outline codes, which were filled in with red during 1991. Ten of the unit's Su-25s and two Su-25UBs were transferred to the 368th OShAP in the northern part of East Germany in April 1992, less than a week before the regiment flew its aircraft to Buturlinovka, where it disbanded. Its aircraft were reassigned to other regiments.

The **368th OShAP** formed at Zjovtnevoye on 12 July 1984, moving to Kalinov to begin operations in September 1984 and then to Chirchik in Uzbekistan in 1986. The regiment fought in Afghanistan between October 1986 and November 1987, operating from Bagram and Kandahar. The 368th moved back to Chortkov in the Ukraine and then to Demmin-Tütow in East Germany in December 1988. The unit withdrew to Buddyenovsk in the northern Caucasus, leaving Germany on 15 June and arriving on 17 June 1993. As far as can be ascertained, the unit is now based at Maikop, Abkhazia. The aircraft wore red codes outlined in white.

The **378th OShAP** fought in Afghanistan during the late 1980s, and may

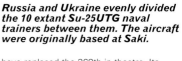

Russia and Ukraine evenly divided the 10 extant Su-25UTG naval trainers between them. The aircraft were originally based at Saki.

have replaced the 368th in-theatre. Its aircraft wore red codes, thinly outlined in black. The unit returned to Postavy in what is now Belarus and now forms part of the Belarus air force.

The **397th OShAP** was also based at Postavy and was transferred to the control of the newly independent Belarus air force.

The **433rd OShAP** has been described as having been an Su-25 unit, at an unknown airfield. Its present status is unknown.

The **456th OShAP** was based at Chortkov in what is now independent Ukraine, and forms part of the Ukrainian air force.

The **461st OShAP** is another little-known unit, sometimes described as an Su-25 regiment. Its present base is unknown, and the unit may no longer exist.

The **760th ISIAP** at Lipetsk is a tactical training unit equipped with a wide variety of aircraft types. At least one of the unit's squadrons flies the Su-25.

A similar training unit is the **802nd UAP** (Training Aviation Regiment). It is believed to be based at Krasnodar, and operates Su-25s alongside Su-17s and Su-24s.

The **200th OShAE** was a squadron-strength operational evaluation unit, and may have been formed from the initial service trials/state acceptance trials unit. The unit formed at Sital Chai on 4 February 1981 and received the first 12 production Su-25s from Tbilisi during April 1981. On the evening of 18 June 1981 the 200th OShAE became the first Su-25 unit in Afghanistan, flying in to Shindand. The unit began combat operations a few days later. Soon afterwards the squadron was doubled (and later tripled) in strength to become the 60th OShAP.

An unidentified target-towing flight, based at Damgarten in East Germany, operated 12 Su-25BMs in support of the Baltic gunnery and missile ranges. Its yellow-coded aircraft are believed to have reverted to the fighter-bomber role when they were reassigned to the 368th OShAP at Demmin in 1991 or 1992.

A unit reported as the 13th Fighter-Bomber Regiment (perhaps the **13th Aviatsion'nyi Polk Istrebitelei-Bombardirovchikov/APIB**) is based at Galinonki, north of Vladivostok. This regiment's first squadron maintains the tradition of the French 'Normandie-Niémen' volunteer unit that fought alongside Russian units during World War II. As such, it received a high-level courtesy visit from French representatives in March 1997.

The **AV-MF** operated a number of Su-25s in the land-based attack role, primarily for the support of amphibious landings. The aircraft were handicapped by a lack of range and equipped only two regiments. The first of these was the **297th ShAP** at Severomorsk, which later parented the Su-25UTGs transferred from Saki to equip the *Kuznetsov*'s air group, which was shore-based at the same airfield.

The **299th ShAP** was based at Saki and was absorbed by the armed forces of the Ukraine when that country became independent. A stylised white gull fin badge was applied to the unit's Su-25UTGs.

This Su-25K , in 'Afghan camouflage', was one of those operated by the Brandis-based 357th OShAP. A second unit was based at Tütow.

Above left: Russia's 'Sky Hussars' display team is, in fact, the third squadron of the Kubinka-based 234th IAP 'show wing'.

Left: This Su-25UBK is one of those previously allocated to the Group of Soviet Forces in Germany. It is seen wearing the Ulan-Ude factory badge.

Former republics and CIS states

Abkhazia

During the Abkhazian war for independence from Georgia, Russia clandestinely handed over a number of Su-25s for the infant state's forces. They were flown by Russian pilots of Abkhazian origin, and one was shot down. Their eventual fate is unknown. Abkhazia does not currently exist as a legally constituted and recognised state, although Georgian government forces have largely been expelled from Abkhazia.

Armenia

Although most sources suggest that Armenia does not have an air force, and relies on Russia for air defence, it does have an army aviation helicopter element, and a government VIP flight operated by Armenian Airlines. The republic may also have a small combat element at Yerevan, with about five Sukhoi Su-25s.

Azerbaijan

Azeri rebel forces received their first Su-25 on 8 April 1992 when an Azeri pilot (Lieutenant Vaghif Kurbanov) defected to Yevlakh from the **60th OShAP** then based at Sital Chai in Azerbaijan. This aircraft was subsequently used to mount raids against Armenian forces and was eventually shot down (with its original pilot) during fighting in Nagorno Karabakh in June or July. By the time he was shot down, Kurbanov had downed a pair of Armenian helicopters and an impressed civil Yak-40. When Azerbaijan became independent upon the dissolution of the USSR, in December 1991, it gained a handful more Su-25s which were left behind at Sital Chai, though Russia claimed that all aircraft returned to Russia. More may have been purchased from Georgia. The number of Su-25s appropriated was often overestimated, not least by Armenia's inevitable claims that every aircraft it shot down was an Su-25, because for some time that was the only aircraft type known to be in service. Azerbaijan confirmed the losses of single Su-25s on 24 June and in July and August 1992; the pilot of the third aircraft, Captain Yuri Balichenko, ejected and was captured. Current strength is less than three Su-25s. Another Su-25 was shot down on 10 October 1992, the pilot ejecting unsuccessfully.

Belarus

Belarus retains close military ties with Russia, and the two republics have signed a range of bilateral agreements and treaties. About half of the former Soviet air force units in Belarus actually come under Russian jurisdiction, although most tactical fighter/bomber units transferred to Belarus.

This view of the Ukrainian Su-25K seen opposite shows that the 'rook' symbol associated with the Su-25 is not restricted to Russian aircraft.

The **206th OShAP** is based at Lida and now forms part of the Belarus air force. The **378th OShAP** returned to Postavy after its service in Afghanistan and now forms part of the Belarus air force. The **397th OShAP** was also based at Postavy, but its present status is unclear, though it may now form part of the Belarus air force. Between 87 and 99 Su-25s are estimated to be in service.

Georgia

Although the main Su-25 production plant is located in Georgia at Tbilisi, the Republic of Georgia air force operates only a handful of Su-25s (variously estimated at between five and eight Su-25s). Seven additional examples were shot down by Abkhazian rebels during 1992 and 1993 when Abkhazia successfully attempted to secede from Georgia. These aircraft were acquired from undelivered stocks at the factory upon the dissolution of the USSR in December 1991, and remain based at Tbilisi.

Turkmenistan

When Turkmenistan gained its independence it found itself with large numbers of former Soviet combat aircraft based on its soil. Many were Su-17s, MiG-23s and MiG-27s, which Russia had no interest in redeploying, but there were also a handful of Su-25s and MiG-29s. A national air defence force was established in October 1993, and it is believed to include a small number of Su-25s.

Ukraine

Upon the break-up of the USSR, the Ukraine was left with massive military forces, including units equipped with the most modern aircraft types. Several former Soviet Su-25 regiments were based on Ukrainian soil, and were adopted by the new independent Ukrainian air force and naval air arm. The **456th OShAP** is based at Chortkov and now forms part of the Ukrainian air force's **14th Air Army**. The Su-25 fleet is maintained and any surplus aircraft are stored at Ovruch with the **4070th Aircraft Reserve Base**. Estimates of the number of Su-25s in service with the Ukrainian air force range from 25 to 50. The most reliable estimates suggest that around 30 aircraft are in service. The air force Su-25s are augmented by aircraft operated by former AV-MF elements based in the Crimea and which now fall under Ukrainian command. It is estimated that 45 Su-25s are controlled by the Ukrainian navy, including four or five of the rare carrier-capable Su-25UTGs. These serve with the **299th ShAP** at Saki and wear red codes.

The International Fighter Pilot's Academy (a civilian-run organisation offering flight experience in front-line jets to generate hard currency) moved from its Slovak base to re-establish itself in the Ukraine. Here it offers flights in a range of aircraft types, from the Su-27 and MiG-29 to the L-39 and including the Su-25UB.

The scheme worn by this Ukrainian Su-25, unlike the aircraft in the background, seems to indicate that it is a former AV-MF aircraft.

Other export customers

Afghanistan

Despite the many reports to the contrary, no evidence can be found to support the widely held belief that Afghanistan has ever operated the Su-25. Even during the long Soviet presence in that country, all Sukhoi Su-25s were flown by Soviet pilots and almost inevitably wore Soviet insignia, though a handful may briefly have worn local insignia for disinformation or publicity purposes. No photographic evidence of 'Afghan' (or Afghan-marked) Su-25s exists, and there have been no reliable reports of Su-25s in-country since the Soviet withdrawal.

For the record, Brasseys' *World Aircraft and Systems Directory* stated that 60 Su-25s were delivered between 1986 and 1990, while Jane's *World Air Forces* suggests that 12 Su-25s (survivors of a batch delivered in 1988) are still in service. The same is true of some other sources.

Little hard information is available on the current status of Angolan Su-25s. The aircraft have, however, seen combat against UNITA rebels.

Angola

Reliable witnesses (and reportedly a brief clip shown on Angolan and Portuguese TV) first indicated that a small number of Su-25s were delivered to Angola. As far as can be ascertained, 14 Su-25s (probably including two two-seaters) were delivered during 1988-89. Photographic proof and first-hand confirmation of FAPA Su-25 operations emerged in *World Air Power Journal* Volume 28 in 1996. Angola's single unit of Su-25s was split between bases at Saurimo (formerly Henrique de Carvalho) in the northeast of Angola, and Luanda, the capital, on the western coast.

Bulgaria

Bulgaria became the second export operator of the Su-25K when Soviet instructor pilots flew an initial batch of Su-25s to Bezmer air base, in October 1986. Bulgaria eventually received 36 Su-25Ks plus four Su-25UBKs – though the latter were not delivered until 1988/89. The 'Frogfoots' are flown by the 22nd Iztrebitelno-Bombardirovachen Aviopolk/Fighter-Bomber Regiment (22 IBAP) which has two operational squadrons. The Su-25 replaced MiG-17s and MiG-15UTIs, and the first squadron became operational with all its 18 aircraft in 1987. The second unit followed in 1988. The delay

in delivery of the Su-25UBKs forced the initial pilots to transition to the SU-25K from the MiG-15UTI.

The Bulgarians soon settled into operations with the Su-25, though they have expressed some reservations about the aircraft's relatively short range and very heavy fuel consumption. One aircraft was lost (with its pilot) on 17 April 1989. Bulgaria reportedly relied strongly on the USSR for the supply of heavily subsidised aviation fuels, and, when the Warsaw Pact crumbled on 1 April 1991, these supplies dried up overnight. The Su-25 force was hard-hit, and was virtually grounded in its entirety. The aircraft are understood to have resumed operations only fairly recently.

Component squadrons of Bulgarski Voennvazdushi Sily (Bulgarian air force) wings do not have strongly-defined identities. Some aircraft of the 1st Squadron, 22th IBAP, wear a lion's-head badge, while some of those attached to the 2nd Squadron wear a blue badge with an entire lion. The aircraft wear three-digit white nose codes, outlined thinly in what is understood to be the squadron colours (red or blue).

Croatia

There are persistent reports that Croatia received a 'squadron' of Su-25s (probably from Ukraine) in 1993. They reportedly remained crated because the necessary technical documentation, instructors and technicians could not follow them after the outbreak of civil war in Yugoslavia. This did not prevent the Croatians from successfully assembling the MiG-21 fighters received (perhaps from the same source) and the story should be viewed with some caution.

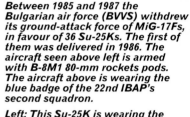

Czechoslovakia

Czechoslovakia was the first export customer for the Su-25, and received 36 single-seat Su-25Ks and a pair of Su-25UBK trainers. The single-seaters were drawn from the fifth batch (eight aircraft), the sixth batch (four aircraft), the eighth batch (10 aircraft), the ninth batch (six aircraft) and the 10th batch (eight aircraft).

The first four aircraft were delivered by Soviet pilots to Hradec Králové on 2 April 1984 where the **30th 'Ostrava' Fighter-Bomber Air Regiment** of the **10th Air Army's 34th Fighter-Bomber Air Division** began conversion to the new type. The two twin-stick Su-25UBKs were not delivered until 21 April 1988, by which

time conversion was complete. The regiment moved to Pardubice in June 1985, where it was redesignated as the **30th Ground Attack Air Regiment** on 1 November 1985.

On 1 January 1993 Czechoslovakia divided into separate Czech and Slovak Republics, and the air force was split between the two new nations. The surviving aircraft in the Su-25 fleet (35 of the 36 original single-seaters and both of the trainers) were divided between the two republics. The aircraft's subsequent history in the former Czechoslovakia is described under separate headings.

Czech aircraft wore four-digit serials based on the last four digits of their Soviet construction numbers, thus combining their production series and their position within that production series. These serial numbers were originally stencilled in black, but aircraft from the fifth, sixth and eighth batches had black serials outlined in white. Aircraft from the ninth and 10th batches had white serials, sometimes stencilled, and sometimes with thin red outlines. As they were repainted, all aircraft received whatever was the latest serial style. The

Left and below: Iraq's 'Frogfoot' force was seriously depleted during Operation Desert Storm, through shoot-downs, defections to Iran and aircraft destroyed in bombed-out HASes. Before February 1991 Iraq had perhaps 30 Su-25Ks.

Between 1985 and 1987 the Bulgarian air force (BVVS) withdrew its ground-attack force of MiG-17Fs, in favour of 36 Su-25Ks. The first of them was delivered in 1986. The aircraft seen above left is armed with B-8M1 80-mm rockets pods. The aircraft above is wearing the blue badge of the 22nd IBAP's second squadron.

Left: This Su-25K is wearing the badge of the 22nd IBAP's 1st Squadron. The wing also operates four Su-25UBKs (which replaced MiG-15UTIs). Bulgaria's need for Su-25 training was so great that single-seat MiG-15bisRs were converted to MiG-15UTIs, while still retaining their two NR-23 cannon.

two trainers had white codes very thinly outlined in red.

The aircraft were originally delivered in standard Soviet-type camouflage with two shades of brown and two shades of green on the upper surfaces, and with light blue-grey undersides. In Czechoslovak service the aircraft were repainted in a similar camouflage scheme using slightly different (more green) shades and separated by a wavier demarcation line. Several aircraft have worn special colour schemes in Czech service.

The first move away from drab uniformity among the Czechoslovak Su-25s came with the application of the 30th Fighter-Bomber Air Regiment's traditional Ostrava city crest badge, consisting of a prancing but riderless horse on a red shield, with a white flower in the top right-hand corner. The first such crest was applied to 6019 on 25 August 1988, along with a red-lipped black sharkmouth (with white teeth), a painting of a nude girl sitting in a field of flowers, and the name *Anca*. Higher authorities did not approve of engineer Antonin Fidransky's artistry, and ordered the removal of all of the markings.

The city crest (which had previously been applied to the unit's MiGs) soon reappeared. Following the dissolution of the Warsaw Pact, 8072 received a black-lipped red sharkmouth (again with white teeth) together with a huge '30 bilp' (standing for Bitevni Letecky Pulk, or attack regiment) on its tailfin. Immediately before its 1992 visit to the IAT at Boscombe Down, 9013 received an even more spectacular scheme, with a patchwork camouflage of light brown and two shades of green (the patches being separated by a pale khaki) over the front half of the aircraft's upper surfaces. The rear fuselage and tail surfaces were grey, with occasional patches of green on the fuselage and a huge cartoon frog on the fin. The frog held a tank in one hand, and a hammer in the other, reflecting the type's role and NATO codename. The aircraft was nicknamed *Zabi Noha* (Frogfoot).

The Czech Su-25Ks were to virtually the same standard as Soviet Frontal Aviation aircraft, and eighth series aircraft (at least) were compatible with the Kh-29L missile.

The Czech Su-25Ks were serialled 5003, 5006, 5007, 5008, 5033, 5036, 5039, 5040, 6017, 6018, 6019, 6020, 8072, 8073, 8074, 8075, 8076, 8077, 8078, 8079, 8080, 8081, 9013, 9014, 9093, 9094, 9098, 9099, 1002, 1003, 1004, 1005, 1006, 1007, 1008, and 1027, while the Su-25UBKs were 3237 and 3348. 5033 did not survive to see the division of Czechoslovakia.

Czech Republic

When Czechoslovakia divided into independent Czech and Slovak republics, the new Czech Republic inherited two-thirds of most of the former country's military aircraft types. The country retained 24 Su-25Ks and a single Su-25UBK which initially remained with their old unit, the **30th Ground Attack Air Regiment**, at its original Pardubice base. The regiment came under the command of a new **1st Mixed Air Army**. The aircraft moved to the **32nd Základna Taktického Letectva** (Tactical Air Base) at Namest and became the **322nd Taktická Letka** (Tactical Squadron) on 23 September 1994, as part of a major Czech air force reorganisation. Aircraft retained by the Czechs were Su-25s 5003, 5006, 5007, 5008, 5039, 5040, 6019, 6020, 8076, 8077, 8078, 8079, 8080, 8081, 9013, 9014, 9093, 9094, 9098, 9099, 1002, 1003, 1004, 1005, and Su-25UBK 3348.

The Su-25s retained by the new Czech Republic included the specially marked 9013. It was later joined by 8077, which received a red, white and blue tailfin advertising 'Lubrifilm Metal'.

Hungary

There are enduring reports that Hungarian forces began to transition to the Su-25 (reportedly re-equipping a MiG-21-equipped fighter-bomber unit at Dombovar), but that the order for the aircraft was cancelled. The story is persistently denied, and there is no photographic evidence of Hungarian Su-25s (or even of Russian Su-25s operating in Hungary). Hungary used Su-7s and Su-22s in the fighter-bomber role, and not MiG-21s, and Dombovar is not a name normally associated with any of the known Hungarian airfields. There are, however, credibly detailed reports of two 'Hungarian' Su-25 crashes, which occurred during preparations for an 'entry into service' flypast. The first Su-25 crashed into a train and taxi at Linkota after its Hungarian pilot ejected, and the second crashed at Matyasfold, killing the Czech pilot.

All that can be said with confidence is that the Su-25 never entered squadron service. One explanation for the story may be that Hungarian pilots were involved in the training and transition of the first Czech 'Frogfoot' pilots, or that Czech pilots and aircraft were training in Hungarian airspace.

Iran

Seven of the Iraqi Su-25s which escaped destruction by coalition bombing are believed to have reached safety in Iran, where they may have been absorbed into the Iranian Islamic Air Force, although this cannot be confirmed.

Iraq

Western estimates of aircraft numbers delivered to Iraq before the Gulf War should be treated with some caution; they were inflated by the difficulty of making accurate estimates when both supplier and customer were paranoid about security, and by a desire among Western intelligence agencies not to underestimate the scale of the threat. The estimated 36 MiG-29s delivered turned out to be only 14 aircraft, for example.

Some reports suggested that Iraq received 84 Su-25Ks and Su-25UBKs, and others suggested that the true number was 45, or 30 (probably the most likely total).

Above: This Czech aircraft wears the prancing horse badge of the 332nd Tactical Flight – inherited from the original 30th Attack Regiment.

There is no photographic evidence of any Iraqi Su-25UB trainers, although, since the aircraft of the Iraqi air force are seldom photographed, this is hardly conclusive. The USSR was a long-standing supplier of weapons to Iraq, which the USSR regarded as a useful source of hard currency and oil, and a useful bastion against Islamic fundamentalism in the form of Iran, which the USSR worried might export its revolutionary ideas to some of the Soviet Union's southern Islamic republics, including Armenia, Azerbaijan and Kazakhstan.

The aircraft were delivered crated, by sea, between 1986 and 1987. The aircraft were painted in a unique sand, earth and drab camouflage, with light blue undersides, and carried five-digit serials commencing 25. Aircraft 25590 was displayed statically at Saddam Hussein International in May 1989 as part of a major exhibition of Iraqi military strength. It may have been the first aircraft delivered. The Su-25s played only a minor role in the long war with Iran, and may have used Spanish EXPAL BR-500 500-kg (1,100-lb) bombs and locally produced mustard gas and Tabun (nerve gas) bombs (produced by SEPP, the State Enterprise for Pesticide Production) in addition to Soviet weapons. The aircraft moved from base to base and are known to have operated from Tallil, Jalieh and Bassorah, among other airfields. About 20 Su-25Ks (including a handful of UBKs) are believed to have been extant at the start of Operation Desert Storm, and they were immediately dispersed and hidden, often in the open.

Two Su-25s were credited to Lieutenant Robert W. ('Gigs') Hehemann, an F-15C pilot of the USAF's 36th TFW, flying from Incirlik in Turkey. He shot them down on 6 February 1991 using two AIM-9s as they attempted to flee to safety in Iran. They were trying to join the seven Su-25s which are believed to have successfully fled to Iran on 25 January, and have not been returned. There is photographic evidence that at least one more (black 25591) was destroyed on the ground by coalition bombing, caught in the open at Jalieh airfield. More were almost certainly destroyed in their shelters.

North Korea

Links between Russia and North Korea grew closer following visits to Moscow by North Korea's President Kim Il Song in May 1984 and October 1988. Intelligence co-operation and basing agreements were accompanied by the delivery of much new Soviet equipment, initially including MiG-23s, and later Su-25s and MiG-29s. The first batch of six Su-25Ks was delivered to North Korea in 1988, and these aircraft were followed by 30 more Su-25s in 1989, including (or perhaps augmented by) either two or four Su-25UBKs. These were assigned to a single three-squadron *Shturmovik* regiment reportedly based at an airfield with hangars carved into solid hillside. Details of serials and markings remain unknown.

Slovakia

When Czechoslovakia divided into separate, independent Czech and Slovak Republics, military equipment was divided between the new nations in a 2:1 ratio. Slovakia waived its allocation of some aircraft types, but was determined to retain its share of the Su-25Ks.

Above: Czech (and Slovak) Su-25s have a tradition of wearing sharkmouths, but the shark theme was taken to new extremes by this aircraft, during 1996.

Below: After the split of the Czech and Slovak Republics in 1993, the Czech air force's 322 TLt acquired this single Su-25UBK.

Eleven of the surviving Su-25Ks and a single Su-25UBK were assigned to the **2nd Mixed Air Regiment** at the **2nd Air Base** at **Piestany** as the unit's **1st Flight** in October 1992. The aircraft were subsequently detached to **Trencin**, and then on 23 September 1994 moved to **Malacky-Kuchyna** to form the **3rd Flight** at the **33rd Air Base**, officially redesignating on 1 January 1995.

Slovakian Su-25s retained their Czechoslovak camouflage and serials, with a new national insignia based on that used during the Slovak National Uprising during World War II. New squadron markings were not applied, but a handful of aircraft retain their 30th Ground Attack Air Regiment markings. Following Czech practice, a number of Slovak Su-25s have received special colour schemes. 8074 received a coloured nose, with stylised red, orange and yellow flames, and with similar flames on the engine intakes. 1027 received an even more ambitious colour scheme, with the nose serial painted in beautifully variegated reds, yellows and oranges, and with the tail fading from black at the tip trailing edge through a dull orange to a bright yellow at the leading edge of the fin-root. Superimposed upon this was a galloping bison and the outline of an ancient city. On the port side only, a nude woman reclined along the back of the bison. The aircraft assigned to Slovakia were 5036, 6017, 6018, 8072, 8073, 8074, 8075, 1006, 1007, 1008, 1027 and Su-25UBK 3237. 8072 has since been written off, having been badly damaged in a landing accident at Sliac.

A specially-painted Slovak air force Su-25K (below) wore this remarkable 'fin-art' and graphic unit badge (above and left) throughout 1993 and 1994.

Tornado Variant Briefing
Part 1: IDS and Recce

Some of Britain's early attempts at international collaboration in the design and production of military equipment proved to be less than auspicious. The trinational Panavia Tornado programme, though, generally has been a textbook example of how successful such collaborative ventures can be, although it has never enjoyed the good press it deserved. Much was made by ill-informed journalists of a supposedly high loss rate in the Gulf War, but the aircraft actually performed with great distinction, attacking some of the most difficult targets and doing so with a loss rate much lower than had been expected.

The Royal Air Force maintains eight squadrons of strike/attack Tornados, arranged into four pairs of squadrons each with a secondary speciality (reconnaissance, maritime strike, defence suppression and laser designation). This trio from Nos IX and 31 Squadrons represents the ALARM-capable radar attackers based at Brüggen in Germany.

The Tornado was designed in the early 1970s after the failure of the AFVG strike-attack aircraft programme, primarily to meet a Royal Air Force requirement for a Canberra replacement in the interdictor, strike and reconnaissance roles. The Germans soon 'came aboard' and the aircraft rapidly became an F-104G replacement as well. The programme eventually overcame the hurdles and difficulties to become a prime example of successful international collaboration. By 1997 the Tornado was still in production (23 years after its first flight) and almost 1,000 had been built, making it one of the most successful European aircraft programmes of the post-war era. As well as being a political and industrial success, the Tornado has been a military success, too, becoming one of the most effective and popular aircraft ever fielded by a European air arm, and standing comparison with the best that the USA or the Soviet Union could produce.

Although it did not need to prove itself in battle, peacetime exercises (including demanding Red Flags over the Nevada desert) confirmed that the Tornado was well-nigh unstoppable in the low-level strike/attack role,

Above: A rare formation comprises one aircraft from each of the nations involved in building the aircraft. They are from the Trinational Tornado Training Establishment, where aircraft from all three users serve side-by-side.

Left: A key secondary role of the Tornado is reconnaissance; the aircraft is able to carry either internal or podded sensors. Here an MFG 2 aircraft carries an MBB multi-sensor pod.

and confidence was high that the force would have acquitted itself well in a real war. Following the end of the Cold War, the Tornado has had more opportunities to demonstrate its prowess, not least because the world has become less stable. The aircraft has demonstrated its ability to meet new requirements for mobility, deployability and for the flexible employment of many new weapons, from medium level as well as at rooftop height.

Tornado in the Gulf

The Tornado's new role was perfectly demonstrated during the Gulf War, in which aircraft operated in a number of different roles with a wide range of weaponry, and flew a diverse array of sortie profiles. Contrary to media reports, the Tornado was a great success in the war, and its performance helped raise morale.

Six RAF Tornados were lost in action during Operation Desert Storm (four of them during the opening phase, in low-level anti-airfield attacks) and this was taken by an ill-informed media as being evidence that the aircraft was incapable of performing its intended mission. There were allegations that the Tornado had been forced to switch to the less risky medium-level bombing role. In fact, once the decision had been made to attack Iraqi airfields, there was little option but to do so from low level, and there was no aircraft available to the coalition that was better able to perform this vital role than the Tornado. Had the RAF's

Tornados not attacked with JP233 and conventional HE bombs, USAF F-15Es and F-111s would have had to do so, probably with Durandal and HE bombs; they would almost certainly have suffered equally heavy (or heavier) losses. Until low-level airfield attacks had cut airfield runways and taxiways, and until it was clear that coalition forces could conduct their operations unmolested, the coalition air forces could not conduct their high-profile precision attacks against hardened aircraft shelters and other targets. In many respects, the low-level Tornado attacks against Iraqi airfields

were as vital to the subsequent coalition air campaign as were the F-117 'Stealth Fighter' attacks against air defence network targets.

The use of the JP233 necessitated a straight-and-level, predictable, low-level overflight of the target, imposing a degree of vulnerability to ground fire. The application of good tactics, with diversionary toss-bombing of AAA and SAM sites, minimised exposure to hostile fire, and only one Tornado was lost during a JP233 attack, egressing from a forewarned target. The remaining three low-level losses were of toss-bombing aircraft, which would have been more vulnerable had they attacked from medium level and delivered their weapons in a shallow dive.

With its good load-carrying ability and sophisticated nav/attack system, the Tornado is a natural for the anti-ship role. German and Italian (illustrated) aircraft carry the Kormoran missile, while the RAF's GR.Mk 1Bs are armed with the further-reaching Sea Eagle.

During Desert Storm the RAF's Tornado fleet flew at low level for the first few days, before switching to medium-level operations. For the latter the 1,000-lb (454-kg) laser-guided bomb was widely employed, chiefly during the anti-bridge and anti-aircraft shelter campaigns.

The RAF's Tornados flew over 1,500 sorties in Operation Desert Storm, expending nearly 100 JP233s, dropping 4,200 free-fall bombs and almost 1,000 LGBs. Placed against these figures, the loss of only six aircraft was extremely modest, and apparently well below most expectations. The British Secretary of State for Defence had declared before the war that Tornados had been deployed to "deal with any Iraqi armoured thrust," but this had been little more than political window dressing, giving the aircraft an overtly defensive role. The truth was always that the aircraft would fly a more dangerous and more offensive mission.

There were important lessons to learn from the Tornado's participation in the Gulf War. Air Marshal Bill Wratten (now ACM Sir

Tornados are currently involved in several peacekeeping operations. While RAF Tornados man the detachments in Turkey and Saudi Arabia monitoring Iraq, German and Italian aircraft fly from Italy over former Yugoslavia. Here a Luftwaffe reconnaissance Tornado from EJG 1 refuels from a USAF KC-135 over the Adriatic.

William Wratten), the RAF's Gulf War air commander stated, that, "The need for stand-off weapons is one of the main lessons of the Gulf War." This was hardly news, since long before the Gulf War many had questioned the unnecessary exposure to ground fire imposed by weapons like JP233. That had been one of the driving forces behind the Tornado Mid Life Upgrade (MLU).

The most vital lesson offered by the Gulf War was that the entire military situation facing Britain's armed forces had changed almost beyond recognition. This meant that the Tornado would have to operate in a totally new environment, with very different constraints and considerations, using new tactics and new weapons.

Nuclear role

During the Cold War, the Tornado's most important role was nuclear strike, a role now being jettisoned by the RAF as the WE177 laydown nuclear bomb is withdrawn. The USSR and the Warsaw Pact were effectively the only serious threat to NATO, since each superpower kept its client states on a tight reign, avoiding the escalation of minor conflicts. NATO's response to the Warsaw Pact's numerical superiority was to maintain small, high-quality conventional forces sufficient to delay any Warsaw Pact advance and provide a breathing space for negotiation, before using nuclear weapons if necessary.

Once the Cold War ended, the credibility of the old threat diminished rapidly, but new threats began to appear as new states emerged and former Soviet client states were freed from the controlling influence of the old USSR. Nuclear proliferation became increasingly more likely. This is a remarkable development, and one which does not seem to be entirely comforting. In an era in which all-out nuclear war with Russia seems increasingly unlikely, the ability to breach Moscow's anti-ballistic missile defences no longer seems relevant. The UK has proceeded with procurement of the Trident missile, and the Tornado's nuclear role was dropped.

Low-level conventional operations have become far more likely, yet the end of the Cold War has been treated as an excuse to slash conventional forces and to reduce defence expenditure. Some observers have suggested that the need to restructure armed forces to meet the post-Cold War threat inferred a need for increased force levels and increased expenditure. They point at the increased requirement

for rapid-reaction forces, air mobility and out-of-area capabilities. Moreover, the removal of the USSR as a common threat served to make expensive autonomous national capabilities more important than ever. In the new environment it became increasingly likely that a specific NATO partner might find itself undertaking military operations to which its allies were unwilling to commit forces. However, throughout the Western world politicians gave the populace the 'peace dividend' it expected, reducing defence spending to fund tax reductions or popular social programmes.

In both Germany and the UK, the Tornado force found itself cut back, with reductions in numbers of squadrons, aircraft and manpower levels. In Britain a force of nine front-line Tornado bomber squadrons was reduced to four, albeit with two more operating in the maritime role, replacing Buccaneers. These squadrons are barely adequate to cover existing commitments, and it has been suggested that the force could no longer mount an operation similar to Operation Granby, when some 60 aircraft were deployed to the Gulf to take part in the operation to evict Saddam Hussein from Kuwait. The argument exists that the RAF has lost its ability to mount viable autonomous operations at anything but the most modest scale, and there is some evidence to support the view that the force is too small to sustain extended small-scale peacekeeping operations in more than one area simultaneously.

Fortunately, the reduction in aircraft numbers will eventually be compensated for, to a certain extent, by upgrades to the aircraft, which will enhance and improve its capabilities, and through the use of more accurate and more effective weapons. The Tornado remains a highly effective fighter-bomber today, broadly comparable with any of its rivals, including the much-vaunted F-15E. The upgrades now planned will keep the aircraft viable in the future, keeping it competitive with tomorrow's attack aircraft. This is a remarkable achievement for an aircraft designed in the 1960s.

Roots

The Tornado can trace its roots back even further than that. The studies into polymorphic aircraft configurations (those that can change shape) by Vickers's Barnes Wallis eventually resulted in the BAC P.45, a variable-geometry fighter-bomber design study, upon which the AFVG (Anglo-French Variable Geometry) strike-attack aircraft (intended as an interceptor for France) was based. This was a troubled project, born as the British-led partner to the nominally French-led Jaguar. The reasons for a collaborative project remain a mystery to some, since there was little commonality in the British and French requirements, and since a unilateral design would then actually have been easier and cheaper. Britain already had the P.45 airframe design, the R.B.153 engine and the TSR.2's avionics waiting for a home. Without French design leadership, the AFVG never stood much of a chance, since Dassault continued with its own variable-geometry Mirage G and the French government did everything possible to delay and complicate the collaborative aircraft, changing its specification and the numbers required. They simultaneously used their participation to wring the best possible terms out of

the British for the collaborative helicopter deals (which thus became somewhat one-sided) and on the Jaguar programme. It did not help that the British side was pursuing the project as much for political aims (primarily to ease entry into the Common Market) as to meet a real military requirement.

Inevitably, the French pulled out of the project, but the aircraft continued as the UKVG, with the Anglo-French M45 engine being replaced by the RB.153, which had been running since 1963. Instead of proceeding with the aircraft as a purely British project (the Labour administration had stated that Britain would never again go it alone on a combat aircraft), BAC approached MBB as a potential partner, finding the German company disillusioned by the imminent demise of the overambitious VTOL AVS. Discussions began on 10 June 1967, and a brochure was issued on 30 November 1967. MBB had already begun work on the Neue Kampfflugzeug (NKF), a lightweight, single-seat, single-engined fighterbomber that was incompatible with the big British twin-engined two-seater; at the same time, it fulfilled a requirement closer to the RAF's than had the Armée de l'Air's requirement for the AFVG. Britain suggested the Jaguar as an interim G.91 replacement, with the UKVG aircraft as an Anglo-German collaboration to meet the Luftwaffe's need for an aircraft to replace the F-104G.

One stumbling block to co-operation was German insistence on design leadership. Germany felt that it should have this because it required a larger number of aircraft than any

potential partner (though this assumption was based on unreasonably optimistic figures). BAC was relaxed about who had nominal design leadership, having shaped and driven the Anglo-French Jaguar despite not having titular leadership. They were nervous, however, that if the inexperienced Germans led in more than name, the result could be disastrous. Another problem was the apparently irreconcilable difference in the sizes of the aircraft which were required by the RAF and the Luftwaffe.

The programme takes shape

Sales efforts by Northrop (intended to sell its P.530 Cobra) had little effect other than to persuade the Luftwaffe that its G.91 and F-104 replacement requirements could be met by a single aircraft type, and the NKF seemed to be such an aircraft. In January 1968 Germany was joined by the other major NATO F-104 users – Italy, Belgium and the Netherlands (Canada standing apart as an observer) – for what became MRA 75 (Multi-Role Aircraft for 1975).

The UKVG petered out, to be replaced by the lighter ACA, and the twin BS-143-engined FCA (marginally smaller than UKVG), which was offered as a solution to the MRA-75 requirement. On 25 July 1968, Britain, Germany, Belgium, Canada, Italy and the Netherlands signed a memorandum of understanding, while Britain, Germany, Canada and

the Netherlands funded feasibility studies. Belgium and Canada soon dropped out of the project, since they required an interceptor-orientated aircraft with high specific excess power. In mid-December 1968, BAC, MBB and Fiat formed a joint industrial company and drew up a formal requirement.

At that stage there were two rival designs. That of MBB had a mid-set wing and outboard wing pivots, with outboard ailerons and an all-moving tail. BAC's design had a high wing and pivots buried within the fuselage, with full-span trailing-edge flaps and tailerons and spoilers for roll control. A compromise solution was adopted, incorporating MBB's outboard pivots and wing glove design but with BAC's high-set wing and new RB.199 turbofans. The German aircraft had a single US TF30 engine, which was bulkier and destined to be disastrous in its other applications, the F-111 and F-14. German requirements for a short-field capability (essentially an ability to operate from war-damaged airfields) were taken into account in the design of the new aircraft. The compromise design closely resembled the UKVG, and became the definitive MRCA (Multi-Role Combat Aircraft). The configuration was finally agreed during a meeting in Munich on 14 March 1969. Interestingly, the British design featured semi-circular intakes (with variable shock cones) much like those of the F-104, while the

The variable-geometry wing is the key to the Tornado's excellent low-level flying capability, the high wing loading providing a comfortable environment for the crew. Demonstrating the aircraft's medium-level agility is an RAF machine from the TTTE, a Batch 1 production aircraft lacking underwing pylons, undernose LRMTS fairing and retaining the low-powered RB.199 Mk 101 engines.

German design had simpler intakes above the wingroot. To optimise high supersonic performance, the Italians pressed for a more sophisticated raked intake with variable ramps, similar to that used on the Concorde or on the Rockwell Vigilante. This also offered good performance at high angles of attack, and was soon accepted.

Remarkably, the partner nations were able to agree what the Tornado's roles should be, listing the seven key ones as interdiction (defined as the destruction of high-value targets in the enemy's rear areas), counter air (airfield denial), battlefield air interdiction (attacking the build-up of forces in the enemy's second echelon), close air support (especially in poor weather, when dedicated CAS aircraft could not operate), reconnaissance, maritime attack (against ship and shore targets), and point air defence at low and medium altitudes.

The British were in no mood for delay. The cancellation of the TSR.2 and of the F-111 had removed the intended replacement for the RAF's long-serving strike-roled Canberras, for

which a replacement was urgently sought. It was felt by many that the Canberra was obsolete and had to be replaced by 1969-1970, although exercise, TACEVAL and NATO competition results suggested that the aircraft was still viable enough in its assigned interdiction and strike roles, often outperforming USAFE F-4s. Moreover, the scope of the new aircraft's intended roles was so wide that many believed that it could not possibly succeed, and would inevitably fall victim to technical problems and political opposition. The cynical suggested that MRCA stood for 'Must Refurbish Canberra Again!'

Panavia was formed from the joint industrial company on 26 March 1969, and shares were allocated on the basis of one-third for BAe; one-third for MBB; one-sixth for Fiat; and one-sixth for VFW-Fokker. It was decided that the MRCA would have three assembly lines, in Britain, Germany and Italy. At this stage there were still two distinct versions of the aircraft. The Panavia 100 was a single-seater optimised for interception and destined for the German, Italian and Dutch air forces. MBB Munich had design leadership on this aircraft. BAe Warton led the Panavia 200, the two-seat strike aircraft destined for the German navy and the RAF and fitted with integral fuel tanks in the wings. An extremely inaccurate (and deliberately misleading) model of the Panavia 100 was shown publicly in September 1969, but revealed little more than the aircraft's overall similarity to the UKVG in its broad configuration. Conical fairings hid the intake design completely, and the canopy was disproportionately small, making the Tornado appear to be a much larger aircraft than it was.

Workshare

BAC was given responsibility for basic flight testing, including envelope proving and expansion, aerodynamic loads, propulsion, stalling and spinning, and all specific two-seat development. The company would build all rear fuselages and the two-seat forward fuselage. Britain's role also included the provision and operation of two Buccaneer avionics testbeds (XT272 and XT285, converted by Marshall of Cambridge) and a Vulcan RB.199-34R engine testbed (XA903). MBB was responsible for avionics integration and the flight control system, and built the centre-section, and the forward fuselage of all single-seaters. Aeritalia was given responsibility for the clearance of external stores, and would build the wings, while Fokker would build the tail and the full-span trailing-edge flaps. The workshare was revised when the Netherlands withdrew from the project, BAC gaining the tail. BAC and MBB each had 42.5 per cent of the project, while Fiat had 15 per cent. The Dutch withdrawal came as no surprise, since the KNLAF needed a replacement for its F-104s in the fighter-bomber and interceptor roles, and not a heavy, long-range interdictor. Surprisingly, the Italians stayed onboard, despite the fact that they required a Mach 2, 60,000-ft (18300-m) interceptor, with short-range interdiction and close support as secondary roles. There have been suggestions that the Italians initially had little faith that they would ever procure the MRCA, and that Fiat stayed in to gain design experience and expertise and to strengthen its position in the event

Tornado Variant Briefing

that licence-production of a US design became necessary. Fiat merged with Aerfer to form Aeritalia in November 1969, a move which had little impact on the company's participation in the MRCA programme except for necessitating some sign-writing and letterhead changes.

Fortunately, Britain was eventually able to persuade its partners that the best possible way of destroying enemy tanks, troops and other forces was to do so far behind the front line, while they were still concentrated, before they could deploy and enjoy heavy AAA and SAM defences at the front line. This inferred that the aircraft's role should include the destruction of roads, marshalling yards, bridges and choke points. The RAF backed up its arguments with hard data, against which other nations could offer only opinion. The case for the efficacy of interdiction (as compared to CAS) proved compelling.

Attack at night

Similarly, the British were able to offer convincing data in support of their belief that the new aircraft should be able to operate at night and/or in foul weather. The key was that attacking under cover of darkness or weather reduced vulnerability, and allowed targets to be attacked more efficiently with lower losses, while modern technology allowed a high degree of accuracy even under such conditions. The arguments were convincing, and the RAF's vision of the MRCA soon translated into a trinational requirement, accepted by all the potential users. Although Britain stuck to its guns on range and all-weather capability, it was prepared to compromise in order to keep the other partners involved. The RAF reluctantly agreed to reduce its low-level combat radius requirement, and agreed to Germany's tough STOL requirements. In order to avoid being accused of dictating the size of the aircraft (having accused Germany's STOL needs of doing just this, and having accused Italy's thrust requirements of sizing the engines), Britain chose not to reveal that it was already looking at a dedicated fighter version for the air defence of the UK, even though it was apparent that such a variant would need a slightly stretched fuselage which could easily (and even advantageously) have been incorporated in the baseline aircraft.

The RB.199 powerplant was similarly of multinational development and construction, although it was actually a single-nation Rolls-Royce design. A trinational engine consortium,

Turbo-Union, was formed from Rolls-Royce, MTU and Fiat to develop and build the engine, should it be selected to power the new MRCA. The engine was selected after the competitive evaluation of other rival engines, including a TF30 derivative and the JTF22 from Pratt & Whitney, and the GE/1/10 from General Electric. The RB.199 was exceptionally small and compact, and tailoring the MRCA to the RB.199's dimensions allowed the smallest possible airframe. It would also ensure that re-engining the aircraft would be almost impossible, since no equivalent engine was small enough to fit the RB.199 engine bay. The small size of the RB.199 was critical in achieving the Tornado's small external dimensions, and it is worth recalling that the aircraft is dimensionally smaller than either the F-4 or the F/A-18, and is only a little larger than the lightweight F-16.

At one stage, it was thought that a trinational consortium would also be formed for the avionics suite, but this proved impractical. Instead, EASAMS was given project leadership, placing work-sharing sub-contracts with ESG and SIA.

The MRCA was named in April 1969 and became the Panther — albeit briefly, and with little publicity. The name was never fully accepted and was soon dropped, one (possibly apocryphal) explanation being its coincidence with the trade name of a leading brand of lavatory cleaner in one of the partner nations.

The obvious capability of the proposed two-seat avionics suite contrasted with that of the single-seater, and the Germans began to worry that the Panavia 100 might prove inadequate for service in the 1980s. In March 1970 the decision was taken to drop the single-seater, and for the German air force to instead receive two-seaters. The Italians quickly followed suit. This was a remarkable occurrence, since neither Italy nor Germany had any fast-jet navigators, and Italy had to pass an act of parliament just to be allowed to train some. The MRCA (or Panther) was still very much a multi-role aircraft, incorporating provision for Sparrow

One role quietly dropped from the original MRCA requirement was that of fighter (resurrected with the ADV), but the Tornado IDS retains a respectable self-defence capability. Here an RAF GR.Mk 1 fires an AIM-9 Sidewinder.

BVR AAMs, Tail Dog IR-homing dogfight missiles and the stillborn Viper AAM, in addition to a range of bombs, CBUs and ASM, including Kormoran and Martel.

MRCA project definition was completed in April 1970, and the development and manufacture of prototype aircraft was authorised in 1970 (or in September 1971, according to some sources). The three governments authorised the industrial partners to prepare for production on 15 March 1973.

Conventional construction

The aircraft's final design was settled too early for much use to be made of composites or other advanced materials, and thus the MRCA became one of the last conventional light alloy fighters to be built, with the usual mix of machined forgings, chemically- and mechanically-milled, integrally stiffened skins and honeycomb stabilised structures. The wing carry-through structure was an electron beam-welded titanium box, and was designed to give the aircraft a fatigue life of 16,000 flying hours, giving the whole aircraft an actual fatigue life of 4,000 hours after application of a 'safe life' ('scatter factor') of four.

The process of getting the aircraft into service did not go entirely smoothly. The German requirement (once estimated at 700 aircraft) was reduced first to 420 aircraft and then to 324 aircraft. The latter reduction was made possible by a Luftwaffe order for 175 F-4Fs (at a unit cost of about £2.3 million) to equip four *Geschwaderen*, which replaced three of the planned MRCA *Geschwaderen* and 100 of the aircraft (at £3.4 million each).

There were many disagreements, and compromises were required in order to provide maximum commonality between the aircraft delivered to each customer. The Germans wanted to use an advanced Autonetics radar, while Britain preferred a European solution, or a cheaper radar from Texas Instruments. Control forces were another area of conflict, with a compromise being found between the British preference for light stick forces and the traditional American heavier controls which were preferred by Germany and Italy. Cockpit design also proved to be fraught with potential disagreements, though in the end, a virtually common panel was designed.

Germany's ECR variant is equipped with infra-red reconnaissance systems and sophisticated RHAWS equipment for the anti-radiation role. The HARM missile provides the offensive muscle in the latter.

The disagreements caused delays, of course, and the very complicated organisation and infrastructure required by a trinational programme inevitably imposed costs and delays which would not have been suffered by a national project. More serious than any actual technical problem or disagreement was a widespread campaign of criticism and disinformation. In Britain this was not sufficient to have much impact on the programme, merely necessitating a more energetic public- and press-relations campaign. But in Germany, especially, the sneers were enough to fundamentally weaken vital political support for the programme. One accusation made in Germany and Italy was that the MRCA as proposed would not meet the requirement as originally stated. This was true, but ignored the fact that the requirement itself had developed, and that the MRCA would be a much more militarily useful aircraft. The inference, however, was that the Luftwaffe (say) would receive an inferior aircraft for 'political' reasons.

In Germany the MRCA (and later the Tornado) was christened 'die eierlegende Wollmilchsau' (the egg-laying, wool-bearing, milk-giving pig) in sarcastic reference to its multi-role capabilities. To others it was simply 'The English Aeroplane'. Every delay, every technical problem, every careless utterance was seized upon by the MRCA's detractors and used against the programme. Many still believe that the campaign was orchestrated, funded and co-ordinated by a number of US aircraft companies, perhaps including Northrop and General Dynamics, who saw the MRCA as a threat to their own potential European fighter sales. This cannot be proven. In Italy, Panavia was forced to enlist the support of some unlikely allies, most crucially the Communists, who were persuaded that the alternative was procurement of another American aircraft type, providing US workers with jobs and further increasing Italian reliance on the USA. The party adopted a policy of what it called 'minimum necessary support' which involved abstaining from votes which threatened the MRCA, allowing the programme's more enthusiastic supporters a narrow majority.

Even under the glare of a harsh and hostile press spotlight, the MRCA's development programme proceeded remarkably smoothly. Flying a new engine in a new airframe is never straightforward, however, and if nothing else doubles the risk of delay. Minor surging problems with the engine delayed the release of a flight-cleared RB.199, although, in retrospect, programme insiders acknowledge that the problem was not really serious enough to prevent the aircraft from flying. Even after fixes had been incorporated, the propensity to surge was serious enough to be noticeable during air show demonstrations, and thus was a source of some embarrassment. More serious was a tendency for fan blades to break away, although they usually did so without causing major damage or drama, and the problem was solved before production engines were released.

German deliberations

While it would have been relatively easy and painless for any one of the partners to pull out of the MRCA programme before a commitment was made to production, once such a commitment was made withdrawal became much more difficult. Between 1976 and 1980, various factions in Germany pushed for a withdrawal from the project, and in 1980 a serious attempt to do so was initiated by German politicians, using a supposed 'massive cost overrun' as an excuse. There had been cost increases, of course, but they were almost entirely due to inflation and to the massive rise in the price of certain raw materials, particularly titanium. Nevertheless, the new Social Democrat government ordered the Ministry of Defence to secretly study the implications of pulling out of the programme. By then, though, materials had been ordered for some 809 Tornados, 485 of them for Britain and Italy. Germany would have had to subsidise these aircraft to maintain their existing unit cost, and would have had to move the production lines for the German sub-assemblies to the other two countries, leaving its own factories empty and without work. Taken together, all of this would have cost almost as much as proceeding with its MRCA buy unaltered, while the Luftwaffe and Marineflieger would have been 'down' 324 aircraft.

The Tornado, of course, has continued to experience its share of problems during its service life, most of which have had little to do with the aircraft itself. Reduced force levels have led to cuts in manpower; this, in turn, inevitably has led to redundancies among both ground and aircrew, and those who have left

Above: Not renowned for its manoeuvrability, the Tornado can nevertheless put on quite a show in the right hands, as demonstrated by this No. II Squadron, Royal Air Force aircraft. The full-span flaps and slats provide large amounts of lift at low speed.

Right: The GR.Mk 1A has an internal infra-red reconnaissance suite, and was the world's first aerial system to dispense entirely with film, relying instead on video recording. With the exception of losing both cannon, the aircraft retains its full strike/attack capability.

have sometimes been the best personnel. Inevitably, morale has suffered, though not to the extent that operational efficiency has been degraded. Some argue that combat readiness has been effected by other changes. A need to generate cost savings (coupled with what some see as a doctrinaire adherence to a holy grail of privatisation) has led to an increased 'contractorisation' of second-line functions within the RAF, under which some maintenance and support services have been taken over by pri-

Tornado remains arguably the world's finest low-level strike/attack platform and, with the upgrades being undertaken by each of the original three users, will hold this position for some time. Its multi-role capacity also makes it a world leader in maritime strike and tactical reconnaissance.

vate companies. Although intended to increase efficiency and decrease costs (primarily by replacing expensive-overhead servicemen with civilian employees), this has sometimes had the opposite effect. Privatised engine servicing, for example, reportedly led to prolonged periods of aircraft unavailability, and a situation in which one station found itself with only six of its 36 aircraft serviceable on a particular day, having lost engines to keep overseas deployments and detachments running. Other examples of contractorisation have proved much happier, and the basic concept can help a military air arm to maintain its operational capabilities more economically.

Although a relatively large number of Tornados have been lost in service, concerns about the aircraft's accident rate are misplaced. Compared with other fast jets (particularly those operating in the low-level role), the Tornado enjoys a remarkably low loss rate, although occasional accidents are inevitable. There is certainly no evidence to support the veiled criticisms and hints of a hidden design defect in the aircraft suggested in a contemporary novel written by a former Tornado navigator. Most aircrew would maintain that the Tornado is an inherently safe aircraft, with excellent handling characteristics, good systems redundancy and excellent battle damage tolerance. **Jon Lake**

Tornado Variants

MRCA prototypes

The early days of the MRCA programme were fraught with delays imposed by the need to get agreement from three partners, to find common solutions which were acceptable to all, and to work out workshare and methods by which unnecessary duplication of effort could be avoided. In order not to lose further time in the flight test programme, it was decided that the development effort would be shared by a relatively large number of prototypes, with a further batch of pre-production aircraft. It had originally been thought that seven prototypes would be sufficient, but the number grew to 13 before a compromise of nine flying prototypes was reached. Construction of the prototypes began in November 1970. Politically, there had to be three flight test centres (one per partner nation) but, as far as was possible, flight test tasks were not duplicated. Britain built and used four prototypes, Germany, three, and Italy, two. This did not give a true impression of the extent of the actual British leadership of the MRCA programme. While BAC operated only one more prototype than did MBB, the Warton trials fleet included a Lightning armed with the Tornado's new 27-mm cannon, and two Buccaneers equipped with Tornado radar and avionics. BAC was also responsible for the Avro Vulcan engine testbed.

The first Tornado prototype was D-9591, which on 12 November 1973 was trucked from the MBB factory at Ottobrun to Manching, where it was assembled with engines which were cleared for ground running only. Flight clearance of the RB.199 had been delayed by technical problems, and by structural and electrical problems with the Vulcan aircraft used as the engine testbed. The Tornado's first flight was delayed while Panavia waited for flight-cleared engines to be delivered. Finally, on 14 August 1974 Paul Millet and Nils Meister took the first prototype aloft, swapping seats on the third flight on 29 August. The callsign used was LUNA 23. Germany had the honour of hosting the maiden flight, which was made in a German aircraft, although the pilot was an Englishman. This was a vital sop to German national pride, as it would later be in the Eurofighter programme. The first prototype,

MRCA prototype P.01

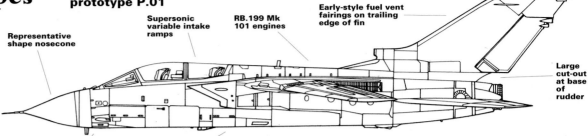

Empty RWR fairings, often used for TV cameras

Early-style fuel vent fairings on trailing edge of fin

RB.199 Mk 101 engines

Supersonic variable intake ramps

Representative shape nosecone

Large cut-out at base of rudder

No cannon fitted to early prototype aircraft

Prototypes initially flown without pylons

later serialled 98+04, was primarily used for engine testing.

The first British prototype was XX946, which made its maiden flight on 30 October 1974 from Warton, flown by Paul Millet and Pietro Trevisan. It was the first aircraft with fully variable engine intakes, and was later used for envelope expansion, engine development and preliminary inflight-refuelling trials. Uniquely, the second prototype was fitted with small square-section fairings on the tips of its tailplanes, although they were later removed, leaving small blisters on the tips (which were also unique to this aircraft). These fairings were exciters for the initial flutter testing. The third Tornado to fly was another UK aircraft, XX947, which made its maiden flight on 5 August 1975, in the hands of Dave Eagles and Tim Ferguson. It was the first Tornado with dual controls, and, as the aircraft destined for stalling and spinning trials, was fitted with an emergency spin recovery chute and a Sundstrand hydrazine monopropellant emergency power unit intended to allow emergency engine relights. XX947 was the first Tornado to be delivered in a representative camouflage colour scheme, although several other early aircraft were similarly repainted, and some later prototypes made their first flights in Panavia's garish red and white 'house colours'. It was also the first aircraft fitted with a nose radome, rather than a representatively shaped fairing.

Prototype fin modification

Six, seven or nine vortex generators added to lower fin

The early prototypes were limited to Mach 1.3 and 40,000 ft (12200 m) by the lack of fully rated engines, but early flight trials still progressed relatively smoothly. One of the most serious problems encountered was excessive base drag, with some directional instability at transonic speeds (Mach 0.9 to Mach 0.95). It was found that airflow around the spine and the base of the tailfin was breaking away. This was eventually solved by the refinement of the fairing below the rudder (filling the gap between the jet pipes and the bottom of the rudder), and by the addition of new vortex generators at the base of the fin, adjacent to the rudder leading edge, and later by using a redesigned rear fuselage, of slimmer form. These improvements considerably improved the airflow around the tail unit and reduced drag, as well as solving the stability problem.

The fourth Tornado was D-9252 (later 98+05), which Hans Friedrich Rammensee and Nils Meister took into the air on 2

P.02 second prototype

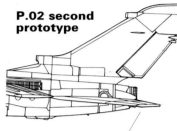

Square fairings on tailplane tips to excite flutter during tests

September 1975. The aircraft was fitted with an almost representative and integrated avionics system, and was used to prove the avionics system. The aircraft was briefly tufted for aerodynamic investigations. It demonstrated low-level automatic terrain following and was later assigned to MW-1 trials, to tests of the digital autopilot, and to navigation and ground mapping radar testing.

Italy's first Tornado (X-586) was flown solo (its rear cockpit full of instrumentation) by Pietro Paolo Trevisan on 5 December 1975. The aircraft was assigned to flutter testing, but was severely damaged landing after its sixth flight. It then had to undergo a long rebuild. The sixth Tornado, Britain's

The second MRCA prototype was XX946. It had small blisters on the tailplane tips where flutter-test fairings had been fitted during aerodynamic trials.

Above: P.01 first flew from Manching on 14 August 1974. The intakes on this aircraft were fixed.

Below: XX947 was the third Tornado to fly. Note the unusual underfuselage conduits.

Above: The second German prototype (P.04) originally flew as D-9592, but was later given test serial 98+05. This is how it appeared in 1977.

XX948, was also flown solo on its maiden flight, by Dave Eagles. The aircraft was assigned to external stores trials (primarily jettisoning rather than delivering weapons). It was the first Tornado fitted with a gun, and the first with the revised slimmer rear fuselage. The gun had previously been test-fired from a Lightning F.Mk 2A operated by BAC. It was also the first Tornado to have had vortex generators on the tailfin, though other earlier aircraft were subsequently retrofitted to a similar aerodynamic configuration.

The next prototype was a German aircraft, 98+06, which was flown by Nils Meister on 30 March 1976, with Fritz Eckert in the backseat. It was the first aircraft with a complete avionics suite and was used for TF and avionics trials. The MRCA was formally named Tornado during the same month. Paul Millet flew the next prototype, XX950, on 15 July 1976, with Ray Woolett in the rear cockpit. The aircraft was used for avionics and weapons aiming development and trials, and was the second dual-controlled trainer.

The last prototype (X-587, an Italian aircraft) and the first pre-production machine (P.11) made near-simultaneous first flights on 5 February 1977. Pietro Trevisan was accompanied by Manlio Quarantelli for this maiden flight. The ninth prototype was used for flutter trials, and for the clearance of external stores, as well as for climatic trials and autopilot development. Among the other duties performed by the second Italian prototype was testing of the Italo-German reconnaissance pod, with its Texas Instruments IRLS (Infra-Red LineScan) and twin 24-in (609.6-mm) focal length Zeiss optical cameras. The aircraft was eventually camouflaged, with prominent Dayglo stripes and a plethora of camera calibration markings.

The 10th aircraft was a static test airframe, and never flew.

All of the aircraft carried extensive instrumentation and telemetry equipment, with some 460 instrumented points per aircraft, capable of transmitting up to 150 parameters simultaneously. Some features seen on the prototypes were short-lived or temporary, including extended, lengthened nose-mounted test instrumentation probes and forward-looking camera fairings which sometimes replaced the forward fin-mounted RHAWS antenna fairing.

The prototypes were upgraded repeatedly during their lives, demonstrating and proving new equipment and systems. The first prototype, for instance, became the first Tornado to fly with the -4 engine in March 1978, allowing clearance beyond Mach 1.92.

Two of the prototype Tornados were lost in service. Britain's P.08 crashed during a simulated toss-bombing manoeuvre on 12 June 1979, killing Russ Pengelly and Squadron Leader John Gray. In April 1980 Germany's P.04 crashed during an air show

X-586 (P.05) was the first of two Italian prototypes, used for many weapons trials after a lengthy rebuild. Heavily instrumented, it carries the CASMU Skyshark stand-off dispenser weapon here.

practice, killing Ludwig Obermeier and Kurt Schreiber. The survivors flew on in the trials and development role into the 1980s, when they were withdrawn for a variety of ground instructional purposes.

Tornado IDS pre-production

The nine prototypes were followed by six pre-production aircraft. They were intended to approximate as closely as possible the planned initial production standard and equipment fit, and introduced the definitive fin/engine nozzle fairing. The fin dressing was also refined, with the seven vortex generators being reduced to six per side (from six, seven or nine on the various vortex generator-equipped prototypes). Their primary task was one of service evaluation and initial instructor training, although the aircraft were used to tidy the loose ends of the development, trials and clearance programme. Three of the pre-production aircraft were built and based in Germany, two in Britain, and one in Italy. The first of the pre-production aircraft was flown for the first time on 5 February 1977, the same day as the ninth and final flying prototype. This was probably no coincidence, it being widely reported that a trinational agreement bound the partners not to fly a pre-production jet before all nine prototypes had got into the air. Certainly the first British and German pre-production machines had been rolled out some months before, well before Christmas 1976.

P.11 (98+01) was the first pre-production Tornado, identified by the production-standard fin fillet. Here it is seen lifting off on its first flight from Manching.

The first of the pre-production batch was 98+01 (P.11), a German twin-sticker flown by Fred Rammensee and Kurt Schreiber. This aircraft had the production-standard fin fillet. The second pre-production aircraft was Britain's XZ630, which flew for the first time on 14 March 1977 in the hands of Tim Ferguson and Roy Kenward. The aircraft had -03 engines, and was to become the first Tornado to be delivered to an official test centre (Boscombe Down). The third pre-production MRCA, 98+02, flown by Fritz Soos, with Rainer Henke in the rear cockpit, on its 10 January 1978 maiden flight. It was the first Tornado with a kinked tailplane leading edge. XZ631 (P.15) flew at Warton on 24 November 1978, in the hands of Jerry Lee and Jim Evans. The aircraft was the first with a production rear fuselage, and the first with the wet fin intended for all RAF aircraft.

The only Italian pre-production aircraft (X-588, P.14) was the next to fly, on 9 January 1979, in the hands of Manlio Quarantelli and Egidio Nappi. This aircraft had full production-standard wings. It was later upgraded to production standards, though it was never issued to a front-line unit. The German P.16 (98+03) rounded off the pre-production batch, flying for the first time on

26 March 1979 in the hands of Armin Krauthann and Fritz Eckert. This aircraft had a production-standard forward fuselage, and was configured to carry the Kormoran anti-ship missile.

A handful of the German and Italian pre-production aircraft were rebuilt to full production standards, but none was actually issued to front-line units.

XZ630 was the second pre-production aircraft (P.12) and the first to be delivered for service testing. It is seen here with the LRMTS fairing fitted.

98+03 was the last of the pre-production batch (P.16) and was used to test the Kormoran anti-ship missile, along with the second prototype (98+05).

Tornado IDS – production

Tornado production was authorised on 10 March 1976, with a planned start date of 1 July, long before the pre-production aircraft had flown. It was estimated that the first batch (20 aircraft for the UK, 16 for Germany and four for Italy) would take 18 months to complete. The basic IDS version is known to the RAF as the Tornado GR.Mk 1, while the Germans, Italians and Saudis use the IDS designation. Aircraft have been built in eight production batches (detailed below). The differences between British, German and Italian IDS aircraft lie mainly below the skin, and are limited to minor equipment and avionics items. Uniquely, all RAF IDSs have an extra 121-Imp gal (551-litre) fuel tank in their tailfins, additional to the standard IDS internal fuel capacity of 1,285 Imp gal (5842 litres). A good indicator of the minor nature of the differences between Tornados from the three partner nations is provided by the ECM fit. RAF aircraft carry a BOZ-107 pod to starboard and a Sky Shadow to port (though they initially carried a pair of Sky Shadows, one probably being a dummy to prevent an asymmetric load-out), while German aircraft carry a BOZ-101 to port with a Cerberus II, III or IV ECM pod to starboard. More recently some German aircraft are believed to have used the US AN/ALQ-119 instead of Cerberus, though this may be due to a misidentification of the newer marks of Cerberus. Marineflieger Tornados may use Ajax ECM pods instead of Cerberus. Italian aircraft use the BOZ-102 with Cerberus or with the Elettronica EL/73 ECM pod. Over Bosnia, Italian Tornados have most usually been photographed carrying a BOZ pod under each wing, presumably one loaded with chaff, one with flares.

Tornado GR.Mk 1 and IDS bombers from the various production batches look externally identical, though new batches introduced important improvements and modifications. The best way to tell different batch IDS Tornados apart is by serial number, but squadron markings, fit (e.g., the presence of LRMTS) and weaponry (the presence of HARM) can provide strong (if sometimes misleading) clues. For example, some early-batch aircraft have been retrofitted with equipment normally associated with later batches, while squadrons nominally equipped with aircraft from one particular batch might use a few earlier aircraft as attrition replacements.

The Tornado customer nations do use a range of different weaponry, some shared and some nation-specific. In the strike role, RAF Tornados use the indigenously designed and produced WE.177B. This marks a major difference from Italian and German Tornados, which can carry the US B61 (upon which WE.177 is based), but which operate under a dual key system, with US/NATO rather than national control over their use. A 950-lb (430-kg) weapon measuring 12 ft (3.66 m) in length, and with a 2-ft (0.6-m) tailfin span, WE.177B had a yield of 100 kT and entered service in 1966, initially equipping RAF Avro Vulcans. Yield of the various sub-variants of WE.177 is thought to have been varied by altering the amount of tritium in the warhead. The WE.177B was once intended to have been replaced by a stand-off nuclear missile, for which Air Staff Requirement 1244 was issued. A great deal of money was spent on secret study contracts to examine

potential replacements, but this weapon requirement was cancelled on 18 October 1993, when it was decided that WE.177B would instead be withdrawn in 2005. It will then be replaced by Trident missiles with low-yield warheads assigned to the tactical role. This withdrawal subsequently has been brought forward, and the last RAF WE.177Bs will be retired in 1998.

The main conventional weapons used by RAF Tornados are the Mks 1-12 500-lb (226-kg) bomb (actually weighing 570 lb/174 kg in free-fall configuration, and 620 lb/281 kg with a Hunting Mk 118 retarding tail), and the Mks 13-22 1,000-lb (454-kg) medium case high-explosive bomb. This weapon is used 'slick' for delivery from medium level or for lofting attacks, with a Hunting Mk 114 tail. The weapon weighs 1,030 lb (467 kg) in this configuration. For low-level use, the same weapon can be fitted with a Hunting Mk 117 parachute retarding tail, which increases weight to 1,130 lb (513 kg). For precision use, the bomb can be fitted with a Paveway II guidance kit (a new nose incorporates the laser sensor and control fins) and a new tail incorporates pop-out stabilising tailfins. This brings the basic 1,000-lb bomb to the standard of a US GBU-16, and raises the weight to 1,210 lb (549 kg). The Tornado force was unable to designate targets for its LGBs for many years, and the war role of the Buccaneer OCU would have been to provide designation using their AN/AVQ-23E Pave Spike pods. This system has since been replaced by the GEC TIALD pod, described below.

Following the Gulf War, both the 500- and 1,000-lb bombs were fitted with the Type 960 multi-function bomb fuse. In addition to weapons based on the basic 500-lb and 1,000-lb bombs, RAF Tornados can and do carry a range of more specialised weapons. The Hunting BL755 cluster bomb, and the Improved BL755 can both be carried by the Tornado GR.Mk 1, although both are primarily used in the anti-armour role and that is not normally a Tornado task. A unique Tornado weapon is the Hunting JP233 bomblet dispenser, used primarily in the anti-airfield role. These weapons weigh 5,148 lb (2335 kg) each, and two may be carried side-by-side below the fuselage. Each dispenser contains 30 57-lb (26-kg) SG357 parachute-retarded concrete-cratering bomblets and 215 5.5-lb (2.5-kg) area denial mines. They can be dispensed at two rates, giving either a long, narrow swathe or a short broad one. The weapon may be used against targets like railway marshalling yards, motorway intersections, and airfield runways and taxiways. In peacetime, Tornados more often simply carry ML Aviation CBLS 200 practice bomb carrier. A 3-kg (6.6-lb) bomb made by Portsmouth Aviation accurately simulates the ballistic characteristics of a BL755 or a retarded 1,000-lb bomb; a 15-kg (33-lb) bomb is used to simulate full-size 1,000-lb bombs, and can be lofted up to 4

Above: Tornado production was undertaken at Warton, Manching and Caselle. Seen at the latter are aircraft from the first Italian batch.

Below: The RAF and RSAF adopted the Hunting JP233 runway-denial weapon. BAe trials aircraft ZA354 performed the initial tests.

miles (6.5 km). The practice bombs incorporate a flash and smoke cartridge, to give a clearer view of impact.

Luftwaffe Tornados use a range of weapons, including some taken over from the F-104G Starfighters which they replaced. In German service the Tornado IDS can carry various US Mk 80 series bombs, slick or retarded, the Hunting BL755 CBU, and B61 nuclear weapons. One Tornado-specific weapon is the MBB/Diehl MW-1 dispenser weapon. This is a massive slab-sided box (with streamlined ends) which ejects sub-munitions horizontally outboard from 224 apertures (one at each end of the 112 tubes), using different strengths of explosive charge in the centre of each tube to ensure an even coverage of the target. The unit can carry five different types of sub-munition, which are carried in different combinations and proportions according to the type of target under attack. STABO

bomblets are used for cratering runways, MUSA and MUSPA are used as fragmentation and passive fragmentation mines, MIFF is a passive anti-personnel mine and KB44 is a penetrator used against armour or hardened buildings. The number of bomblets carried varies according to the type of weapon being used. The KB44, for example, is carried in bundles of seven bomblets, giving a total load of 4,500 individual bomblets. They could cover an area about 180 x 500 m (590 x 1,640 ft), with one bomblet every 20 m² (215 sq ft), all 4,500 bomblets being fired within half a second. Another unusual store occasionally carried by the Luftwaffe Tornados is the Dornier Aerial Target System 3, used for gunnery training. The system consists of a winch carried on the port underfuselage pylon, with a target dart suspended from the starboard pylon until launch. This loadout was first flown by Erprobungsstelle 61 in September 1984.

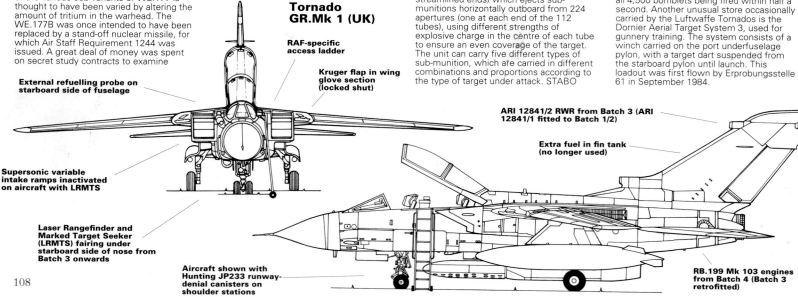

Tornado GR.Mk 1 (UK)

RAF-specific access ladder

Kruger flap in wing glove section (locked shut)

External refuelling probe on starboard side of fuselage

Supersonic variable intake ramps inactivated on aircraft with LRMTS

Laser Rangefinder and Marked Target Seeker (LRMTS) fairing under starboard side of nose from Batch 3 onwards

Aircraft shown with Hunting JP233 runway-denial canisters on shoulder stations

ARI 12841/2 RWR from Batch 3 (ARI 12841/1 fitted to Batch 1/2)

Extra fuel in fin tank (no longer used)

RB.199 Mk 103 engines from Batch 4 (Batch 3 retrofitted)

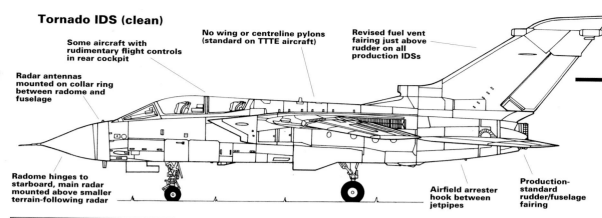

Tornado IDS (clean)

Some aircraft with rudimentary flight controls in rear cockpit

No wing or centreline pylons (standard on TTTE aircraft)

Revised fuel vent fairing just above rudder on all production IDSs

Radar antennas mounted on collar ring between radome and fuselage

Radome hinges to starboard, main radar mounted above smaller terrain-following radar

Airfield arrester hook between jetpipes

Production-standard rudder/fuselage fairing

Tornado Variants

The Tornado received its baptism of fire in the Gulf War. RAF aircraft like this No. 31 Sqn machine at Dhahran dropped 1,000-lb LGBs, designated by Pave Spike-equipped Buccaneers or by TIALD Tornados.

The Marineflieger uses many of the same weapons as the Luftwaffe Tornados. MFG 2 pioneered the introduction of the HARM missile and the 380-kg (840-lb) MBB/Aeritalia reconnaissance pod. Naval Tornados inherited a stock of 350 Kormoran Mk 1 missiles when the F-104 was retired, and then received 174 Kormoran Mk 2s from 1989. A final store used by Marineflieger Tornados is the Sargent Fletcher 28-300 buddy-refuelling store, 73 of which were delivered. Some 96 Marineflieger aircraft (probably those with the MWCS) were equipped for carriage of this pod.

Italian Tornados used the same weapons as their German counterparts, including HARM and Kormoran. Reports that AGM-65

Maverick ASMs would be integrated with Tornado have not been confirmed, although the missile has been used by attack-roled Luftwaffe Phantoms.

A number of aircraft in each production batch were delivered with primary flying controls (including throttles) and flight instruments duplicated in the rear cockpit to allow an instructor pilot to replace the navigator for conversion, continuation or standardisation training. One of the navigator's MFDs was dropped, and the radar hand-grip controller was moved to the starboard console. None of these trainer versions was given a separate designation, although the RAF aircraft were sometimes referred to unofficially as GR.Mk 1Ts or GR.Mk 1(T)s.

Batch 1

The 43 aircraft in Batch 1 were assigned plane set numbers 001-043.

The batch included 23 RAF IDS aircraft, including 12 twin-stickers. The RAF serial numbers ran from ZA319 to ZA330 and from ZA352 to ZA362. The operational

aircraft (BS001-BS011) were randomly interspersed with the trainers which were ZA319, 320, 323-326, 330, 352, 356-358 and 362 (BT001-BT012). They were assigned to the TTTE and have remained with that unit, though a handful have moved on, mainly to development and trials duties. TTTE aircraft have not been retrofitted with LRMTS, and retain RB.199 Mk 101 engines. They are down-rated (reportedly to 36 kN/8,093 lb) because the aircraft routinely fly without pylons, and are thus regarded as being 'rather slippery'. Reducing available thrust ensures lighter fatigue life usage. The RAF's three ADV prototypes (ZA254, ZA267 and ZA283, respectively AA001, AB001 and AC001) were part of Batch 1.

Seventeen German aircraft were from Batch 1, including 14 trainers (GT001-014) serialled from 43+01 to 43+17. The strike aircraft were 43+12, 43+13 and 43+14 (GS001-003). Virtually all were assigned to the TTTE, and have remained with that unit ever since.

There were no Italian aircraft in Batch 1.

Batch 2

The 110 Batch 2 Tornados were assigned plane set numbers 044-153.

There were 55 RAF IDS aircraft in Batch 2 (ZA540-564, ZA585-614), including 16 twin-stickers (ZA540, 541, 544, 548, 549, 551, 552, 555, 562, 594, 595, 598, 599, 602, 604, and 612 (BT013-028)). The 39 operational aircraft (BS012-050) were randomly interspersed. The RAF Batch 2 aircraft were initially assigned to the TWCU and to No. IX Squadron, and to the other first UK-based squadrons, Nos 27 and 617. The RAF's Batch 2 Tornados were powered by the 40.0-kN (8,992-lb st) RB.199 Mk 101, which was derated to 38.70 kN (8,700 lb st) on squadrons to enhance serviceability. The original Mk 101 was said to have been rated to 35.98 kN (8,090 lb st), or 70.95 kN (15,950 lb st) with afterburning.

Developments to increase thrust were ongoing, resulting eventually in the Mk 103 engine.

Batch 2 also included 40 German aircraft (GS004-GS030 and GT015-GT027), 24 for the Luftwaffe and 16 for the Marineflieger, although early plans had suggested that virtually all of Batch 2 would be taken up by 40 aircraft for the Marineflieger's first two-*Staffel* wing. The German Tornados were serialled from 43+18 to 43+57. The 13 dual-control aircraft were 43+21, 43+22, 43+23, 43+29, 43+31, 43+33, 43+35, 43+37, 43+42, 43+43, 43+44, 43+45, and 43+51. The German aircraft were shared between the TTTE, JBG 38 and MFG 1 (4342-4357). Among the Marineflieger aircraft in Batch 2 were the first Tornados equipped with the Multiple Weapon Carrier System (MWCS), which added a centreline underfuselage pylon to the two 'shoulder' pylons to allow a wider range of stores to be carried, with additional electronics in the centre fuselage to confer compatibility with the Cerberus ECM pod, Kormoran missiles and some other stores. The MWCS was subsequently fitted to all German and Italian Tornados, and the centreline pylon made its appearance on later RAF aircraft.

Finally, Batch 2 included 15 Italian aircraft including 10 operational aircraft, IS001-IS010 (MM7002-MM7011), and five twin-stickers IT001-IT005 (MM55000-MM55004). The twin-stickers initially went to the TTTE, but most of the operational aircraft went to 154° Gruppo.

Batch 3

Batch 3 was the largest Tornado production batch, with 164 aircraft, which were assigned plane set numbers 154-317.

Sixty-eight of the Batch 3 aircraft were RAF IDS aircraft, including eight twin-stickers. These aircraft should have had ZB-series serials, but an administrative error allocated them elsewhere, and the aircraft had to be given ZA serials (ZA365-376, ZA392-412, ZA446-475, and ZA490-494) actually 'lower' than the Batch 2 aircraft which preceded them. The 60 operational aircraft (BS051-110) were accompanied by eight dual-control trainers (BT029-036). The latter were randomly interspersed and were serialled ZA365, 366, 367, 368, 409, 410, 411 and 412.

The RAF Batch 3 Tornados introduced

Dual-control aircraft like this TTTE machine retain full combat capability, but have a rearranged rear cockpit.

Italian Tornados use the US Mk 83 1,000-lb bomb as the primary free-fall weapon. The sand scheme was first applied for the eight-aircraft participation in Desert Storm.

the undernose LRMTS, which reportedly imposed an airspeed limitation sufficient to encourage the RAF to disable the intake actuators, giving the aircraft what was effectively a fixed intake, and limiting performance to well below Mach 2. Batch 3 aircraft had a Marconi ARI 18241/2 RWR in place of the original Elettronica ARI 18241/1. These aircraft were primarily delivered to the Laarbruch wing, though the first 11 (and some later Batch 3 examples) went to the TWCU, and the next few went to the Marham wing. The Laarbruch-based aircraft (50) were subsequently re-engined with the 9,650-lb st (42.93-kN) RB.199 Mk 103. Reports suggest that the aircraft were physically re-engined, and that existing engines were not simply brought up to Mk 103 standards. The Mk 103 had an afterburning rating of 16,900 lb st (75.26 kN), and was fitted with a new negative *g* oil system. The Mk 103-engined aircraft had their mechanical engine control units modified.

Attrition among the RAF Batch 3 aircraft

Below is the front cockpit of an RAF Batch 4 aircraft, dominated by the circular moving-map display. The control column hinges at its base for pitch control, but pivots half-way up for roll control.

was relatively high, including some aircraft destroyed during Operation Desert Storm. Fourteen surviving Batch 3 Tornados were converted to GR.Mk 1A standards, mainly for No. II (AC) Squadron, and an additional 26 were converted to GR.Mk 1B standards, primarily for use by Nos 12 and 617 Squadrons. This has left only a handful of RAF Batch 3 aircraft in anything close to their original configuration.

There were 68 German aircraft in Batch 3, including 12 trainers (GS031-GS086 and GT028-039), of which 32 of the operational aircraft were originally delivered to the Marineflieger. The trainers were serialled 43+90, 43+91, 43+92, 43+93, 43+94, 43+97, 44+01, 44+05, 44+10, 44+15, 44+20 and 44+25, and the remainder from 43+58 to 44+25. Aircraft 43+91 introduced the new three-tone green wrap-around lizard camouflage used by Luftwaffe Tornados today, which has been retrospectively applied to almost all aircraft during maintenance. The Luftwaffe aircraft were delivered mainly to JBG 38 and JBG 31, though 43+58 to 43+89 (all operational aircraft) were delivered to the Marineflieger, initially serving with MFG 1.

Italian production within Batch 3 amounted to 28 aircraft, including five twin-stickers, IT006-010 (MM55005-55009). The operational aircraft were IS011-IS033

Right: The rear cockpit of a single-stick Batch 4 aircraft: the circular display at centre is for the radar, flanked by the two TV-tabs. Flight instrumentation is restricted to attitude, altitude and speed.

(MM7012-7034). They were initially delivered to 154° Gruppo.

Batch 4

Tornado Batch 4 comprised 162 aircraft, allocated plane set numbers 318-479. Of these, 18 were F.Mk 2 fighters (described separately) and 144 were IDS aircraft.

Fifty-three RAF IDS aircraft (BS111-155) included eight twin-stickers (BT037-044). They were serialled from ZD707-720, ZD738-749, ZD788-793, ZD808-812, ZD842-851 and ZD890-895; the twin-stickers were ZD711, 712, 713, 741, 742, 743, 812, and 842. All were powered from the start by the RB.199 Mk 103. The RAF Batch 4 Tornados were produced primarily for the Brüggen wing, and the last of them was delivered on 30 September 1985. Since it has been reported that the first Tornado GR.Mk 1s armed with nuclear weapons received their WE 177Bs in RAF Germany in 1984, it may be assumed that the Batch 4 aircraft were the first with nuclear delivery systems.

Batch 4 production for Germany totalled 64 aircraft, including eight twin-stickers (GS087-142 and GT040-047). All were for

the Luftwaffe. Their serials ran from 44+26 to 44+89. The trainers were 44+36, 44+37, 44+38, 44+39, 44+72, 44+73, 44+74, and 44+75. The aircraft were delivered mainly to JBG 31 and JBG 32.

Italian Batch 4 production totalled 27 aircraft (IS034-IS060), with no twin-stickers. Serials ran from MM7035 to MM7061.

Batch 5

Batch 5 consisted of 173 aircraft, which were allocated plane set numbers 480-651, and 653.

It had been planned to include 20 aircraft for the RAF, but only two were actually delivered and were completed as GR.Mk 1As. They were BS156 and BS160, serialled ZD996 and ZE116. The rest of the RAF aircraft planned for Batch 5 were sent to Saudi Arabia as CS001-CS014 and CT001-006, Saudi serials 751-754 (also briefly 701-704) and 757-770. The two-seaters were 754, 755, 756 759, 768 and 769. The Saudi aircraft had originally been allocated BS157-159, BS161-171 with serials ZD997, ZD998, ZE114-126, and ZE144-147. The twin-stickers were BT45-50 (ZE115, 120, 125 and 147). The last two trainers (768 and 769) had once been planned as German operational aircraft GS201 and GS202, serialled 45+53 and 45+54. As such, they never had RAF serials.

The Batch 5 Tornado IDS aircraft featured a MIL STD 1553B digital databus, a new 128k Litef Spirit III computer, and integrated ECM transmitter, chaff/flare dispenser and RWR operation. ADA (language) was used in the missile control unit, conferring an AGM-88 HARM capability in the German and Italian Batch 5 aircraft, although initially the missile was integrated only on aircraft delivered to the Marineflieger.

Batch 5 also included 52 RAF F.Mk 3 fighters

Germany took 70 aircraft from Batch 5. They bore the variant identities GS143-GS207 and GT048-052, and were serialled from 44+90 to 45+59. Twenty-two of the 65 operational aircraft were for the Luftwaffe, with 43 (plus five twin-stickers) for the Marineflieger, primarily for that service's second Tornado unit, MFG 2. They were the last Tornados built for the Marineflieger, though there was some interchange of airframes between the air force and navy, which thus received a handful of later aircraft. The five dual-control aircraft were serialled 45+12 and 45+16.

MFG 2's first *Staffel* had a

Above: Batch 2 RAF aircraft, like this pristine TTTE display aircraft, were not fitted initially with the LRMTS fairing. They were retrofitted to some aircraft.

Right: Following difficulties in refuelling from KC-135s, four of the AMI's Gulf War Tornados were equipped for buddy refuelling, as demonstrated at the 1991 Paris show.

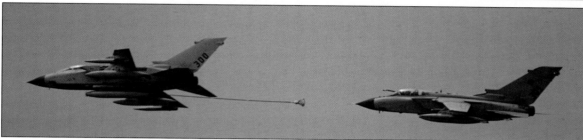

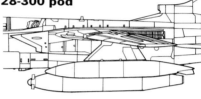

reconnaissance role using the MBB/Aeritalia recce pod, and its second *Staffel* had HARM missiles for its primary anti-ship role. Before they were built an initial batch of 23 AGM-88s had been ordered for evaluation, and Germany was offered 866 more, with spares, test and support equipment, for $390 million. A Germany navy Tornado flew with HARM for the first time in December 1985.

Italian Tornado production concluded with the 29 AMI aircraft which formed Batch 5. These aircraft were IS061-IS087 (MM7062-MM7068) and IT011-IT012 (MM55010-MM55011).

Batch 6

Some 155 Tornados were built in Batch 6, allocated the plane set numbers 652 and 654-807. Batch 6 included 68 RAF and 24 Saudi F.Mk 3 and ADV fighters.

The remaining 63 were IDS variants for Germany. All were originally destined for the Luftwaffe, with none for the Marineflieger. The aircraft were GS208-GS255 and GT053-067, serialled from 45+60 to 46+22. The 15 twin-stickers wore the serials 45+60, 45+61, 45+62, 45+63, 45+70, 45+73, 45+77, 45+99, 46+03, 46+04, 46+05, 46+06, 46+07, 46+08, and 46+09. Twenty-four of the aircraft were diverted to the Marineflieger before delivery, primarily to MFG 2.

There were no Italian aircraft in Batch 6.

By the time the last Batch 6 aircraft was delivered, Panavia had produced 807 Tornados, two more than the original target figure of 805. By then Batch 7 was already taking shape.

Batch 7

The 122 aircraft built as Batch 7 wore the plane set numbers 808-929.

BAe's production of Batch 7 airframes included 27 IDS aircraft for the RAF (BS172-BS192), encompassing six twin-stickers (BT51-56, ZG750, 752, 754, 756, 769, and 771) and 14 built as GR.Mk 1As (BS172-185, ZG705-714, ZG725-729). The GR.Mk 1As went to equip the newly formed No. 13 Squadron (with one being retained for

trials use by the SAOEU) while the twin-stickers went to a number of units. The remaining seven non-reconnaissance-configured operational aircraft in the batch were BS186-192 (ZG773, 775, 777, 779, 791, 792 and 794). They mainly went to Brüggen-based squadrons. The company also delivered 28 Saudi IDSs (including eight twin-stickers and six built to GR.Mk 1A standards) as part of Batch 7. They bore the variant identities CS015-034 (RSAF serials 6610-6619, 6624-6633) and CT007-015 (RSAF serials 771-774, and 6620-6623, respectively).

Batch 7 also included 24 RAF F.Mk 3 fighters and another eight ADVs ordered by Oman but diverted to the RAF as F.Mk 3s.

Germany's 35 Tornado ECRs (described separately) used the final 35 German variant identities GS256-290, and were delivered as part of Batch 7. They wore serials running from 46+23 to 46+57.

There were no Italian aircraft in Batch 7.

Batch 8

Batch Eight was to have consisted of 26 aircraft for the RAF, and 35 for the Luftwaffe, but they were subsequently cancelled. The Luftwaffe aircraft would have equipped the new JBG 37 at Husum. The eight IDS aircraft for Jordan (including three twin-stickers) in Batch Eight were also cancelled, but not before they had been allocated plane sets 930-937 and variant identities FT01-FT03 and FS01 to FS05.

Batch 9

Batch 9 consisted of 48 IDS aircraft for Saudi Arabia, described in detail under the Tornado IDS (export) heading. They brought

Tornado production to 978.

Some (perhaps even most) RAF Tornados from all batches can now carry the enlarged 495-Imp gal (2250-litre) tank designed for the ADV, and colloquially known as the 'Hindenburger'. German and Italian Tornados carry only the 220- or 330-Imp gal (1000- or 1500-litre) standard IDS fuel tanks. The big 712-lb (323-kg) tank is surprisingly complex, and has five compartments and a proportioner to maintain the tank's centre of gravity when partially full. Its fuel load is 3,968 lb (1800 kg). The first routine use of the larger ADV tank by the Tornado IDS was made during the run-up to the Gulf War, and provision for their carriage was part of a package of emergency modifications made to the Tornado GR.Mk 1 and GR.Mk 1A to prepare them for active service over Iraq. When the ADV carries the larger tanks, its flight control system is automatically 'aware' that the tanks are fitted, and wing sweep is limited to 63.5° maximum (rather than the

Sargent Fletcher 28-300 pod

normal 67°). On the IDS, a metal stop was added to the manual wing sweep lever, similarly limiting the wing sweep. All of the aircraft deployed to the Gulf were from RAF Germany-based squadrons, so all already had RB.199 Mk 103 engines and the enhanced RHAWS.

Following the first squadron-strength deployment during Desert Shield all Tornados deployed to the area had further modifications incorporated in a programme

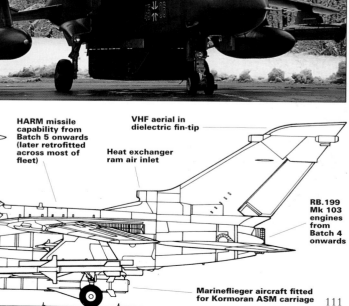

The Luftwaffe adopted the bulky MW-1 dispenser for area/runway denial missions. A variety of sub-munitions can be fitted, including those for anti-personnel and anti-armour operations.

Tornado IDS (Germany)

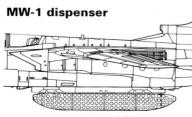

Outer wing pylons for Cerberus ECM pod and BOZ-101 chaff/flare pods (not shown). Italy uses Cerberus and BOZ-102

MW-1 dispenser

HARM missile capability from Batch 5 onwards (later retrofitted across most of fleet)

VHF aerial in dielectric fin-tip

Heat exchanger ram air inlet

RB.199 Mk 103 engines from Batch 4 onwards

German-style access ladder

Marineflieger aircraft fitted for Kormoran ASM carriage

Tornado Variants

This WTD 61 test aircraft lands at Manching carrying the two main German anti-ship weapons: Kormoran 2 under the fuselage and HARM on the wing pylons.

known as Phase One, undertaken at RAF St Athan and at a number of front-line stations. There were 23 possible planned modifications, and 19 new modifications known officially as Special Trials Fits. Few aircraft incorporated all the mods and STFs, with 18 and 13 being typical. The possibility of battle damage led to the incorporation of a long-planned modification to the Tornado's fin-mounted fuel tank, with a nitrogen purging system being fitted to remove any fuel vapour once the tank was empty. Sand ingestion caused a glass-like coating to form on the turbine blades, and to counter this a number of modifications were made to the engine. Fan blades were not a problem, contrary to some reports. The turbine blades were single-crystal blades (chemically milled) which gave them a longer life, and greater reliability. The old metal blades overheated and burned, giving a reduced life. Problems could go undetected if the blades did burn through, leading to catastrophic failures. This forced increasingly frequent boroscope inspections. To solve the problems caused by sand build-up, cooling holes were made in the blades' leading/trailing edges. If these

holes became blocked, the blades overheated and disintegrated. In Saudi Arabia, the main action taken was to use a high-pressure rig (lance) firing a water/air mix into the turbines to clear the cooling holes.

Since it was obvious that RAF aircraft would be operating as part of a force dominated by the US Air Force, all Tornado GR.Mk 1s deployed had their Cossor SSR-3100 Mk X IFF equipment removed and replaced by a Mk XII Mode 4 set. The aircraft were provided with Have Quick secure voice radios and some carried a hand-held GPS receiver. All leading edges

were painted with SWAM (surface wave absorbent material), and RAM (radar absorbent material) was applied to the intake area. SWAM is applied like paint, though it is much denser (more like car underseal) and so heavy that it takes two men to lift a 5-litre (1.1-Imp gal) tin. RAM was applied in steel-backed tiles, necessitating removal of the engines to allow them to be bonded to the intakes adjacent to the first stage of the fan. The optional bolt-on retractable inflight-refuelling probe was fitted (though inflight refuelling was not then a routine part of Tornado operations within RAF Germany), and

navigation and communications equipment was upgraded. Some aircraft were also compatible with the use of NVGs, which were widely used during the war, particularly by the reconnaissance crews. Most obviously, the aircraft were repainted (or more accurately overpainted) with a coat of Trimite's alkali-removable temporary finish (ARTF) paint. Some modifications were subsequently removed after Desert Storm, while others were retained.

All Italian aircraft are Kormoran-capable and all are capable of carrying the MBB/Aeritalia reconnaissance pod, an unknown number of which were acquired.

Tornado IDS (export)

Saudi Arabia: The only export customer to have taken delivery of Tornados is Saudi Arabia. The Saudi order has often been characterised as being somehow inevitable, and made without a true competition; an ally placing a routine order with its traditional supplier. In fact, nothing could be further from the truth. Although Saudi Arabia had previously bought BAC Strikemasters and Lightnings, the Kingdom was far more used to buying US equipment, as a massive fleet of F-5s, and other American types, bore witness. The Tornado faced stiff competition from the F-15 (including the then-new Strike Eagle). The F-15 did have to struggle against some artificial constraints, including a US refusal to supply conformal fuel tanks or multiple ejector racks (at Israeli prompting), and a demand that the aircraft could not be based at Tabuk, the northern Saudi airfield which most threatened Israel. In the end, though, the attack-configured F-15 (with or without CFTs and MERs) was judged to be too much of an unknown quantity, and the Tornado IDS had reached a level of proven maturity. The Strike Eagle, in any case, was a very different aircraft then to today's F-15E. It used a Pave Tack laser designator rather than the current LANTIRN pods, and lacked various systems. Saudi aircrew flew Tornado evaluation sorties from RAF Honington in 1984, and the massive £4,000 million Al Yamamah deal was announced in September 1985, covering the supply of 48 Tornado IDSs, 30 Hawks, 24 Tornado ADVs, two radar-training Jetstreams and 30 BAe-built Pilatus PC-9s. Saudi aircrew began training at Cottesmore in October 1985, and deliveries (at four aircraft per month) began in March 1986, with 18 IDS aircraft diverted from RAF Batch 5 orders and all 24 ADVs diverted from the RAF's Batch 6. The remaining 28 IDS aircraft were built in Batch

7, along with the replacement aircraft for those the RAF had diverted from Batch 5.

The first batch of Saudi Tornados was diverted from RAF orders in Batch 5 and built in Batch 7. The aircraft reportedly were delivered with Sea Eagle ASMs, JP233 airfield attack weapons, and ALARMs. Fourteen of the Saudi aircraft were dual-controlled trainers. The last six Saudi Tornado IDSs in the first batch were delivered in GR.Mk 1A configuration, partially replacing recce-configured F-5Es. The Saudi aircraft had the fin fuel tanks.

Batch 5 Saudi Tornado IDS

RAF variant	RAF serial	New variant	Saudi serial
BS157	ZD997	CS001	751
BS158	ZD998	CS002	752
BS159	ZE114	CS003	753
BT45	ZE115	CT001	754
BS161	ZE117	CS004	757
BS162	ZE118	CS005	758
BS163	ZE119	CS006	760
BT46	ZE120	CT002	755
BS164	ZE121	CS007	761
BS165	ZE122	CS008	762
BS166	ZE123	CS009	763
BS167	ZE124	CS010	764
BT47	ZE125	CT003	756
BS168	ZE126	CS011	765
BS169	ZE144	CS012	766
BS170	ZE145	CS013	767
BS171	ZE146	CS014	770
BT48	ZE147	CT004	759
BT49	None	CT005	768
BT50	None	CT006	769

Batch 7 Saudi Tornado IDS

The second part of the first Tornado IDS order was filled by aircraft built from scratch for Saudi Arabia, with no RAF serials or

variant identities. The aircraft consisted of CT007-014 and CS015-034. The twin-stickers carried the Saudi serials 771, 772, 773, 774, 6620, 6621, 6622, and 6623, and the operational aircraft were 6610-6619 and 6624-6633. The final six, 6628-33, were in GR.Mk 1A configuration.

Saudi Arabia provisionally agreed Al Yamamah II in July 1988, covering the delivery of another 12 Tornado IDSs and 36 more ADVs. The contract was cancelled in July 1990, but was then reconfirmed in June 1993, by which time its terms had been changed to cover the supply of 48 IDS aircraft, with no ADVs.

Batch 9 Saudi Tornado IDS

Variant	Saudi serial	Ferry serial
CT015	7501	ZH905
CT016	7502	ZH906
CT017	7503	ZH907
CT018	8301	ZH908
CT019		ZH909
CT020	8303	ZH910
CT021		ZH911
CT022		ZH912
CT023		ZH913
CT024		ZH914
CS035		ZH915 GR.Mk 1A equivalent
C?		ZH916 to ZH952

Pre-delivery photos of an Al Yamamah II Tornado IDS in GR.Mk 1A-type configuration showed the aircraft carrying ALARM missiles inboard, with BOZ-107 pods (perhaps one fitted with a TRD) outboard. This led to speculation that the reconnaissance aircraft in the Saudi order might actually be configured for SEAD duties, perhaps also being fitted with some kind of emitter locator system. This would make them similar to the aircraft once proposed for Malaysia, Thailand and South Korea. The truth was more prosaic, the aircraft having been 'caught' by a 'spotter' en route to Boscombe Down for electro-magnetic clearance trials using a number of

instrumented stores which it was self-ferrying to Wiltshire.

Potential customers

Canada: Although the MRA-75 partners reduced to three to produce the MRCA, one partner later showed a renewed interest in the production Tornado. Canada was passed Tornado data from 1972, and began to see the aircraft as a potential candidate for its requirement for a New Fighter Aircraft (NFA) to replace the F-104 and F-101, fulfilling a primarily air-to-air role in Canada, and a predominantly air-to-surface role in Europe. This interest was encouraged and nurtured by Panavia, which put together a highly attractive package that incorporated a significant amount of local industrial participation. This would have included a Canadian assembly line for aircraft and engines ordered by the CAF, and Canadian manufacture of components for all Tornados. CAF aircrew flew the Tornado during January 1978, and Panavia made a formal proposal to Canada in February 1978; in the end, however, the air-to-air aspect of the Canadian requirement ruled out the Tornado, and Canada purchased F/A-18 Hornets.

Oman: Oman was the first nation to actually order the Tornado, although that order (for eight ADV F.Mk 2s) was subsequently cancelled. Interestingly, the order included provision for the delivery of eight additional aircraft, which could have been IDS or ADV airframes, or a new version combining features of both. Oman was reportedly very interested in obtaining Terprom for these aircraft.

Jordan: Jordanian attempts to acquire Tornado ADVs via Saudi Arabia are described in the section on export ADVs. Their efforts came to nothing, as reported, but direct negotiations between BAe and Jordan led to the Hashemite Kingdom revealing an interest in acquiring eight IDS aircraft (with perhaps 12 more) in March 1988. A contract was signed in September 1988, and eight positions were reserved on the production line for plane sets FT001 to FT003 (IDS twin-stickers) and FS001 to FS005 as part of batch eight. Jordan, however, was in a parlous financial state, and was forced to cancel its order in March 1989 until 'more favourable circumstances prevail'.

Malaysia: Malaysia first began to show serious interest in acquiring Tornados during the late 1980s. The country reached

The first Saudi Tornado is seen during a test flight from Warton, in completely clean configuration. In addition to the IDS aircraft, the Saudi deal also included ADVs, Hawks, PC-9s and Jetstreams.

Left: The left-hand Tornado in this No. 66 Sqn pair is one of the unspecified number supplied to Saudi Arabia in GR.Mk 1A configuration, with infra-red reconnaissance system installed in place of the cannon.

Below: Seen departing Warton, another Saudi GR.Mk 1A equivalent is also carrying ALARM missiles. Note the build number on the fin, which identifies single-control (CS) or twin-stick (CT) aircraft.

preliminary agreement on a package of British defence equipment in September 1988, at which time the package included 12 Tornados. The Malaysian requirement comprised four SEAD aircraft, which it was felt would be broadly equivalent to the RAF's GR.Mk 1A with a new Marconi emitter-location system. The package was subsequently retailored, with the Tornados replaced by cheaper armed Hawks.

South Korea and Thailand: Elsewhere in Asia, South Korea had a requirement for some 50 Tornados (including up to 40 SEAD aircraft). This resulted in a competition between Germany (offering ECRs) and Britain (offering modified GR.Mk 1As as offered to Malaysia). Thailand was another potential prospect for the Tornado, with four SEAD-configured aircraft thought to be required among the 16 aircraft expected to be ordered. A complementary requirement for a light attack aircraft held out the promise of a Tornado/Hawk or Tornado/MB.339 package, but the prospect came to nothing.

Spain, Greece and Turkey: There were a number of other failed attempts to export the Tornado, which usually proved too sophisticated and too expensive – especially by comparison with subsidised F-16s, repeatedly offered on impossibly easy terms. In Europe, the Tornado was considered by Spain (which took F/A-18s instead) and Greece, where the vital air-to-air role forced adoption of the Mirage 2000 and F-16. In 1984 Turkey actually ordered 40 Tornados, but the UK Export Credits Guarantee department refused to fund the deal, and it fell through.

Japan: The Tornado looked like a strong contender in Japan, whose initial requirement was stated to be 24 aircraft, with options on 76 more, and with an eventual requirement for up to 130 aircraft. Japan required an attack aircraft to replace the F-1, particularly in the maritime strike role. The Tornado in its IDS form was favoured by many senior JASDF officers, and a dedicated ship-killing variant (based on the stretched ADV airframe) was even

offered as the Tornado J. Japan eventually procured the indigenous Mitsubishi F-2
Iraq: Another possible customer for the basic Tornado IDS was Iraq, which

evaluated the aircraft in 1982, and which anticipated ordering 100 aircraft. The Iran-Iraq war led to sanctions which ruled out acquisition of British military equipment.

Tornado GR.Mk 1 'Pathfinder'

The RAF's requirement (AST 1228) for an anti-radar missile to replace the anti-radar version of Martel was eventually fulfilled by an indigenously developed weapon, the BAe ALARM. Unlike the Martel, or the contemporary US HARM, the ALARM is not a simple direct-fire point-it-at-the-emitter-and-shoot weapon. Before take-off, the missile is programmed with the signal parameters of enemy radars, and their priority for attack. The missile can be fired in a direct mode, climbing to height before homing onto an appropriate pre-programmed target in the designated target area. If the target stops emitting it homes onto the last known target position.

The missile is usually fired in the loiter mode, again going into a climb (to anything between 40,000 and 70,000 ft/12190 and 21335 m). The missile deploys a small parachute and descends slowly from directly above the designated target area, its seeker still 'looking' for a target. When one is seen the chute is jettisoned and the missile engine fires again, and the weapon homes on to the target. While the missile descends under its target it effectively has a long loiter. If it forces the enemy radar to stay 'off line' then it is judged to have achieved a soft kill (having 'killed' the radar

for the important period during which coalition aircraft are in its engagement zone). If the enemy radar starts transmitting, a hard kill is virtually inevitable.

A third mode is available, known as dual. In this, the missile will home onto a suitable target if it sees one during its climb; otherwise, it will continue until it reaches the target area and deploy its parachute thereafter, acting in the loiter mode. An ALARM attack can be planned so that when the missile is launched it has been told (for example) to turn 20° to port, fly 20 miles (32 km) and look for an SA-6 radar and, if none is found, search for SA-2 or gun-laying radars in a particular order of priority. Ideally, the missile will arrive at the target area as the attack aircraft it is covering begin their attack. The missile can be updated by the navigator to change the launch parameters, threat priorities or routings at any time up to launch.

BAe was awarded a fixed-price development and production contract in 1983, covering an initial batch of 750 missiles, though production was planned to reach 2,000. Carriage trials of inert missiles (by BAe's IDS hack ZA354) began on 13 February 1985, with nine missiles arrayed on underwing and underfuselage pylons. Captive carry trials of real missiles began in January 1986. Firing trials were delayed until November 1988 by problems with the Nuthatch rocket motor. Following the firing trials, which were conducted by ZD708 (a BAe-operated test aircraft) at Yuma, and which were completed in October 1990, No. 32 JTU prepared to start the formal acceptance trials. This process was interrupted by the Gulf War. Although they

retained the basic GR.Mk 1 designation, the first of 18 No. IX Squadron Tornados had already been modified for the carriage of ALARM, and it was intended that the squadron would convert to the SEAD/Pathfinder/Escort role. They were the first RAF IDS Tornados capable of carrying the BAe ALARM missile, although it was planned that all RAF Tornados would eventually be capable of carrying a pair of ALARM missiles.

These aircraft were taken over by No. 20 Squadron, whose crews were rapidly trained in the new role before deploying to Tabuk with nine of No. IX's Tornados (ZD719, ZD746, ZD747, ZD748, ZD789, ZD810, ZD850, ZD851 and ZD893). The ALARM missile was by no means a mature weapon by this stage, since, although firings had been made at Yuma, only one had been against a representative radar target, and the missile had never had to differentiate between radar targets of different priority. The JTU acceptance tests would have been expected to include many more firings, with a fair amount of development fine-tuning. But this was cancelled, and the ALARM went straight to war. Before the Gulf War, aircraft flew with two ALARMs underwing, and by January 1991 had switched to the carriage of three missiles under the belly. The aircraft generally operated with three missiles in early missions, and were often sufficiently light to be able to get airborne up to an hour before the bomber packages they were tasked with protecting, and to fly to the target area without inflight refuelling. The aircraft flew escort missions and dedicated anti-radar and anti-missile sorties, with two

Above: BAe trials aircraft ZA354 was used for captive-carry tests of the ALARM missile from 1985. Here it carries the theoretical maximum of nine (three under the fuselage and three arrayed around each wing pylon). In practice, only the fuselage weapons are carried.

Right: Today, Nos IX and 31 Squadrons at Brüggen are the RAF's ALARM specialists. Shown here is a No. IX Squadron aircraft, complete with mission markings from the Gulf War. It was one of the original nine aircraft converted for ALARM carriage.

Tornado Variants

The standard ALARM load-out consists of three missiles on specialised launch rails. Two are mounted on the mid-shoulder stations, with one slightly further forward on the centreline.

Right: ALARM was another weapon blooded during the Gulf War. For Operation Granby, No. 20 Sqn ('Gx' tailcodes) hastily took over aircraft from No. IX Sqn, the crews working up quickly on the new weapon.

missiles underfuselage (with underwing 'Hindenburgers') becoming the standard warload. The ALARM Tornado can carry a maximum load of nine missiles: three underfuselage, and three under each wing.

Some 121 ALARM missiles were fired during 24 missions (48 individual aircraft sorties, plus four aborts), exhausting RAF stocks of the new missile and necessitating deliveries direct to the theatre from BAe's Longstock plant. The missiles were fired from medium level and from low level (200 ft/61 m); the pilots pulled up the nose for launch in the latter case, to compensate for the slightly downward-sloping launch rails and to make sure the missile did not hit the ground after launch. On occasion, the ALARM climbing from low level looked like a SAM directed at the higher-flying bombers, and in these circumstances the ALARM Tornados broadcast a coded warning that they were firing. The missile enjoyed a great deal of success, although

some missiles failed to work. During early missions it was typical for four aircraft to fire 10 successful missiles, of 12 carried. Since the Gulf War, ALARM has been used by No. IX and, since 1995, by No. 31 Squadron. The first peacetime ALARM firing was conducted by No. IX Squadron in August 1994.

Following the Gulf War, tactics were refined and developed. The RAF Tornado's lack of an autonomous emitter location system was addressed by the development of co-operative tactics with the Luftwaffe's Tornado ECRs, and armed SEAD tactics have also been worked out in order to increase the chances of achieving a hard kill. Tornados operate with a mixed load of two or four ALARMs and conventional or cluster bombs. The ALARMs are fired first, and if the radar then shuts off it is attacked with dumb bombs. If it comes up again, the ALARM will achieve the hard kill; if it stays off, then the bombs finish the job.

Tornado GR.Mk 1 tanker

While Marineflieger Tornados routinely operate in the buddy refuelling role, the RAF (whose range requirements for the Tornado had always been the toughest) initially ignored the possibility of using buddy refuelling pods. This lack of interest continued until the build-up to the Gulf War, when there were worries that the RAF's dedicated tankers might be reduced by attrition or unserviceability. Fifteen Sargent Fletcher 28-300 refuelling pods were acquired from the Marineflieger and eight twin-stick Tornados were modified at RAF St Athan (under Special Trials Fit 238) to carry them. One more aircraft was similarly modified at RAF Honington (probably ZD812). The first aircraft (ZA410) emerged from conversion on 13 January 1991, and the programme was concluded on 6 March. The eight aircraft (ZA365, ZA367, ZA410, ZA411, ZD712, ZD714, ZD741 and ZD743) were held in reserve in the UK and Germany.

Tornado GR.Mk 1 TAP

The GEC Ferranti TIALD (Thermal Imaging Airborne Laser Designator) pod was developed to meet the RAF's SR(A) 1015 which called for a laser designator for the Tornado. It was envisaged that TIALD would be delivered to No. IX Squadron in RAF Germany, which would also be equipped with ALARM missiles and would function as a 'Pathfinder' unit for other RAFG squadrons. Until TIALD entered service the RAF would have to rely on Pave Spike-equipped Buccaneers to designate for LGB-equipped Tornados. TIALD drew on the extensive experience of the development and production of the LRMTS (Laser Ranger and Marked Target Seeker) used in the Harrier, Jaguar and Tornado, and the various sensors developed in response to Air Staff Target 1006, which aimed to assess the feasibility and effectiveness of a range of electro-optical devices, including low-light-level TV; thermal imagers; and laser rangers, marked target seekers and designators. Various combinations of laser, TV and thermal imager were test flown between 1973 and 1980, when the experience gained was incorporated into the day/night attack pod (DNAP). GEC Ferranti was contracted to produce a technology demonstrator pod to be flown on RAE Farnborough's Nightbird Buccaneer, and this became known as TIALD.

TIALD consists of a pod containing a TV operating at 0.7-1.0 microns, a laser designator operating at 1.06 microns and a thermal imager operating at 8-10 microns. All shared common optics, with a common multi-spectral window in an articulated seeker head with a stabilised mirror. The use of common optics guaranteed the smallest possible pod diameter, and ensured that all sensors were boresighted to the same aiming point. The articulated head could roll through 360°, and could move from +30° (although this angle was blocked by the Tornado's nose) back to -155°. An obscuration profile stored within the pod prevented the laser from hitting any part of the airframe. TIALD has a large field of regard for viewing the target area, with a narrower 'wide field of view' for target acquisition, and an even smaller 'narrow field of view' for target identification and designation. This has further electronic x2 and x4 magnification facilities.

The RAE flew a five-phase 116-flight trials programme between 26 January 1988 and 10 December 1990. This culminated in the TIALD Buccaneer designating targets for an LGB-equipped No. 13 Squadron Tornado GR.Mk 1A. It scored a direct hit on the floating target with its first bomb. In the meantime, the thorough, deliberate and considered peacetime development programme had been interrupted by the invasion of Kuwait by Saddam Hussein on 2 August 1990. It soon became clear that force would be required to liberate Kuwait, and the British MoD proposed a TIALD Accelerated Programme (TAP) to give deployed RAF Tornados an autonomous day/night laser designator capability.

Such a programme was considered only

Only two prototype TIALD pods were available for service in the Gulf War. This is one of them, named 'Sandra' after a Viz comic character (one of the 'Fat Slags'). Five aircraft shared the two pods in-theatre.

A production TIALD pod is seen on a No. 14 Sqn jet, fitted with the special STF pylon. The ball mounting for the sensor and laser swivels while the whole nose of the pod rotates, combining to provide full articulation.

Left: No. 617 Squadron was charged with bringing the TIALD into use during the Gulf War, the TIALD detachment being led by the 'Dambusters' CO, Wing Commander Bob Iveson.

Above: No. 14 Sqn took over the TIALD role from No. 617, two of the unit's aircraft being shown here. The furthest aircraft carries the pod, which is usually mounted on the port forward shoulder station.

because TIALD's flight trials had already reached an advanced stage, and had made excellent progress. Initial investigation showed that the MoD's timescale could not be met due to the time it would take to rewrite the necessary software (BAe estimated that the programme would take six months). Undaunted, GEC Ferranti approached its sister company EASAMS, which estimated that the Operational Flight Program software could be rewritten to accommodate TIALD inside six weeks. This was much more useful, and an initial technical meeting was held on 30 November, when pod interface requirements were defined. On 19 November a contract was issued, with the MoD's Directorate of Avionic Equipment and Systems acting as project authority, GEC Ferranti as prime contractor (responsible for pod modifications), and with EASAMS undertaking aircraft software modifications, RAF Honington rewiring the selected aircraft, RAE Farnborough providing control panels, and the A&AEE at Boscombe Down flight- and rig-testing the equipment. The RAF allocated five Tornado GR.Mk 1s (with Gulf modifications and painted in desert pink), to allow the modification of the trials TIALD pod and another produced from components and spares, and their integration on the aircraft.

The first TIALD pod was delivered to the A&AEE on 14 January (Day 27).

Operation Desert Storm began on 17 January (Day 30), and TIALD made its first flight under a Tornado the following day. The TIALD/Tornado combination was initially flown by CTTO (SAOEU) crews, before the remaining TAP aircraft were delivered to Boscombe Down on 23 January (Day 36), together with four crews from No. 13 Squadron. The TIALD laser was fired against a laser target in Scotland on 30 January (Day 43) and a live bomb was dropped on 2 February (Day 46) resulting in a direct hit. On 6 February 1991 four of the five TAP aircraft were flown to the Gulf, exactly 50 days after the programme began. Operating from King Faisal Air Base at Tabuk, the Tornados (flown by the No. 13 Squadron crews and by two crews from No. 617 Squadron) carried out familiarisation and tactical training flights, culminating in the drop of a single bomb on the Badr range on 9 February. TIALD was then ready to go to war, and the first of missions was flown on 10 February. The aircraft attacked Iraqi airfields (mainly hardened aircraft shelters and pilot briefing facilities, but also runways), ammunition and fuel storage areas and bridges. The revetted ammunition dump at Ubaydah bin Al Jarrah was attacked on 19 February, sending a

mushroom cloud 15,000 ft (4570 m) into the air and prompting reports of a nuclear explosion.

The five TAP aircraft were ZA393/CQ (*Cool Queen*, later *Sir Galahad*), ZA406/DN (*Dog's Nob*), ZD739/AC (*Armoured Charmer*), ZD844/DE (*Donna Ewin*), and ZD848/BC (*Bacardi and Coke*). The fifth aircraft flew out to the Gulf on 20 February, having been maintained at Boscombe Down as a spare. Despite having only two pods and five aircraft capable of carrying them, the TIALD fleet typically flew six sorties per day. The original six crews were augmented by single crews from Nos II and 14 Squadrons, and by two crews from No. 16 Squadron. This allowed five shifts to be formed, each with two crews, who flew one day sortie, one night sortie, and then had a day off.

The pod-equipped aircraft flew 72 successful sorties and designated for a force of 14 bomber Tornados, which scored 229 direct hits with their 1,000-lb Paveway II laser-guided bombs. Typically, a pair of TIALD-equipped aircraft would each escort a package of four bombers, with a third TIALD-capable aircraft readied as a spare. Some 20 miles (32 km) from the target, the TIALD was slaved to the radar, with narrow field of view being selected 15 miles out (24 km). The navigator then refined the aim

point using a hand controller, placing the aiming point over the target. Auto track was selected to allow the TIALD to remain locked on. The laser would typically be fired for up to 30 seconds, until bomb impact, when it would be redirected to the next target to provide guidance for bombs already released by the second bomber in the package. Up to four targets could be designated in a single pass. The TIALD aircraft could self-designate for a single bomb carried on the starboard underfuselage station beside the pod on the port station, though this was rarely practised. The designator aircraft would fly at 20,000 ft or more (6100 m), and stand off at least 4 miles (6.5 km) from the target. Using TIALD was sufficiently easy that five of the 10 navigators who operated the system during the war flew only one training mission. TIALD proved invaluable as a reconnaissance and bomb damage assessment tool, with the thermal imager providing good enough pictures at night to be a useful navigation aid. TIALD images were best viewed on the ground, using a 625-line monitor, because the Tornado's 200-line monitor provided less definition.

Since the Gulf War more RAF Tornados have been made compatible with TIALD. The system was used initially by No. 617 Squadron, and subsequently by No. 14 Sqn.

Tornado IDS (Luftwaffe reconnaissance version)

After the end of the Cold War, the availability of surplus Tornado IDS aircraft in Germany allowed the retirement of the McDonnell Douglas RF-4E Phantom, and their replacement by specially equipped Tornados. Panavia was asked to develop five options for the conversion of Tornados to reconnaissance configuration, to be of varying levels of sophistication and capability. They included a version similar to the RAF's GR.Mk 1A, perhaps with the addition of Zeiss optical sensors. Another option involved a Vinten 4000 or Honeywell IRLS mounted in a reinforced nose; yet another outlined using similar equipment in an external pod. It was even suggested that the new variant might use Eurofighter 2000-type EJ.200 engines, although in the end, a more modest solution was found.

A 'conversion' programme for some 40 ex-Marineflieger Tornados, mostly from MFG 2, was announced in early 1994. These aircraft equipped AKG 51 'Immelmann', which took over the insignia and traditions of AKG 52. It is unclear which type of conversion was necessary. Nine of MFG 1's HARM-capable aircraft were

AKG 51's recce-configured Tornados have adopted the two-tone pale-grey scheme. This aircraft carries a Cerberus ECM pod and AIM-9Ls.

Tornado Variants

The MBB/Aeritalia reconnaissance pod, as used by both German and Italian air forces, houses an infra-red linescan and a panoramic camera. The sensors are hidden behind rolling-blind windows when not in use.

MBB/Aeritalia reconnaissance pod

retained by the Marineflieger, meaning that almost one-third of the new reconnaissance aircraft were compatible with AGM-88 HARM missiles. The unit soon gained a number of aircraft from other Luftwaffe wings, transferring out some of the former Marineflieger aircraft.

In fact, the reconnaissance capability of the new Tornados was initially very limited. The aircraft delivered to the Luftwaffe originally shared only nine MBB/Aeritalia reconnaissance pods (three from the Marineflieger, and six procured from Italy), although more were quickly obtained. The

Marineflieger had originally acquired 26 reconnaissance pods. The existing pod contained a pair of Zeiss optical wet-film cameras and a Texas Instruments RS-710 IRLS, and was regarded as being purely an interim piece of equipment; the Luftwaffe ordered a new reconnaissance system for service entry in 1998. The new pod will be autonomously air-conditioned, and will carry two optical cameras, an IRLS, a data-

storage system and comprehensive built-in test equipment. A new reconnaissance management unit will give the backseater full control over the pod, and will allow the real-time display of imagery as it is gathered. The pod will be supported by a new ground station, probably with a real-time datalink. Six of AKG 51's reconnaissance Tornados were deployed with Einsatzgeschwader 1 to take part in

operations over Bosnia (Operation Deliberate Force). EG-1 was established at Piacenza in August 1995 to co-ordinate operations by the six AKG 51 Tornados and eight JBG 32 Tornado ECRs. They remained there even after the withdrawal of the ECRs on 22 November 1996.

The newly acquired ex-Marineflieger Tornados retain their simple IDS designation, as do the aircraft transferred from other Luftwaffe units.

Tornado GR.Mk 1A

One of the roles inferred in the Tornado's original MRCA appellation was reconnaissance, and the aircraft was seen from the start as a potential replacement for some of the Canberras, Phantoms and Jaguars then being used in that role. Throughout the 1970s the three Panavia partners tried to arrive at a common reconnaissance version of Tornado. Unfortunately, the requirements were all slightly different and it proved impossible to reach agreement. Therefore, in 1982, the UK decided to begin development of a 'national', 'internal', dedicated reconnaissance version. Some consideration was given to providing Tornado with a reconnaissance pod, as had been designed for use with the Jaguar, the Phantom and even the Harrier. This was thought to impose an unacceptable drag penalty, while a jettisonable pod would be inappropriate for very high cost sensors. The last thing anyone wanted was for a Tornado to jettison its sensors and imagery upon being bounced by enemy air defence aircraft. The focus moved to the design of a semi-conformal, low-drag, fixed pallet or 'slipper' and eventually to a completely internal installation.

The lack of internal volume available in the Tornado precluded the fitting of a full multi-spectral reconnaissance suite (though a camera nose, like that of the RF-4 Phantom, could have been designed had the radar been sacrificed). Instead it was decided to concentrate on the development of small electro-optical sensors, recording direct on to video tape. A similar system would be applied to the second-generation Harrier GR.Mk 5.

An IR-based digital, filmless reconnaissance system was developed for the new Tornado GR.Mk 1A by BAe (responsible for integration), Vinten (sensors) and CDC (recorders). The system drew heavily on the UK's TICMS (Thermal Imaging Common Module System) and used SPRITE (Signal Processing In The Element) detection technology, with cooling by a Stirling Cycle cryogenic cooling system. This sensor package was mounted

Tornado GR.Mk 1A

- **Cannon armament deleted to make room for reconnaissance system**
- **Reconnaissance system control panel in rear cockpit**
- **BOZ-107 chaff/flare pods carried on one or both outer pylons**
- **Full nav/attack capability retained**
- **IRLS fairing with airflow baffle**
- **Standard 220-Imp gal wing drop tanks (depicted) often replaced by 495-Imp gal 'Hindenburgers'**
- **Side window for SLIR (side-looking infra-red) sensor. Underfuselage bulge for panoramic IRLS (infra-red linescan) sensor**
- **LRMTS fairing offset to starboard**

in the nose, displacing the internal cannon. Externally, the Tornado GR.Mk 1A is distinguished by a shallow fairing below the fuselage and by a pair of IR-transparent 'windows' in the sides of the forward lower fuselage. The underfuselage fairing incorporates a panoramic window giving virtually horizon-to-horizon coverage for the BAe/Vinten Linescan 4000 IR linescanner, and the side 'windows' serve the BAe SLIR (Sideways-Looking Infra-Red), with its 10° FoV out to the sides.

Because the Tornado GR.Mk 1A has no conventional optical cameras, it requires no wet-film processing support, and this allows very fast turnarounds between missions and a faster delivery of imagery to the end user. The use of a video-based system allows inflight editing and review of imagery, while both the pilot and navigator can record 'event markers' on the tape to allow specific targets to be found more rapidly for interpretation or evaluation. The

use of digitised imagery means that it would also be possible to transmit data to an appropriately equipped ground station in real time, although an appropriate datalink has yet to be procured.

Apart from the loss of the cannon, the GR.Mk 1A retains full ground attack capability, and the RAF's Tornado GR.Mk 1A squadrons are dual-tasked.

A single Tornado GR.Mk 1, ZA402, was delivered to Warton for other development work during June 1984 and was then nominated to serve as the prototype GR.Mk 1A, making its maiden flight in its new configuration on 11 July 1985. The kit was not fitted, and the aircraft was used for vibration level tests and for the measuring of pressures and airflow around the IRLS slot. Trials of the intended sensor package began in late summer 1985. ZA402 had a trial installation of the reconnaissance kit. It was followed by a 'production batch' of 13 more Batch 4 GR.Mk 1 conversions (ZA369-373, 394, 395, 397, 398, 400, 401, 404, and 405). The first two Tornado GR.Mk 1As built as such were the only

aircraft actually delivered to the RAF from Batch 5; the rest (standard GR.Mk 1s) were diverted to the Saudi air force. The two aircraft were delivered in December 1986 and January 1987 and were initially flown by 'ordinary' squadrons until the formation of No. II Squadron, the first specialised Tornado reconnaissance unit. The two new-build GR.Mk 1As were ZD996 and ZE116 (BS156 and BS160). They were initially provided only with structural provision for the new equipment, losing their internal cannon and gaining the distinctive undernose fairing, but not receiving the 'windows' on the sides of the nose. One aircraft remained with BAe for trials, and the other 14 were sent to RAF Germany from 3 April 1987, where they were initially issued to most of the Brüggen- and Laarbruch-based squadrons, pending fitting of their reconnaissance role equipment at No. 431 MU at RAF Brüggen. Others were briefly used by the TTTE.

No. II Squadron took on the converted Tornado GR.Mk 1As in late 1988, but its aircraft were originally delivered without side windows (and presumably without reconnaissance equipment), and there were reports that reconnaissance training did not begin until 1989. Side windows started to appear in October 1989, indicating imminent installation of reconnaissance equipment. The equipment was late, and slow to arrive, and by January 1990 only eight of the 20 extant Tornado GR.Mk 1As were sensor-equipped. The squadron later moved from Laarbruch to Marham.

Fourteen more GR.Mk 1As were newly built as part of Batch 7 (ZG705-714, 725-727, and ZG729). No. 13 Squadron reformed with the new-build Tornado GR.Mk 1As at Honington on 1 January 1990, the first of these aircraft having been

This No. 13 Squadron GR.Mk 1A shows off the external evidence of the TIRRS fitted to the aircraft: gold-tinted side windows for the side-looking sensors and a bulged fairing under the forward fuselage for the panoramic linescan. Note the lack of cannon.

Up close for the camera, this No. II(AC) Sqn GR.Mk 1A is carrying the Vinten GP.1 external pod used for medium/high-level work. The rear slit window for the panoramic tracking camera can be seen, while the nose housing the mirror for the main camera is rotated so that the window is pointing to the oblique position for LOROP work.

delivered on 13 October 1989. This unit also later moved to RAF Marham. Six Tornado GR.Mk 1As received a Computing Devices Co.-devised package of modifications (known as Granby 2) for participation in Operation Desert Storm. They were operated by a joint detachment drawn from Nos II and 13 Squadrons and were based at Dhahran from 14 January 1991. The modifications were trialled at Laarbruch between Christmas 1990 and New Year 1991. The six aircraft deployed to the Gulf (all drawn from No. II Squadron) were

ZA370, ZA371, ZA372, ZA373, ZA397 and ZA400. They flew 128 night reconnaissance sorties, totalling about 300 flying hours. The aircraft often flew with four standard IDS tanks under the wings and fuselage, or with a pair of the larger ADV 'Hindenburgers' underwing. This meant that the internal fuel load of 1,400 Imp gal (6364 litres) could be more than doubled by the addition of 1,650 Imp gal (7500 litres) of external fuel, and that at a typical operational take-off weight of 26 tonnes, the GR.Mk 1A would be carrying 11 tonnes of fuel. The reliability improvements of Granby 2 were subsequently incorporated in all GR.Mk 1As.

Some of the Tornado IDSs delivered to Saudi Arabia were built to a similar standard to the RAF's GR.Mk 1A. The first of these was 6628, delivered to the Royal Saudi air force for No. 66 Squadron. A number of aircraft from the Saudi Al Yamamah II batch were built to a similar standard. Although these aircraft look like GR.Mk 1As, they may be more capable, perhaps carrying an emitter location system to allow them to operate in the SEAD role. One of the Al

Yamamah II aircraft was certainly seen carrying ALARM missiles before delivery.

In monitoring operations over Iraq (flown from Turkey and Saudi Arabia), RAF Tornado GR.Mk 1As have flown at about 15,000 ft (4575 m), and have carried the GP.1 pod (actually a Vinten Series 18-601) containing optical cameras, rather than operating at the low levels for which the onboard sensors are optimised. This is the same pod that has been used by GR.Mk 1s and GR.Mk 1Bs participating in Operation Warden over northern Iraq. The pod has an F144 (Type 690) LOROP camera forward, with an 18-in (450-mm) focal length lens giving a 14° field of view. This records onto conventional 5-in (127-mm) film. The pod's tactical stand-off lens/mirror assembly and rotating nose allows any depression, from horizon to horizon, and allows the camera to be 'aimed' by the pilot. Aft is a Type 900 A/B panoramic magazine-loaded camera, with a 3-in (76.2-mm) lens recording onto 17.8-in (70-mm) film and giving horizon-to-horizon coverage. The camera can operate at up to 16 frames per second. Vinten is coy about

the number of GP.1s delivered, saying only that 'a considerable number' are in service, and that the pod is in service 'with two export customers'. The RAF uses the GP.1 on its Jaguars and Harrier GR.Mk 7s, as well as on the Tornado GR.Mk 1 and GR.Mk 1A.

In the near future, the RAF will receive the urgently needed day-night, medium-level, stand-off imaging capability which the Tornado lacks. Simultaneous operation in the visual and thermal spectrums is thought to be essential, with a required target recognition range of 40-nm (46 miles; 74 km) visually and of 20 nm (23 miles; 37 km) in the IR spectrum, and with a minimum slant range of 20,000 ft (6100 m). Staff Requirement (Air) 1368 for a RAPTOR (Reconnaissance Airborne Pod for Tornado) is intended to bring a suitable system into service as quickly as possible, with an IOC of December 1998. RAPTOR consists of external sensor pod suitable for carriage on the shoulder pylon of the Tornado GR.Mk 1A and, subsequently, for carriage by the GR.Mk 4A. It will incorporate a real-time/near real-time datalink and a deployable datalink ground station (DLGS) capable of operating with up to four aircraft, and will be compatible with the RAF's current Transportable Reconnaissance Exploitation Facility (TREF).

A number of companies are competing to provide elements of the RAPTOR system, including Vinten and Per Udsen (for the pod), Normalair Garrett, Schlumberger Industries and Amplex (recorders) and CDC (the DLGS).

Tornado GR.Mk 1B

Early plans for the allocation of Tornados to the maritime strike role were cancelled in the early 1980s, the Buccaneer force 'running on' in order to make two extra Tornado squadrons available on NATO's central front. The end of the Cold War led to a reduction in the number of Tornados committed to the overland strike role, with the two four-squadron wings in RAF Germany being reduced to a single four-squadron wing. Three squadrons (Nos XV, 16 and 20) were simply disbanded, while a fourth (No. II) returned to the UK. Some of the surplus aircraft were used to re-equip the two remaining maritime strike Buccaneer squadrons.

Some 26 former Laarbruch-based RB.199 Mk 103-engined Batch 3 Tornado GR.Mk 1s were converted to GR.Mk 1B configuration, the first as the 'Pinst' (proof of installation) airframe by BAe at Warton, the rest at RAF St Athan. Two (ZA409 and ZA411) were twin-stickers, and are sometimes erroneously referred to as GR.Mk 1B(T)s. One was 'plumbed' for the carriage of a Sargent Fletcher 28-300 refuelling pod during the Gulf War. The first conversion was ZA407, which made its first flight in GR.Mk 1B configuration on 18 September 1993. The conversion was relatively simple and straightforward and, apart from serial numbers, squadron markings and armament (when carried), it

A Tornado GR.Mk 1B from 'Six-foot' (No. 617 Sqn) clutches a brace of Sea Eagles to its belly. The missile requires a dedicated launch rail which attaches to the shoulder pylons.

Tornado GR.Mk 1B

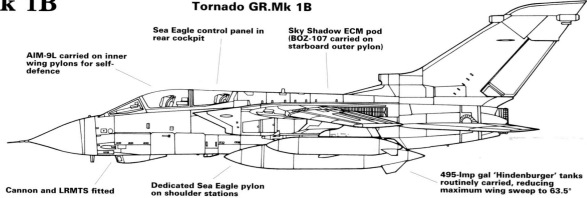

- **AIM-9L carried on inner wing pylons for self-defence**
- **Sea Eagle control panel in rear cockpit**
- **Sky Shadow ECM pod (BOZ-107 carried on starboard outer pylon)**
- **Cannon and LRMTS fitted**
- **Dedicated Sea Eagle pylon on shoulder stations**
- **495-Imp gal 'Hindenburger' tanks routinely carried, reducing maximum wing sweep to 63.5°**

is virtually impossible to distinguish a Tornado GR.Mk 1B from a standard GR.Mk 1.

The GR.Mk 1B conversions were: ZA374 (BS056), ZA375 (BS057), ZA399 (BS066), ZA407 (BS074), ZA409 (BT033), ZA411 (BT035), ZA446 (BS076), ZA447 (BS077), ZA450 (BS080), ZA452 (BS082), ZA453 (BS083), ZA455 (BS085), ZA456 (BS086), ZA457 (BS087), ZA459 (BS089), ZA460 (BS090), ZA461 (BS091), ZA465 (BS095), ZA469 (BS099), ZA471 (BS101), ZA473 (BS103), ZA474 (BS104), ZA475 (BS105), ZA490 (BS106), ZA491 (BS107), ZA492 (BS108).

The conversion basically covered the provision and installation of a new stores management system and (removable) Sea Eagle pylon adaptors, which provide an interface between the launch aircraft and

the missile. This gives the missile a slight nose-down 'sit' and allows the missile's onboard navigation system to be updated with data from the launch aircraft. It is then possible to use the missile's computed mode, allowing off-boresight launch from high or low level and allowing the missile to discriminate between targets, being programmed to attack the largest, smallest, nearest, furthest, leftmost or rightmost target within a group. The Sea Eagle can be carried on a non-dedicated pylon, but can then only be used in its reversionary mode. In this, the missile must be fired at a boresighted target, flying at a set height until its pre-set pop-up, when it turns on its own radar and attacks the first target 'seen'. The reversionary mode may have a narrower altitude band. In either mode, Sea Eagle is a genuinely

fire-and-forget weapon, flying to the target using inertial guidance before turning on its own active radar seeker. The weapon has a formidable ECCM capability, and a classified launch range of more than 50 nm (57 miles; 92 km).

There are suggestions that the RAF's Tornados were not the first to carry Sea Eagle. Some reports suggest that the weapon was also delivered for use by Saudi Tornados. It is not known whether any or all of the Saudi Tornado IDSs have been given the new stores management system used on the GR.Mk 1B, or even whether the aircraft can carry the dedicated Sea Eagle pylons which provide an interface between missile and aircraft.

The Tornado GR.Mk 1B remains compatible with the Paveway LGB, relying on third-party designation, although the aircraft could easily be made compatible with the TIALD laser designator pod. The GR.Mk 1B squadrons spend only about 40 per cent of their time training for the maritime strike role, retaining a full overland strike/attack capability via a range of weapons.

Plans have been outlined for at least some of the GR.Mk 1Bs to be modified to enable them to carry the Flight Refuelling Mk 20B HDU pods previously carried underwing by the RAF's recently retired Victor K.Mk 2 tankers. The Buccaneer (which already enjoyed a small, though significant, payload/range advantage over the Tornado) routinely operated with a buddy inflight-refuelling store, and the addition of such a store to the GR.Mk 1B would undoubtedly enhance operational flexibility. Unfortunately, financial

Tornado Variants

constraints led to the plan being dropped. Interestingly, a previous plan to give some RAF Tornados a buddy refuelling capability was implemented, then rapidly abandoned during the Gulf War. Fifteen Sargent Fletcher 28-300 pods were acquired from the Marineflieger, and nine aircraft were modified to carry them before the programme was abandoned, when it was realised that sufficient large tankers were available. These aircraft comprised ZA365,

In common with the rest of the RAF's fleet, the GR.Mk 1Bs are slowly acquiring a medium sea-grey paint scheme. This example is seen with two drill rounds for the Sea Eagle.

ZA367, ZA410, ZA411, ZD712, ZD714, ZD741, ZD743, and ZD812. ZA411 subsequently became a GR.Mk 1B.

Tornado ECR

The Tornado ECR, known as the EKA (Elektronische Kampfführung und Aufklärung) in Germany, was developed to meet a German requirement for a dedicated reconnaissance aircraft (primarily to replace the RF-4E and RF-104G), though from an early stage it was decided that the aircraft would also operate in the suppression of enemy air defences (SEAD) role. All German Tornados from Batch 5 onwards are compatible with the AGM-88 HARM missile (though only Marineflieger aircraft used the weapon), but the Tornado ECR was perceived as being more than a mere launch platform for the missile, having its own Texas Instruments Emitter Location System to allow it to locate, identify, plot and engage threat radars.

Since the Tornado ECR was designed to have an ODIN (Operational Data Interface) datalink, the aircraft could also conduct real-time electronic reconnaissance missions, and could transmit data concerning the location and status of enemy air defences to strike aircraft it might be escorting, or for which it was 'pathfinding'.

The Emitter Location System uses six 1750 digital processors, a surface acoustic wave channeliser and a cued analysis

receiver to determine the signal characteristics and location. It uses antennas in the wing glove and forward fuselage, giving only forward hemisphere coverage (unlike the 360° F-4G). This is a relatively unimportant detail, however, since the ECR would usually operate in pairs, flying in a racetrack pattern so that one aircraft was nose-on to any threat. The system relies on a comprehensive pre-programmed threat library, with no ability to be rapidly reprogrammed in the air (or even on the flight line). The ELS was developed by Texas Instruments, and integrated into the Tornado by DASA. It began flight tests in 1989, and was fully qualified by the end of 1993. The ELS was augmented by a Honeywell/Sondertechnik horizon-to-horizon IRLS (also known as an Imaging Infra-red System, or IIS) below the forward fuselage, incorporating an AN/AAD-5 IR scanner. Installation of the IIS necessitated the removal of the ECR's twin 27-mm cannon, but otherwise the aircraft retains the usual ground attack capabilities of the baseline IDS.

The panoramic IIS is augmented by a steerable forward-facing Carl Zeiss FLIR in a turret below the starboard forward fuselage. The sensor can rotate through 180° to face back into the trailing-edge fairing when not in use, protecting its 'window'. This passive IR sensor was

intended to allow covert penetration of enemy airspace. The IR image can be displayed on the pilot's HUD or on his new Combined Electronic Display and Map (CEDAM), and on the WSO's TV tabs. The image in the HUD can be overlaid with flight data and steering commands, allowing fully head-up operation.

Threat information was handled by a MIL STD 1553B digital databus, and displayed to the WSO on two dedicated screens. ELS data could be superimposed on imagery from the IRLS to produce an IR threat map. The pilot could elect to view the same data on his combined map display. The ECR can transmit ELS or IIS data and imagery to other aircraft or suitably equipped ground stations using the aircraft's ODIN datalink. Work on the ECR Tornado began in early 1984, and a formal Panavia proposal was made to the German Ministry of Defence in January 1985. This outlined the building of 40 dedicated SEAD Tornados, at an estimated cost of DM3,700 million.

The first of two ECR prototypes (actually P.16/98+03, the final pre-series Tornado) made its maiden flight on 18 August 1988, with 98+79 (GS217, formerly 45+75) joining the programme on 30 November 1988 (or two months later, according to some sources). The first prototype initially looked extremely unprepossessing, in a well-worn Marineflieger colour scheme with extensive areas painted only in primer, and with 'ECR' crudely stencilled on the tailfin. The aircraft lacked the definitive FLIR fairing, but did have the bulged undernose fairing for the IIS, and did have the new Emitter Locator System. A flight test instrumentation pod was carried on the aircraft centreline.

The definitive ECR features many of the improvements of the standard Batch 6 IDS, with 128 K computer and MIL STD 1553B digital databus, plus MIL STD 1760 weapon interfaces. The aircraft has a digital engine control unit, although the engines themselves are RB.199 Mk 105s, which deliver 10 per cent more thrust than the RB.199 Mk 103s. The engine has a new type 62B fan LP compressor, giving increased pressure ratio, and the engine also incorporates single crystal blade technology in the intermediate and HP turbines. The Mk 105 engine was flown for the first time in May 1987. HARM firings were subsequently conducted at NAS China Lake in early 1990; among the aircraft involved were 45+29 and 98+02. As well as AGM-88 HARM, the Tornado ECR was designed to be able to use the AGM-65D Maverick, visually or by using the FLIR, radar or ELS to boresight the missile's own seeker head to the target. It is unclear if the

weapon has actually been delivered to the Luftwaffe's ECR units. There is speculation that the Israeli Litening laser designator pods which the Luftwaffe has selected (but not ordered) would equip the ECRs if they are ever delivered.

Thirty-five Tornado ECRs were ordered in June 1986, to form the German part of Batch 7. The first of these, 46+23 (GS256), made its maiden flight on 26 October 1989. This first production ECR was handed over by MBB at Manching to the co-located Defence Material Test Centre (WTD.61) on 3 May 1990. Deliveries to JBG 38 at Jever began on 21 May 1990, and were finally completed in April 1991. The final 17 aircraft were delivered to JBG 32 at Lechfeld from June 1990, with the last aircraft arriving there on 28 January 1992. All but five of the Tornado ECRs were initially delivered without their vital ELS equipment, and operated at a much reduced level of capability, relying on RHAWS and the HARM missile's own seeker heads to acquire and pinpoint targets. The five ELS-equipped aircraft were used for trials, and used test equipment rather than production-standard kit. The majority of newly delivered ECRs were originally equipped only with the FLIR, the IIS and the ODIN datalink. The first aircraft with the ELS fitted was delivered to the Luftwaffe at Manching on 8 February 1993. The 35 aircraft initially equipped a single *Staffel* with JBG 32 and another with JBG 38, though they were subsequently concentrated in JBG 32. This unit which became the Luftwaffe's sole ECR unit on 1 July 1994, receiving the last of the JBG 38 ECRs in October 1994. Between August

Above: This close-up shows the panoramic IIS reconnaissance system, and the steerable turret for the FLIR.

Texas Instruments ELS antennas in wing glove and forward fuselage

Two IDS aircraft (98+03 and 98+79) were converted from IDS standard as testbeds for the ECR system. Here the second aircraft carries a centreline reconnaissance pod.

Tornado ECR

Full overland strike capability retained, although cannon are deleted

Honeywell/Sondertechnik IRLS in underfuselage fairing

Carl Zeiss FLIR in steerable turret offering forward/lower hemisphere coverage

ECRs were dispatched from JBG 32 to Einsatzgeschwader 1, the operational unit based in Italy for monitoring flights over Bosnia. In addition to the usual two HARMs, this aircraft has AIM-9Ls for self-defence.

1995 and November 1996 a rotational detachment of up to eight Tornado ECRs of JBG 32 were deployed to Piacenza in Italy to participate in Operation Deliberate Force. These aircraft received unspecified new equipment and were painted in a new overall light grey colour scheme, which was subsequently refined and then applied across most of the ECR fleet. Ten ECRs (those with the original unmodified equipment fit) have remained in the dark green Lizard camouflage.

Operational experience rapidly demonstrated that simultaneous operation in the reconnaissance and Wild Weasel roles was not practical, and that the ECR's Honeywell/Sondertechnik imaging infra-red system would be better used in a new pod by the dedicated Tornado reconnaissance aircraft of AKG 51. The removal of the IIS will have an impact on the SEAD role, since it can be used at the moment to help provide an accurate threat map display which relates to specific 'seen' features.

There was considerable speculation that Tornado ECRs (variously reported as 24 surplus Luftwaffe aircraft converted to ECR standards or 40 new-build ECRs among a total Tornado buy of 50 aircraft) might be sold to South Korea, but no order has materialised.

Germany's ECRs were basically the last 35 German IDS airframes (GS256-GS290), and wore the serials 46+23 to 46+57. None was dual-controlled, and were plane sets 817, 818, 821, 823, 827, 830, 833, 837, 839, 842, 844, 847, 848, 851, 854, 856, 858, 860, 864, 866, 869, 871, 873, 876, 879, 881, 884, 887, 890, 894, 896, 898, 900, 903, and 906.

Tornado ITECR

When Italy decided to obtain a SEAD capability, the Tornado was the obvious platform to use. As an interim step, a contract was issued to provide HARM capability to some Italian IDS aircraft in March 1991, following combat experience in the Gulf War. Integration tests on the first proposed HARM-shooter were completed in October 1991, and 20 Tornado IDS aircraft were modified to carry HARM missiles at the Italian air force's Central Maintenance Depot at Cameri and at Alenia's Turin plant, for interim service with 50° Stormo. The first two aircraft were handed over in February 1992, and were operated by 155° Gruppo, which also maintained a reconnaissance commitment using the MBB/Aeritalia reconnaissance pod. At the same time, in early 1992, the decision was taken to provide HARM capability across the Italian IDS fleet. Despite this, it was already apparent that a more capable SEAD aircraft was required, with enhanced emitter location systems.

After a protracted period of uncertainty and indecision (which included the cancellation and reinstatement of the ECR itself), Italy finally elected to procure 16 full-spec Tornado ECRs. Even after L286 billion ($235 million) had been spent on avionics, the programme came under threat, with vague proposals that the new equipment should be fitted to Tornados as part of a less ambitious upgrade. The Italian ECR as flown is a full-standard ECR, however, and

The Italian ECRs are externally identical to the German aircraft, but exhibit differences internally, notably the inclusion of a video recorder for reconnaissance imagery in place of film.

differs from the German aircraft in being converted from existing IDS airframes (rather than being newly-built), thus retaining its original engines. The aircraft also have higher Italian avionics content as a result of revised workshare agreements. They also have an alternative RHAWS, produced by Elettronica. The Italian aircraft retain their IIS, but record to video tape rather than to dry silver film, and to enable this the aircraft have a Tape Recorder Formatter Unit instead of the usual ECR Recorder Film Processor Unit. The first Italian ECR (MM7079) was converted by Alenia at Turin and made its maiden flight in July 1992, only three years after the German ECR prototype.

MM7079 was subsequently handed over to the AMI as the Luftwaffe received the last of its new production ECRs, illustrating how far behind the Italian ECR programme had fallen. The aircraft subsequently went to the RSV (311° Gruppo) at Pratica di Mare. The Italian ECRs will reportedly equip 155° Gruppo at Piacenza, which should have been operational with the ECR during 1995, though there is still little sign of service.

Tornado GR.Mk 4

While the Cold War was still raging, the RAF drew up a requirement (SR(A)417) for an upgrade to its Tornado GR.Mk 1s to enhance their ability to penetrate hostile airspace, and to make increased use of more accurate weapons, from greater stand-off ranges. The concept behind the requirement was that an upgraded Tornado should be able to make a covert, electronically silent penetration, using a non-emitting system for terrain following and navigation, instead of using its existing attack and terrain-following radars. Although all three of the original Tornado partners recognised the need for their aircraft to be upgraded, it soon became apparent that a joint MLU requirement would have imposed unacceptable delays and unnecessary cost, since there was little agreement on the details of what such an upgrade might include.

Britain became increasingly aware that its own doctrine differed from those of its partners, and decided to go it alone. Originally, it was intended that the upgraded aircraft would use GEC's Spartan terrain-referenced/terrain-following navigation system, in conjunction with the same company's TICM II FLIR. As Terprom (TERrain PROfile Matching), this system was subsequently flown in BAe's trials IDS, XZ630, and not the RAE's raspberry ripple-painted GR.Mk 1, as has often been stated. The equipment had begun flight trials in 1979 in a Jetstream, before flying aboard an F-16 testbed, and finally in the Tornado from early 1985.

In the early days of the Tornado MLU (Mid-Life Upgrade), the extent of the modifications was ambitious. There were suggestions that the fuselage would be stretched to provide extra space for avionics, and that new, 'stealthy' air intakes would be fitted. More modestly, it was proposed that the aircraft would be fitted with the all-composite taileron developed by BAe, and flown in 1982. It was 17 per cent lighter than the existing component. The canopy was to receive a thin gold coating for reduced radar cross-section and there were propositions that the aircraft might even be fitted with the 20,230-lb st (90.0-kN) Eurojet EJ200 engines designed and developed for the Eurofighter 2000. The UK had always insisted that the Eurofighter engine (originally known as XG40) should be dimensionally compatible with the RB.199, primarily to allow it to be used in a Tornado retrofit programme. This also allowed the RB.199 to be used in the first Eurofighter

The principal external characteristic of the GR.Mk 4 is the new fairing under the port forward fuselage which houses the FLIR. Night-vision goggles are also standard equipment.

prototypes, avoiding having to fly a new airframe and a new engine simultaneously. The EJ200 is lighter than the RB.199, with half the number of parts and with 50 per cent greater dry thrust, giving virtually the same thrust dry (13,490 lb st/60.0 kN) as the basic RB.199 had in full reheat (14,840 lb st/66.0 kN). Alternatively, it was suggested that the aircraft could be fitted with the 16,075-lb st (71.50-kN) RB.199 Mk 103B (which reportedly enjoys running costs 12 per cent lower than those of other RB.199s), or with the RB.199 Mk 105 fitted to German Tornado ECRs. It was envisaged that, whichever engine was used, Full-Authority Digital Engine Control (FADEC) units would be incorporated.

Other features originally outlined for the Tornado upgrade included a new Ferranti wide-angle holographic HUD, and a new Smiths Industries MFD HDD for the pilot. A Marconi Zeus RWR was to replace the existing Sky Guardian equipment, and the new variant would also receive a new GEC stores management system plus a digital FBW control system. Finally, the upgrade included provision for the GEC TIALD laser designator, and for stub pylons on the outboard face of each underwing pylon, these being dedicated to the carriage of ALARMs. It was also hoped to incorporate provision for huge 592-Imp gal (2691-litre) auxiliary fuel tanks.

A development and investment contract for the MLU was issued to Panavia on 16 March 1989, under which three aircraft

The first of 142 production Tornado GR.Mk 4s made its first flight from Warton on 4 April 1997, crewed by Graham Wardell and Phil Compton. The introduction of the GR.Mk 4 will allow greater commonality and weapons flexibility within the RAF Tornado fleet.

would be converted to serve as prototypes. They were XZ631 (the original P15), ZD708 and ZG773 (never actually delivered to the RAF); XZ631 received most systems, and the other two prototypes were converted to full GR.Mk 4 standard. A number of other aircraft have been used in support of the GR.Mk 4 programme, including the SAOEU's ZG706.

The RAF hoped to order 26 new-build Tornado GR.Mk 4s in Batch 8, the first to be delivered. It was intended that they would be followed by 165 conversions from pre-Batch 7 GR.Mk 1s and GR.Mk 1As. The budget for the upgrade was estimated at £1 billion. Each conversion would take 10 months, and 20 aircraft could be upgraded simultaneously. It was planned that the first 70 aircraft would be converted by BAe in a 'return to works' rebuild, with the next 15 being produced by joint BAe/RAF working parties at RAF St Athan. The organisation conducting the remaining conversions would be decided by competitive tender.

As defence cuts bit harder, the scope and extent of the upgrade was progressively reduced. The new-build Batch 8 aircraft were cancelled on 18 June 1990, and it became apparent that the number of conversions would be reduced. As the number of GR.Mk 4s fell, BAe pushed to have the tender element of the contract removed, hoping to do all of the work itself.

The MLU ran into some development problems, while the constantly moving 'goalposts' caused even greater delays. By 1993 the entire project was running 18 months behind schedule, and the Treasury pressed for its cancellation. With the collapse of the Warsaw Pact threat, it became increasingly difficult to justify the upgrade, which had been designed to allow the aircraft to continue to penetrate Warsaw Pact defences at low level. Instead, the budget was reduced to £750 million, and the number of aircraft to be converted was further decreased. This reduction was accompanied by the deletion of some of the MLU's major elements, including the abandonment of the major structural modifications (fuselage stretch and stealth intakes), for example. Even more significantly, on 4 May 1993, Sir Michael Graydon, Chief of the Air Staff, announced that the GEC Spartan and covert radar altimeter had been dropped from the upgrade.

The first GR.Mk 4 (XZ631) was not ready to make the type's much delayed first flight on 29 May 1993, so the second aircraft (ZD708) was used instead. Apart from a huge 'GR4' logo on the fin, the aircraft had a forward-facing test camera in the leading edge of the fin RWR fairing and a new FLIR fairing below the nose, offset to port, adjacent to the usual LRMTS fairing. This

first flight did little to obviate the uncertainty surrounding the GR.Mk 4 programme, which still faced the threat of cancellation. Eventually, following the government's Front Line First defence review, on 14 July 1994 BAe received a £640 million order for the conversion of only 80 aircraft, with an option to convert 62 more during 2000 and 2002, a total of only 142 aircraft. By this time the scope of the upgrade had narrowed, and covered only the installation of a digital map display, GPS, an enhanced weapons control system, a new wide-angle holographic HUD (allowing standard HUD symbology to be overlaid on the FLIR image), a video recorder, the pilot's MFD HDD, and a new fixed FLIR sensor.

This was a very much more modest upgrade than had originally been planned, when the changing international situation perhaps should have demanded that the aircraft should have been given increased flexibility and enhanced capabilities. RAF Tornados now face a less well-defined (but no less potent) threat than they did during the Cold War, yet the scope of the upgrade has been slashed to save money. RAF Tornados may have to operate in new roles, and without the NATO and USAF fighter and SEAD support which could once be taken for granted.

In September 1996, a Tornado GR.Mk 1A masqueraded as a GR.Mk 4 for static display at the Farnborough SBAC show. The aircraft, ZA401, had big GR.Mk 4 logos applied, but was otherwise unmodified. The choice of a reconnaissance GR.Mk 1A was not entirely inappropriate. The first aircraft to be upgraded was a GR.Mk 1, albeit from No. 13 Squadron, and arrived at Warton on 1 April 1996 after a brief period at RAF St Athan. The second aircraft, however, was a GR.Mk 1A, ZA371, which arrived on 3 June 1996. It seems likely that a high proportion of the upgraded aircraft will be GR.Mk 4As, perhaps indicating the importance attached

ZG773 was one of three aircraft used as GR.Mk 4 'prototypes'. Most of the changes are internal, including a new digital moving-map display, wide-angle HUD with holographic display and a new head-down display.

to upgrading the RAF's tactical reconnaissance capability.

During 1996 BAe's own Tornado IDS test workhorse was used to trial US-style low-intensity formation strip lights. They may eventually be incorporated as part of the GR.Mk 4 upgrade.

The Tornado MLU requirement was accompanied by separate requirements intended to find new stand-off and precision-guided munitions, primarily intended for use by the new variant (and for subsequent use by the new Eurofighter). SR(A) 1244 called for a new stand-off nuclear weapon, and was subsequently abandoned, along with the Tornado's existing nuclear role. Before the programme was abandoned, the MoD reportedly examined the Aérospatiale ASLP (an extended-range derivative of the ASMP used by the Mirage 2000N), the Martin TASM and the Boeing SRAM 2.

SR(A) 1236 outlined a need for a CASOM (Conventionally Armed Stand-Off Missile), for which a wide range of weapons was proposed. For a while, the favourite seemed to be the GEC Pegasus or Centaur, which are turbofan-powered, imaging infra-red derivatives of the Al Hakim family of weapons ordered by the UAE. GEC reportedly ran into problems obtaining licences to use the weapon's Microturbo engine, SNPE warhead and Sagem INS. Hughes proposed the Airhawk (an air-launched cruise missile) and Rockwell offered an extended-range derivative of the AGM-130 (tested on an SAOEU Tornado at Eglin AFB during 1994). Hunting teamed with McDonnell Douglas to offer the Grand SLAM (a derivative of the AGM-84 SLAM), and Shorts teamed with Texas Instruments to offer JSOW P31. Rafael offered a derivative of its Popeye (already in USAF use as AGM-142 Have Nap) and Benz Aerospace put forward the KEPD 350. The winning weapon, however was Storm Shadow, a stand-off dispenser weapon derived from the German Apache and to be developed by BAe and MATRA.

SR(A) 1238 was drawn up to find a new stand-off anti-armour weapon, envisaged initially as a dispenser system, but actually filled in the end by the Brimstone missile. SR(A)1240 called for a short-range anti-radiation missile.

A final weapons requirement was SR(A) 1242, which called for a low-level stand-off bomb. A go-ahead for purchase of the free-fall Texas Instruments Paveway III was given in July 1994, in preference to GEC Marconi's rocket-boosted Lancelot, which offered greater stand-off range but had a 50 per cent greater price tag. Britain became the first European customer for Paveway III.

Attempts have been made to sell new-build Tornado GR.Mk 4s overseas. In 1996, for example, BAe offered the UAE a batch of 24 new-build Tornado GR.Mk 4s (with an interim lease of 12 ex-RAF GR.Mk 1s). Saudi Arabia is also seen as a customer for a GR.Mk 4 type upgrade.

Tornado GR.Mk 4A

As far as can be ascertained, reconnaissance Tornados upgraded to GR.Mk 4 standards will be designated as

GR.Mk 4As. They may be the only aircraft cleared for the carriage of the RAPTOR/EO LOROPS pod defined in SR(A) 1368, and

described in more detail in the Tornado GR.Mk 1A entry.

Reconnaissance Tornados were among the first aircraft to undergo the MLU which turned them into GR.Mk 4As. An unmodified GR.Mk 1A (ZA401) was shown

statically at the 1996 SBAC Farnborough air show marked up as a GR.Mk 4, while the second aircraft delivered to BAe to undergo the MLU (ZA371 on 3 June 1996) was a GR.Mk 1A.

Tornado IDS upgrade (Germany)

German Tornados have received a succession of modifications and modernisations aimed at improving capability. During the late 1980s, early aircraft were brought up to virtual Batch 5 standards under the Tornado First Upgrade. This programme saw the installation of a MIL STD 1553B databus, a new stores management system, improved EW

capability, HARM compatibility, a mission data transfer system and DECUs for the RB.199 engines.

Luftwaffe Tornados assigned to the strike/attack role will receive a further multi-step MLU (the first stage of which was known as KWS, or Kampfwertanpassungs-programm – combat efficiency enhancement programme) from Benz

Aerospace. This initially incorporates a new main computer and a MIL STD 1760 digital data bus, which are intended to allow the subsequent integration of a variety of new systems. The original Assembler software package is transformed into an ADA software package in the first step of the upgrade, which is known as the Neue Avionikstruktur. It is envisaged that later

modifications will initially include a steerable FLIR, a new laser INS with integrated GPS, and improved cockpit displays. Under the KWE (Kampfwerterhaltungsprogramm – combat efficiency upgrade programme) the aircraft will gain a new defensive aids computer, with a new missile warning system, improved RHAWS and enhanced ECM.

As in Italy and the UK, increased emphasis is being placed on the use of stand-off and precision-guided munitions, and after evaluation of a number of laser

The first major upgrade for German aircraft was undertaken in the mid-1980s, when AGM-88 HARM capability was added. This was especially useful to the Marineflieger aircraft, which used the weapon on anti-ship duties.

targeting pods (including GEC's TIALD, Lockheed Martin's LANTIRN and Thomson-CSF's CLD) the Luftwaffe selected the Rafael Litening. This selection was allegedly made primarily on cost grounds, and there are reports that the pod has been selected but not actually ordered, with the project so far being limited to the incorporation of suitable, compatible software. If pods themselves are ordered, Zeiss will be responsible for maintenance, repair and logistics support, following a 1994 agreement with Rafael.

The KWS upgrade will allow Luftwaffe Tornados to use the new, enhanced HARM III, and the Apache Modular ASM. The aircraft will also be compatible with a new reconnaissance pod with comprehensive day/night sensors, digital data recording and real-time image display capability.

At one time it was thought likely that the upgrade might include the Low-Altitude Terrain-Aided Navigation (LATAN) and flight guidance system, a German-developed equivalent to Britain's Terprom and Spartan that uses a radar altimeter in conjunction with a digital terrain map to ensure obstacle clearance and to allow terrain-following flight. The system was tested on 43+89 (GS62) from February 1991 and used its memory to search for a corresponding pattern in its own digital map, which

Currently under test for the German Tornado fleet is the Apache-MAW, which is a stand-off weapon carrying various sub-munitions.

included natural and terrain features and man-made objects ranging from power-lines to villages. It produced a digital display of the terrain showing aircraft position, and could be integrated with the FLIR or GPS.

Tornado IDS upgrade (Italy)

Like Britain and Germany, Italy has announced a Mid-Life Upgrade programme for its Tornado fleet. The aircraft will receive an enhanced main computer, using ADA software, advanced RHAWS equipment, improved Active ECM (AECM Mk 3) equipment, a microwave landing system, compatibility with HARM III and a true autonomous PGM capability.

Italy's requirement for a PGM capability for its Tornado force led to the modification of an initial six aircraft by Alenia and the AMI's maintenance centre at Cameri to carry the first of 20 Thomson-CSF CLDP laser designators ordered in 1995. These aircraft will be able to self-designate (or to designate for other LGB-carrying aircraft) and will initially be armed with GBU-16B Paveway II LGBs. They may later receive some of the 1,700 IAI Griffin LGBs reportedly purchased in November 1993. Some sources suggest that the AMI might also use Paveway III or Elbit Opher LGBs on the aircraft.

This 6º Stormo Tornado is one of the original six AMI aircraft modified to carry the CLDP, seen carried under a shoulder station.

Tornado FOWW (Follow On Wild Weasel)

The USAF first evaluated the Tornado as a potential competitor in its Enhanced Tactical Fighter competition. There were suggestions that a USAF buy of the Tornado for use in that role might have led to an RAF buy of two-seat F-15s by the RAF for use in the air defence role, and to cancellation of the Tornado ADV. This competition was subsequently shelved, however, and when it was finally revived (as the Dual Role Fighter) it was won by the F-15E Eagle.

Following the Tornado's unsuccessful participation in the USAF's Enhanced Tactical Fighter programme, another Tornado derivative was optimistically proposed to meet the USAF's Follow-On Wild Weasel requirement, tracked by Panavia from 1986. This envisaged the development of an existing, in-production, two-seat aircraft capable of incorporating new technology and a high degree of automation to reduce crew workload. Low cost of ownership was held to be a key requisite. The requirement was for 150 SEAD aircraft, and was important enough to

prompt Panavia to sign an agreement with Rockwell North American Aircraft. Although all partner companies were involved, MBB took the lead, not least because of the experience it had built up integrating HARM on the Luftwaffe's Tornado ECR. The agreement, signed on 16 December 1988, made the US company an agent for the modified Tornado, and appointed the North American division as integrator of the AN/ALQ-99 emitter locator system. Rockwell would also be responsible for final assembly of the aircraft at its Palmdale plant. The aircraft proposed incorporated advanced emitter location systems and a HARM targeting system, differing from German and Italian Tornado ECRs in having all-round coverage for its integrated RHAWS and jammers. A contract award was expected in 1990, with service entry prior to

This impression shows the FOWW proposal armed with Maverick and Shrike, although HARM would have been the operational weapon.

2000. Tornado was in a strong position, not least because the most important unit to be re-equipped was the 52nd TFW at Spangdahlem in Germany, where inter-operability with German Tornados could

have offered useful advantages. Other competitors included F-15 and F-16 derivatives, and ATF and ATA versions.

In the end, the USAF's RFP was not issued, and the USAF's dedicated F-4G Wild Weasels were not directly replaced. Instead, they have been supplanted by HARM-equipped F-16s which lack a full emitter locator system.

Tornado 2000

The Tornado 2000 designation was applied to an unbuilt proposal for a modernised Tornado for use in the strike/attack role, intended to enter service at the turn of the millennium. The project was studied in 1991, in the immediate aftermath of the Gulf War. The aircraft was described as an 'advanced multi-role low-level penetrator for the 21st century'. It featured a fuselage stretch (for extra fuel, or avionics, or both) and a number of features intended to reduce frontal RCS. They included a faceted nose and redesigned intakes, and there was provision for the carriage of a large, semi-conformal centreline fuel tank. The aircraft had a 25 per cent increase in radius of action by comparison with the basic Tornado IDS.

There have been suggestions that the Tornado 2000 also formed the basis of a 'Long Range Penetrator', with an even more dramatically chined forward fuselage, a fixed, highly swept delta wing, and prominent LERXes. This aircraft would have retained the Tornado 2000's massive conformal tanks, with ASMs carried semi-conformally on its sides.

Tornado 2000 (provisional)

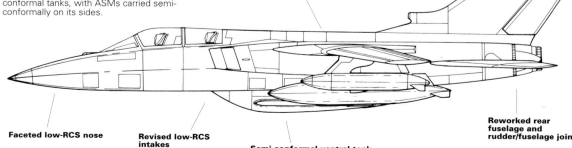

Lengthened fuselage for additional fuel and avionics

Faceted low-RCS nose

Revised low-RCS intakes

Semi-conformal ventral tank

Reworked rear fuselage and rudder/fuselage join

The Japan Air Self-Defence Force

A photo-feature by Katsuhiko Tokunaga

Above: This 306 Hikotai F-4EJ Kai is one of those exchanged by the squadron for the F-15J in 1996/97. 306 and 303 Hikotai (already an F-15 unit) are based at Komatsu on the western coast of Japan's main island, Honshu.

Centre left: In addition to the JASDF's baseline F-4EJs, the RF-4EJ fleet has also undergone the Kai upgrade programme. The chief elements of this include a new Texas Instruments AN/APQ-172 radar (replacing the APQ-99), IR linescan, INS, new radios and digital cockpit displays.

Left: The JASDF aerobatic team, 'Blue Impulse', is based at Matsushima AB, alongside the Mitsubishi T-2 and regular Kawasaki T-4 trainers of 21 and 22 Hikotai. 'Blue Impulse' transitioned from the T-2 to the T-4 in 1995/96.

Right: The JASDF's dedicated aggressor force is the Hiko Kyodotai, which flies F-15s from Nyutabaru, on the southern-most island of Kyushu. This unit swapped the T-2 for the F-15.

Above: These F-4EJ Kais are flown by 302 Hikotai – the combat element of Nansei Koku Konseidan (Southwestern Composite Air Division), based at Naha AB, Okinawa. 302 Hikotai also operates T-33As and T-4s, for squadron liaison/support tasks. It shares Naha with the Queen Airs and T-33As of a dedicated command support flight unit.

Left: In June 1996, 306 Hikotai painted up this F-4EJ Kai to mark the squadron's transition to the F-15J – the last JASDF squadron to make that change.

Below: 304 Hikotai is part of 8 Kokudan (Air Wing), Seibu Koku Homentai (Western Air Defence Force), based at Tsuiki AB on the northern coast of Kyushu. The squadron operates F-15Js, with T-4s in support.

Above: Newly arrived *F-15CJs* formate with surviving *F-4EJ Kais* of 306 Hikotai, in January 1997. Note the differences in schemes between the two *Phantoms*. The F-4 remains an important element in the *JASDF* inventory, with over 100 on strength (plus nearly 40 RF-4EJ Kais).

Below: The Hiko Kyodotai operates F-15DJs in the aggressor training role. It shares its Nyutabaru base with 202 Hikotai (F-15C/DJ) and 301 Hikotai (F-4EJ Kai).

Right: The black panther badge marks this Mitsubishi F-1 as an aircraft of 8 Hikotai (3 Kokudan), based at Misawa alongside sister squadron 3 Hikotai. Both units operate F-1s, with T-2s and T-4s in support.

Above: Tsuiki-based 6 Hikotai has the maritime attack role with the Mitsubishi F-1, as part of 8 Kokudan, Western Air Defence Force. It is pictured here with an F-15CJ of 304 Hikotai. 6 Hikotai transitioned to the F-1 from the F-86F in 1980; in 1990, 304 transitioned from the F-4EJ to the F-15.

Left: 201 Hikotai (seen here) and 203 Hikotai are part of the Chitose-based 2 Kokudan. This wing, and Misawa-based 3 Kokudan, make up Hokubu Koku Homentai (Northern Air Defence Force). The two squadrons of 3 Kokudan both operate F-1s.

Below: These Mitsubishi F-1s of 3 Hikotai (3 Kokudan) are armed with the F-1's primary weapon, the Type 80 ASM-1 anti-ship missile. The missile entered service in 1983 and has a 50-km (31-mile) range with a 150-kg (330-lb) HE warhead.

Above: The F-1 is the first type slated for replacement by Japan's new indigenous fighter, the F-2 (FS-X). In the meantime, it is likely that some F-4EJ Kai Phantoms will be reroled to take over the maritime strike mission.

Below: Fuji's veteran T-1 trainer survives with 13 Hiko Kokudan (Flying Training Wing) at Asiya. The first T-4s arrived at this unit in 1996 and the T-1 will have been retired by 1999.

Right: The JASDF ordered 169 F-15CJs and 44 F-15DJs, and the final deliveries from Mitsubishi are imminent. Seven front-line units fly Eagles (plus the Hiko Kyodotai and the JASDF test unit).

Above: Sengi Kenkyuhan ('Blue Impulse') is formally attached to 21 Hikotai which is based alongside 22 Hikotai as part of 4 Kokudan, at Matsushima. These two squadrons fly a mix of T-2s and T-4s. Along with 31 and 32 Hikotai (both flying T-4s), 1 Kokudan, they make up the JASDF's Koku Kyoku Shudan (Air Training Command), headquartered at Hamamatsu.

Left: The Mitsubishi F-2 (FS-X) is an advanced development of the Block 40 F-16C, which will replace the JASDF's F-1/T-2s. This, the first aircraft, made its maiden flight on 7 October 1995. Plans are to acquire 83 single-seat F-2s and 58 F-2B trainers.

Right: Japan is a member of the exclusive club of nations which operate the Boeing 747-400 as a transport for their head of state (the others are the USA and Brunei). In JASDF service two 747-47Cs are operated by 701 Hikotai, based at Chitose, as the Rinji Tokubetsu Koku Yusotai (Special Air Transport Group).

Below: Another Boeing type is unique to JASDF service – the E-767. The first of the JASDF's four AEW&C-configured 767-27CERs flew on 9 August 1996 (with its radar installation in place). It will be handed over in March 1998.

Above: *The Fuji T-3 serves with 11 and 12 Hikotai Kyoijudan, based at Shizuhama and Hofu, respectively. The T-3 is the JASDF's primary trainer and was originally developed for the JMSDF as the KM-2 (itself based on the Beech T-34). A total of 50 was acquired from 1978 and none has been lost.*

Right: *The Kawasaki T-4 is intended to replace the JASDF's remaining T-33s (approximately 40) and all its T-2s (85). Deliveries began in 1988. The T-4 serves with dedicated training units and front-line squadrons.*

Above: *The JASDF followed the USAF's lead and acquired the Raytheon Beechjet T-400 as a crew trainer. Ironically, the Beechjet was developed from Japan's own Mitsubishi Diamond 'biz-jet'.*

Right: *The first T-4 made its maiden flight on 29 July 1985 and is the collective product of Fuji, Mitsubishi and Kawasaki.*

Above: *Studies have commenced to find a 'C-X' replacement for the Kawasaki C-1 transport, which entered service in 1973. Today, 27 aircraft equip two squadrons.*

Below: *The first two of nine U-4s (Gulfstream IVs) on order were delivered on 24 February 1997. The cargo door-equipped U-4s will replace Beech Queen Airs.*

Japan Air Self-Defence Force

Above: A variety of NAMC YS-11s soldier on with the JASDF. This is one of the handful of basic transport YS-11s that serve with 402 Hikotai at Iruma, as part of 2 Yuso Kokutai (Air Transport Group).

Below: Kawasaki-Vertol KV-107s are in use with a single JASDF unit, the Koku Kyunandan (Air Rescue Wing), which provides detachments around the country.

Above: Heavily-modified Hawker 800s (BAe 125-800s) were acquired from 1995 for maritime patrol and SAR duties. A total of 27 (U-125As) has been ordered. A navaid calibration version of the U-125 is also in use.

Below: A single EC-1 electronic warfare support aircraft is operated by the Denshi Kunrentai (EW/ECM flight) from Iruma AB. The same unit also flies an active-duty YS-11E jammer.

Above: *The JASDF's dedicated SAR unit (Koku Kyunandan) operates a large mixed fleet of KV-107s, CH-47Js and, as seen here, Mu-2Ss and UH-60Js.*

Below: *The elongated nose, with search radar, marks this as one of 25 Mitsubishi Mu-2Ss in service. A smaller number (four) of Mu-2J calibration aircraft are also used.*

Above: *Japan's 13 E-2C Hawkeyes are operated by 601 Hikotai, based at Misawa. Like the other specialist EW or ECM units, this AEW&C squadron is a direct reporting element of Koku Sotai (Air Defence Command).*

Below: *Specially modified NAMC YS-11E/E-Kai/ELs act as EW aggressor trainers for other units and EW crew trainers in their own right.*

Below: *This rich mix of JASDF aircraft in formation includes a C-1 leading two F-4EJs (302 Hikotai), two T-2s, a single F-15CJ (304 Hikotai), two T-4s (early production aircraft in TRDI/Hiko Keihatsu Jikkendan marks), and a T-33A.*

South America

Part One: *Colombia, Ecuador, French Guiana, Guyana, Peru, Surinam and Venezuela*

This *Air Power Analysis* examines the forces deployed in the northern nations of the South American continent. They include Colombia and Peru, countries whose efforts are directed against the drug war – though Peru also faces off against its regional sparring partner Ecuador. Oil-rich Venezuela and the tiny trio of French Guiana, Surinam and Guyana complete the region.

Colombia

In recent years, Colombia has gained the unenviable reputation of being the drug-producing capital of the world. The many cartels have turned world opinion against Colombia, and yet very few people in the West realistically know anything about the country.

Situated in the northwestern tip of the South American continent and joined to central America by the isthmus of Panama, this country of 1138915 km² (439,770 sq miles) has a variety of terrain. The coastal regions consist of humid lowlands separated from the eastern tropical grasslands by the northern Andes range. This range of mountains runs north to south and splits into three great barriers: the Eastern, Western and Central Cordilleras. The grasslands of the east merge with the tropical rainforest of the Amazon and Orinoco river basins. This fertile terrain allows the country to boast a great variety of cultivated crops including bananas, cereals, cocoa, coffee, cotton, rice and sugarcane. Also to be found are precious metal, emeralds, copper and iron.

The diverse terrain, although high in natural resources, is difficult to police, and it is here that many of Colombia's internal problems exist. Apart from the drug cartels, who are responsible for the manufacture of the raw coca grown elsewhere in the continent, the country has a long history of political unrest and has a number of still-active terrorist factions. Colombia's military structure is therefore predominantly designed to counter this threat, while also working actively in the war against the narcotics barons.

Fuerza Aérea Colombiana

The Fuerza Aérea Colombiana (FAC), headquartered in Bogotá, has an independent status among the country's armed forces. In addition to its major commitment to national defence, it also has support roles in opening up the vast territory for economic development and in protecting the 28 million citizens from several internal factions.

The air force currently comprises six main commands: Comando Aéreo de Combate (CACOM), Comando Aéreo de Apoyo Táctico (CAATA), Comando Aéreo de Transporte Militar (CATAM), Escuela Militar de Aviación, formerly Comando Aéreo de Entrenamiento (CAETO), Comando Aéreo de Mantenimiento (CAMAN), and Servicio de Aeronavegación a Territorios Nacionales (SATENA). These commands are principally self-contained, each having under its control a single Grupo and a number of subordinate Escuadrónes. Both CACOM and CAATA have a number of elements which have their own separate headquarters and are differentiated by the title CACOM-1, CAATA-2, etc.

The country's air defence is centred around the US-supplied Peace Panorama integrated air-surveillance system that became operational in August 1993. Air assets are provided by CACOM-1 at Base Aérea 'German Olano', Palanquero. Here Grupo 21 has under its control two squadrons of Dassault Mirage and Kfir fighters. Escuadrón de Combate 212 operates 10 Mirage 5COA and two 5COD fighters, which are the residue of 15 Mirage 5COAs (14 original and one attrition replacement serialled 3021-3035), two 5COR reconnaissance variants (3011-3012), and two 5COD trainers (3001-3002), procured in 1972 to replace Canadair Sabre 4 and F-86Fs.

The Mirages are gradually being upgraded in a joint programme with IAI to a standard similar in avionics to the Kfir C7s operated by Escuadrón 212's sister unit, Escuadrón 213. Airframe improvements have seen the addition of canards. To date, nine Mirage 5COAs have been through the modification programme and the remaining single-seater plus both twin-seaters are scheduled to be delivered to the unit during 1997.

The Kfirs of Escuadrón de Combate 213 were received during 1989, the final five arriving in August of that year. The contract announced in October 1988, following a cancellation of a similar order in 1981, was for 12 Kfir C2s (3040-3051) and a single twin-seat TC2 (3003), at a reported cost of $200 million. Payments were spread over eight years and included a barter element of coal being supplied to Israel.

One aircraft, 3042, was lost in an accident on 2 May 1995. The bulk of the survivors have been gradually upgraded by IAI to C7 standard, including the twin-seater. Late in 1996 it appeared as though three, possibly four, aircraft were still awaiting the upgraded avionics package which allows them to carry the Python 3 AAM.

Another unit currently parented by Grupo 21 is believed to be Escuadrón de Combate 215, equipped with the Cessna T-37B/C. Employed in the advanced flying phase of flight training, the unit relocated from Grupo 41 at Barranquilla in September 1996 due to conflict with the increased civilian traffic using that airfield's single runway. The 'Tweet', which has now adopted the standard USAF black/white training colour scheme, has had an interesting career within Colombia, being previously tasked with a COIN role while operating with Grupo 31 under CACOM-2 at Apiay. Ten T-37Cs (2101-2110), of which four remain, were delivered direct from the manufacturers in 1980, and more recently eight surplus USAF T-37Bs (2115-2122) were delivered by Colombian pilots from Kelly AFB, Texas, in June 1992. Four additional T-37Bs were believed to have been received, possibly from Chile, but they are no longer in service. The two survivors (2112 and 2113) are being preserved at Bogotá and Barranquilla, respectively. A third example, 2111, resides in an abandoned condition at Apiay along with eight Lockheed T-33As and three RT-33As.

Anti-terrorist/drug operations

Also located at Palanquero is an Escuadrón Aerotactico, a unit with a primary anti-terrorist or anti-narcotics tasking. The squadron is equipped with the recently received Basler Turbo 67 AC-47 Dakota and supported by a number of helicopters drawn from the Comando Aéreo de Apoyo Táctico. It is the FAC's intention to set up four of these units to counter known threats at the strategic locations of Palanquero, Barranquilla, Apiay and Cali.

Use of the AC-47 has been ongoing for some time, the US having funded the delivery of five examples in 1988, one of which was lost in an accident shortly after delivery. From 1992 the four others were sent to Basler Turbo Conversions Inc. in Oshkosh, Wisconsin; three had been returned to service by 1996 for use by these specialised units. The composition of the helicopter element will depend on the operational requirements, but will include armed versions of the Bell 212, UH-1H, Sikorsky UH-60A/L and Hughes 369. It is pre-supposed that these units are being assigned the titles Escuadrón Aerotactico 214, 412, 313 and 614, although crew patches give no confirmation of this and the designations may be applied only locally. Once these tactical air units are fully equipped and trained, they will

Above: Colombia's Kfir C7s re tasked with air defence nd attack missions from heir base at Palanquero.

Right: The FAC's Kfir squadron (Esc 213) is partnered by Esc 212 flying upgraded Dassault Mirage 5Cs, as part of Grupo 21.

bove: A single Kfir trainer was delivered to the AC in 1989. Like the Kfir C2 fighters, this sole C2 has been upgraded to C7 (TC7) standard.

Above right: Esc 314 fields large numbers of turboprop conversion Basler TC-47 gunships. This example is equipped with FLIR.

Left: The Tucanos of Esc 312, based at Apiay, have a dual COIN/training role.

Above: The FAC is unique in being the only South American operator of the T-37.

Above: Colombia's combat helicopter assets belong exclusively to the FAC. This is a UH-1H of Esc 513.

Below: Despite a conspicuous pale grey scheme, FAC Tucanos fly combat missions with gun and rocket pods.

Above and left: Esc 411 flies the A-37B Dragonfly from its base at Barranquilla. Esc 411 is the lead unit of Grupo 41. The first A-37s were delivered in 1980. Note the live Mk 82 bombs on the aircraft to the left.

add an important element to the fight against terrorism and the narcotics industry.

Internal problems provoked by the Revolutionary Armed Forces of Colombia (FARC) and the leftist National Liberation Army (ELN) have necessitated the establishment of these tactical air units to support both police and army units. Since 1986 there have been 437 attacks on the oil pipeline that runs from the Barco Oil Fields (near the Venezuelan border) to the coast at Covenas. At the beginning of 1997 alone, the FARC carried out two major attacks on the security forces. On 16 January three Marines were killed and 10 were captured in a raid on Jurado. The three-day battle at San Juanito in which an army patrol was ambushed was followed by an ELN attack on police headquarters at Cubara.

Although it is thought that these guerrilla factions number 10,000 to 15,000, they are only able to exert control in the outlying rural areas. This is where Colombian peasants help to produce narcotics, for if the trade were destroyed many would subsist below the poverty level.

CACOM-2 is to be found at Base Aérea 'Luis F. Gomez Niño', Apiay, in the Los Llanos region; Grupo 31 is the controlling element. Within this command lies the responsibility for COIN operations and advanced pilot training.

Escuadrón 311 has the main COIN task and is equipped with the OV-10A Bronco, an aircraft it has operated since 1991 when it replaced the inadequate T-37C in this role. Through US-funded aid, 11 former USAF OV-10As (2211-2221) were received and have proven a tough and reliable mount in the war against terrorist and narcotics factions. No losses have occurred although one aircraft, 2221, was hit by small arms fire during an operation in 1994; it recovered safely. An additional three ex-USMC examples (155434, 155436 and 155448/FAC serials 2222-2224) were delivered in 1993, but the type is now suffering from poor serviceability and it is hoped a suitable replacement can be found soon.

As a result, a number of EMBRAER T-27 Tucanos of Escuadrón de Combate 312, including 2250 and 2263, have been fitted with hardpoints to help bolster the COIN commitment. These two aircraft can be fitted with gun and rocket pods. Of the remaining Tucanos, 14 of which were delivered in December 1992, only one (2256) appears to have been lost. They carry out advanced flying training for those pilots streamed from the Cessna T-41D at Cali for combat duties.

An Argentine offer of three IA-58 Pucarás was accepted to assist in anti-narcotics operations. The aircraft, 2201-2203 thought to be formerly A-580/578/579 respectively, arrived in December 1989. They equipped Escuadrón de Operaciónes Especiales 314 but serviceability has been poor, and in spite of an offer from Uruguay (which also operates the type) to prolong service life, the Pucarás are now effectively withdrawn from use.

CACOM-3 is to be found at the most northerly Colombian mainland base, Base Aérea del Atlántico, Barranquilla. Here, under its Escuadrón de Combate 411, Grupo 41 operates the A-37B. The jet is used in the CAS role, for coastal patrols and the interception of narcotic traffickers. An initial delivery of 10 A-37Bs was made in 1980, the aircraft being drawn from surplus USAF stocks and receiving FAC serials 2151-2160. They were followed by successive injections of additional aircraft, including a batch of eight

OA-37Bs in September 1989, and US aid in the anti-narcotics war, which ultimately gave the force a total of 32 different aircraft. Losses have not been significant, although two recent crashes were fatal. 2169 crashed on 28 June 1996, followed by the loss of another on 30 December 1996. In the second instance, neither the aircraft nor the pilot have been located. The jet was engaged in an anti-guerrilla mission over the remote jungle-covered mountains of the Uraba region in northwest Colombia.

Although 20 aircraft are still on strength, probably just over half could be considered operational due to limited amount of available spares. From these the unit has to maintain a two/three-aircraft detachment on San Andres Island, a Colombian territory just off the coast of Nicaragua. They operate from this location under the control of Grupo Aéreo del Caribe.

Helicopters

Tactical helicopter assets are assembled under the Comando Aéreo de Apoyo Táctico, which is divided into two primary operating bases. CAAT-1 at Base Aérea 'Luis F. Pinto', Melgar is the primary helicopter site. Under Grupo 51 the full range of helicopter operation is undertaken, from basic training through to night attack, including NVG training.

Prospective helicopter pilots undergo 75-80 hours of training at Melgar or on detachment to Velasquez. The Enstrom F28F is used for this purpose, 12 of which were delivered new from early 1994. They replaced the Hughes 269C and last few Bell OH-13Ss with the Escuadrón Entrenamiento.

Pilots then progress to either the Bell UH-1H/ Bell 205A with Escuadrón Medianos 512 or the Hughes 369 with Escuadrón 514. Operational taskings take the crews into the various Escuadrónes Aerotacticos (which were described earlier) or to Escuadrón Artillados 515 at Melgar. This is the operational parent unit and is equipped with armed Bell UH-1H/212s and Hughes 369s, both types being NVG-capable.

The FAC currently has 24 Bell UH-1Hs, deliveries of which began in 1996. They supplemented nine earlier UH-1Bs which have since been retired. It is believed that US aid has provided around 40 UH-1s: six or seven initially (281-287), followed by 12 (4228-4239) in 1982, five in 1989 (which might be confused with the Bell 205A-1s) and at least eight more, probably 20, in 1990 (4402-4420). In addition to these are six surviving Bell 205A-1s (4288/91, 92/96, 97/99) and 13 Bell 212s (4215-4221/4001-4009), the last nine of which were delivered in 1996.

The Hughes 369s are a mixture of 369D/E/ F/HN/HS/Ms, the bulk of which are referred to as Hughes 500/530s. The latter are capable of carrying a variety of weapons including TOW missiles, rockets and Miniguns. Some 25 OH-6As or Hughes 500s (241-262/4343-4346) have been received since service introduction in 1968, plus four Hughes 530FF (4301-4304), the first of which arrived in 1989. Only 13 of the earlier derivatives survive, along with three of the four Defenders.

A single OH-13S remains airworthy at Melgar and is displayed on occasions. The helicopter, 4214, is the former FAC 214 and 67-15870 c/n 3919. Another example, 4227, is used as a source of spares. 4226 is preserved at the entrance to the

base and, along with another unidentified example, is used as a technical training aid at Base Aérea Madrid. They comprise the four remaining examples with the FAC. One will eventually be donated to the national collection at Bogotá.

CAAT-2 is at Base Aérea 'Rio Negro' located on Medellin's Jose Maria Cordova International Airport. Inaugurated in December 1990, the base is now home to Grupo 61 and its subordinate Escuadrón 611. The unit is equipped with nine Sikorsky UH-60As from 10 (4101-4110) ordered for delivery in 1988, plus four UH-60Ls (4121-4124) received in 1995. The 'missing' UH-60A, 4102, was destroyed in a crash on 12 December 1990 when it was part of Grupo Aéreo 51.

Initially based at Palanquero, CAAT-2 moved to Melgar before finally relocating to Rio Negro. Tasked with anti-narcotic/-terrorist operations, the helicopters frequently deploy to other locations. Twelve more were requested for the army but, following US Senate objections, they have now been approved for use by the air force; the army opted to purchase the Mil Mi-17 instead.

Some reserialling took place in 1987 whereby all aircraft within the FAC inventory gained four-digit serials. For the tactical helicopters, this was accomplished by the addition of the number 4 at the start of the serial. There also has been a practice of reusing serial numbers as they become vacant. This only seems to occur when it involves a different type, as when the Hughes OH-6A/ 369HSs serialled 251-255 took over the serials previously used by the five Kaman HH-43Bs. In other instances, where reuse within the same type occurs, a letter 'A' was added.

Transport and communication

Air transport is split between two commands: CATAM, which has the purely military taskings, and SATENA, which is a military-run airline serving remote areas deemed to be unprofitable by those in the public sector. CATAM – Comando Aéreo de Transporte Militar – has its headquarters at Bogotá's El Dorado International airport. Here, on a small ramp, can be found the FAC's very mixed fleet of transports which is tasked with support, VIP and communications duties as well as the Presidential Flight.

The backbone of CATAM's fleet is the C-130 Hercules. Today it has two new-build C-130Hs (1004/5) and seven older C-130Bs, not all of which are still airworthy. The Bs include the surviving ex-Canadian air force example, 1001, acquired via Lockheed in January 1969, and six former USAF examples (1006/8-12) supplied as aid since 1989, all of which are painted in the green lizard low-visibility scheme. The two C-130Hs retain their white scheme with red/ yellow cheat lines and full-colour national markings.

Supplementing the overworked Hercules in the communications role is a pair of CASA C.212 Aviocars (1250/51) received in 1991 and two EMBRAER EMB-110P Bandeirantes (1270/71) ordered in December 1992, along with a single Cessna Citation 550 (1211) and Beech Super King Air 300 (5750). The unit also has a specially modified Rockwell Turbo Commander A695A (5198) which it uses for photographic work.

Parented by CATAM is Escuadrón Presidencial, which operates a single Fokker F28 Fellowship (0001) acquired in 1971. The former Korean Air Lines Boeing 707-373C (1201), which had been converted by IAI in Israel to a tanker/transport

Above: Esc 711 has a transport and liaison tasking as part of Grupo 71. This is one of the squadron's King Air C90s.

Below: Cessna 310Rs are flown by Esc 613, part of the FAC flying training school, based at BA Cali.

Above: A variety of Commander twins are in FAC service. This is a Gulfstream 890.

Below: The Beech 300 Super King Air is a newly introduced type with CATAM.

Above: All Escuadrón Presidencial helicopters, such as this Bell 412, operate from BA Madrid.

Below: The FAC's Pucará force has, in effect, been withdrawn from use, the victim of poor serviceability.

Above: A single, highly prized squadron (Esc 311) of OV-10As is based at Apiay.

Right: This FLIR-equipped Bell 212 is one of 17 flown by CAATA-1.

All 12 Enstrom F28Fs are attached to CAATA-1.

configuration during 1991, and the two Bell 412s (0004/5) normally reside at Base Aérea Madrid.

Other communications aircraft include an abundance of Cessna and Piper types mainly acquired following confiscations. Although some of them can be found at Bogotá, most are assigned to the various commands in the liaison role and often adopt an autonomous squadron title within the Grupo. Over the years Colombia has acquired dozens of aircraft from this source but, lacking maintenance records, the lifespan of these aircraft within the FAC can be limited.

The Servicio de Aeronavegación a Territorios Nacionales (SATENA) is run as a structured airline using military crews. Formed in 1961, it is a major component of the FAC's transport system although it is not linked to CATAM. Supporting villages and small towns without a substantial air link with the outside world, SATENA performs a vital social function. The current single Fokker F28, a pair of Boeing 727s impounded from drug smugglers, two HS.748s and a number of CASA C.212 Aviocars procured in 1988 operate with military registrations.

During November 1996 SATENA received the first two of three Dornier Do 328-120s, FAC-1160/1161. This will allow the retirement of the surviving HS.748s acquired in 1971, which are now beginning to suffer from serviceability problems and becoming uneconomical to operate. The third example, FAC-1162, followed on 19 December 1996.

Not directly aligned under CATAM, Grupo Aéreo del Sur (GASUR) is located at Base Aérea 'Ernesto Esguerra', Tres Esquinas, and maintains its own transport element close to the Ecuadorian border. Here the unit utilises a single C-47 and the last two remaining DHC-2 Beavers from a batch that was delivered in the early 1950s.

Training

Aircrew, officer and trade training comes under the responsibility of Comando Aéreo de Entrenamiento through its three main training institutes. The Instituto Militar Aeronáutico based in Bogotá is responsible for officer ground training, while the Escuela de Suboficiales based at Base Aérea Madrid handles technical training.

Flying training begins at Cali with the Escuela Militar de Aviación (EMAVI) located within the Base Aérea 'Marco Fidel Suarez' complex. Under Grupo de Vuelos, the school's constituent training squadrons include Escuadrón de Primario (formerly Esc 611), flying the Cessna T-41D. It is on these 11 T-41Ds that first year students undertake 35 hours of primary flying training. From there they move to Escuadrón Basico (formerly Esc 612) and the Beech T-34A for 120 hours of basic flying over the remaining three years of the course. Students are then streamed either to stay on the Beech T-34A Mentor, to go to Apiay to fly the EMB-312 Tucano, or to Palanquero to fly the Cessna T-37B. Those destined for the rotary-wing world move to Melgar, a situation that has prevailed since helicopter flying was concentrated under one roof in 1992.

Those who stay at Cali to fly the Mentor will have a further two years of study and training within the school prior to an operational posting. At present, Escuadrón de Basico undertakes the basic flying training role with a meagre fleet of nine Mentors, many of which have been in service since 1954. An ongoing upgrade and

overhaul programme is being carried out on the fleet by ENAER in Chile.

Also in use with the school are two and possibly four IAR IS-28B2 gliders (011-014). One of the two preserved airworthy PT-17 Stearmans is kept for sport flying, the other being at Palanquero.

Maintenance

The last major command is Comando Aéreo de Mantenimiento (CAMAN). Located 19 km (12 miles) west of Bogotá, Base Aérea Madrid is responsible for the overhaul and repair of most types in the FAC inventory. The airfield itself was built in 1924 to house the Escuela Militar de Aviación, but as an overhaul base boasts little in the way of facilities. Deep level inspection and repair as well as airframe repainting is carried out by the technicians, and with Israeli assistance the Kfir/Mirage upgrade progresses steadily.

Operationally, the base is the official home of the two Bell 412s of Escuadrón Presidencial, although they frequently are at the main FAC facility at El Dorado International.

Surplus US transfer

The future of the FAC is to some degree rosier than other South American countries, with some latitude in the defence budgets for upgrade programmes. Equally, the energy expended by the Colombian government both in maintaining internal stability and in the anti-narcotics campaign has brought recognition from the United States.

The Clinton Administration is weighing a draft proposal, one of a number under consideration, to transfer surplus US attack and surveillance aircraft to several South American countries for use in setting up an international air wing charged with interrupting drug smuggling flights. This particular proposal calls for the transfer of 70-plus retired US aircraft to the governments of Brazil, Colombia, Ecuador, Mexico, Peru and Venezuela. The aircraft which may be involved are E-2C Hawkeyes, P-3B/C Orions, HU-25 Guardians and 24 A-10As which are likely to have their cannon removed and replaced with infra-red systems, radar and perhaps smaller-calibre machine-guns. It is unlikely that either Peru or Ecuador will be considered for the latter type due to the current tension that exists. Under this proposal the US would retain ownership of the aircraft and maintain them at an international air-interdiction centre, possibly at Howard AFB, Panama. The base would also be used to set up an anti-drug smuggling co-ordination facility.

Fuerza Aérea Colombiana

Comando Aéreo de Combate – CACOM 1

Grupo 21, Base Aérea 'German Olano', Palanquero

Escuadrón de Combate 212	Dassault Mirage 5COA/COD
Escuadrón de Combate 213	Kfir C2/C7, TC7
Escuadrón Aerotactico 214	AC-47, Bell 205A-1,H 369HS, PA-31L
Escuadrón 215	Cessna T-37B/C

Comando Aéreo de Combate – CACOM 2

Grupo 31, Base Aérea 'Luis F. Gomez Niño', Apiay

Escuadrón de Operaciónes Especiales 311	Rockwell OV-10A Bronco
Escuadrón de Combate 312	EMB-312 AT/T-27 Tucano
Escuadrón Aerotactico 313	AC-47, UH-1H, H 369E, Cessna 402C

Comando Aéreo de Combate – CACOM 3

Grupo 41, Base Aérea del Atlántico, Barranquilla

Escuadrón de Combate 411	Cessna A-37B Dragonfly
Escuadrón Aerotactico 412	AC-47, Beech 80, Beech Baron

Comando Aéreo de Apoyo Táctico – CAATA 1

Grupo 51, Base Aérea 'Luis F. Pinto', Melgar

Escuadrón Medianos 512	Bell UH-1H, Bell 205A-1, Bell 212
Escuadrón 513	Hughes 369D/F/HM/HS/M
Escuadrón Entrenamiento (514)	Enstrom F28F
Escuadrón Artillados 515	Bell 212, Hughes 369E, Cessna 210N

Comando Aéreo de Apoyo Táctico - CAATA 2

Grupo 61, Base Aérea Rio Negro

Escuadrón 611	Sikorsky UH-60A/L Blackhawk

Comando Aéreo de Transporte Militar (CATAM)

Base Aérea 'Camilo Daza', El Dorado, Bogotá

Escuadrón (711)	Lockheed C-130B/H Hercules
Escuadrón (712) EMB-110P, C.212, Beech 300, IAI 201, Citation 550	
Escuadrón Aerofotográfico	Rockwell Turbo Commander 695A
Escuadrón Presidencial	Boeing 707-373C, Fokker F28

Comando Aéreo de Mantenimiento (CAMAN)

Base Aérea 'Justin Marino Cueto', Madrid

Escuadrón Presidencial (det)	Bell 412

Escuela Militar de Aviación

Base Aérea 'Marco Fidel Suarez', Cali

Escuadrón Primero (611)	Cessna T-41D Mescalero
Escuadrón Basico (612)	Beech T-34A Mentor
Escuadrón de Transporte (613)	Cessna 310R
Escuadrón Aerotactico (614)	UH-60A, UH-1H Iroquois, H-369E

Grupo Aéreo del Sur (GASUR)

Base Aérea 'Ernesto Esguerra', Tres Esquinas

Escuadrón de Enlace	C-47A, DHC-2 Beaver, PA-23

Grupo Aéreo del Caribe

Base Aérea San Andres

Escuadrón de Combate 411 (det)	Cessna A-37B Dragonfly

Aviación Naval Armada

Although Colombia has a major coast line bordering both the Pacific and Atlantic, the Aviación Naval Armada de Colombiana is a small force. Until 1984 the navy was dependent solely on the FAC for aviation support. The arrival of four MBB-Bolkow BO 105CB helicopters (ARC201-204) in late 1983 gave the navy a limited SAR/ASW capability from their frigates and corvettes. The intervening decade has seen very little change, with only the addition of a number of fixed-wing twins during 1991 to complement the maritime surveillance and communications duties performed by the helicopters. The Naval Air Arm's headquarters is located in

Bogotá alongside all the other military commands. The Grupo Aeronaval del Atlántico (Atlantic Naval Air Group) is home-based at the Rafael Nunoz International Airport, Cartagena.

Aviación Naval Armada de Colombiana

Grupo Aeronaval del Atlántico, Cartagena

Escuadrón	MBB BO 105CB
Escuadrón	Rockwell Aero Commander, Piper PA-28, Piper PA-31

Above: The flagship of the Escuadrón Presidencial is his Boeing 707-373C.

Below: The Presidential unit also operates a single Fokker F28-1000 Fellowship.

Above and below: Colombia's Hercules fleet includes C-130Bs and C-130Hs (as seen here), all operated by Esc 711 at BA El Dorado.

Above: This Cessna 550 Citation II is flown by CATAM's VIP squadron.

Below: 'Lesser' VIP passengers have to be satisfied with an EMB-110P1.

Above: This CASA C.212-300 is one of two in service with CATAM's light transport squadron, Escuadrón 712.

Above and right: Armed MDH 530M Defenders are detached from CAATA-1. Training-dedicated MDH 530FFs are flown by the Escuela Militar de Aviación tactical training unit (Esc 614).

Below: A smaller number of original OH-6As (Hughes 500s) serve also.

Above: Most surviving C-47s have been upgraded with turboprop powerplants, but original C-47As survive in service with GASUR.

Below: A single IAI 201 Arava is in regular FAC service as part of Esc 712, based at BA El Dorado. Aravas are also flown by the Policia.

Above and below: Servicio de Aeronavegación a Territorios Nacionales (SATENA) is Colombia's military-run domestic airline.

Above: From 1987 onwards 14 UH-60A/UH-60L Blackhawks were delivered to Esc 611 for use on anti-narcotics missions.

Ejército de Colombiana

Perhaps the most junior force in Colombia is the aviation assets assigned to the Ejército. The first reports of an Army aviation element emerged in 1991, comprising a single Cessna 404 (EJC-017) and Rockwell Aero Commander 500. In the next five years these assets have increased to around 20 aircraft. The mixed collection of Pipers, Beeches and Cessnas all appear to be used in the communication and liaison role and were acquired following confiscation in anti-narcotics operations. The largest and latest arrival is a Convair CV580 (EJC-121), from the same source.

During 1994 the Colombian army mooted an interest in operating its own rotary-wing element. Following the selection of the UH-60 Blackhawk to fulfil this role, the government accordingly made an approach to the United States for the purchase of 12 examples. At this point concern was raised in Congress that delivery of these helicopters to the Colombian army might see their use in violation of human rights. In spite of assurances from Colombia that they were being procured to combat the growing terrorist and narcotics problems, the United States would only release the helicopters for air force utilisation.

The army has turned its attentions elsewhere and indications are that it will receive around 10 Mil Mi-17s in 1997 at a cost of $40 million. Currently, the army uses a number of leased civil-registered Mi-8MTVs flown by civilian pilots

while their own crews are trained. This training is being undertaken at Base Aérea 'Luis F. Pinto', Melgar under the auspices of the FAC's Grupo 51; the first course commenced in October 1996.

With Ejército headquarters being aligned with those of the air force and navy, the bulk of the aviation assets are to be found operating from El Dorado International Airport, Bogotá. A number of small detachments probably exist, including one at Apiay.

Ejército de Colombiana

Edificio Centro Administrativo Nacional, Bogotá

Escuadrón (Bogotá)	Rockwell Aero Commander 695A, Convair CV580, Beech 90, Piper PA-31, PA-34
Escuadrón (det Apiay)	Cessna TU.206G

Policia Nacional

As with most Latin American police forces, that of Colombia is a paramilitary organisation. The Policia Nacional is responsible for civilian control while working jointly with other organisations in the anti-terrorist and anti-narcotics task.

Five policemen and three civilians were killed on 6 February 1997 when hundreds of ELN guerrillas destroyed the police headquarters in the eastern town of Cubara. The PNC is at the forefront of anti-terrorist activities, but must rely heavily on aviation assets as well as ground forces of the other major services. In a joint operation in February it was forced to call upon FAC helicopter gunships and CAS aircraft to rescue a 16-strong patrol of the 1st Mobile Brigade that had been ambushed by 400 FARC guerrillas in the San Juanito region south of Bogotá.

For general activities and limited anti-guerrilla operations, the PNC is a self-sufficient force. Its primary maintenance facility is at Guaymaral in the suburbs of Bogotá, and the force has a number of detached operating locations. Aircrew training is carried out in-house.

Rotary-wing assets include a mixed fleet of Bell 205L LongRangers and Bell 212s, plus the Bell 205. Fixed-wing assets are primarily used for liaison, communication and logistics support. A number of Ayres Thrush Commander crop-spraying aircraft are used in the Policia Nacional's battle against narcotics.

Policia Nacional de Colombia

Bogotá det	Basler Turbo C-47, Ayres Thrush, Beech 200/300, DHC-6 Twin Otter, Cessna 208, Cessna 206
Guaymaral det	Piper PA-31, Bell 205/206/212
Cartagena det	Bell 206L

Ecuador

One of the smaller South American countries, with a population of fewer than 11 million and an area of 460000 km² (177,600 sq miles), Ecuador, as the name implies, straddles the Equator. Bounded to the south and east by Peru and to the north by Colombia, the country has a 2250-km (1,400-mile) Pacific coastline. Rich vegetation turns into near-desert as it approaches the Peruvian border. Until the early 1970s, the Ecuadorian

economy was largely agrarian. This was revolutionised by the discovery of large oil deposits, which for a number of years resulted in Ecuador enjoying the highest economic growth rate in South America. Major increases in defence expenditure occurred. More recently, the country has begun to feel the effects of world recession, which have brought economies including a progressive reduction in defence spending.

Fuerza Aérea Ecuatoriana

The continuing tension with neighbouring Peru over the 1941 loss of a 400-km (250-mile) wide strip of its Amazonian territory has resulted in a number of border skirmishes. They culminated in early 1995 with aerial combat between the opposing forces, leading to at least three confirmed kills for the Kfir fighters that spearheaded the Fuerza Aérea Ecuatoriana (FAE).

The FAE comprises a balanced force of interceptors, fighter-bombers and COIN aircraft operating from 'hardened' bases and forward operating locations constructed during the 1980s in the remaining part of Amazonia. From its headquarters in Quito, the FAE administers some 4,000 personnel and approximately 120 aircraft. Included within this total are a number of passenger/transport aircraft operated by the paramilitary airline TAME, although Ecuador differs in having an external operator as part of the FAE.

Below air staff level, the force is divided into two elements: I Zona Aérea, administering the transport and communications force, and II Zona Aérea with three combat wings and a flying school. Each of these wings (Ala) has a two-figure designation number beginning with either 1 or 2 depending on the element to which it is assigned, and occupies a separate base, its responsibilities embracing the management of the complete flying structure. The flying operations are undertaken by an individual Grupo, which has its own three-figure designation conforming with the wing number. Subordinate to this are a number of flying squadrons with designated four-digit numbers commensurate with that of the Grupo.

I Zona Aérea

Base Aérea 'Mariscal Sucre', otherwise known as Quito International Airport, is the principal

operating location of I Zona Aérea and its component Ala de Transporte 11. Here, under Escuadrón de Transporte 1111, the air force centralises its mixed force of four Lockheed C-130Bs (894-897), single examples of the C-130H (892) and L-100-30 (893), along with the TAME-operated Boeing 727 series, Fokker F28 (220), BAe 748 Series 2 and McDonnell Douglas DC-10.

Short-field and remote location support is provided by the unit's three DHC-6s acquired in the early 1980s which supplement the surviving DHC-5D. One of the three surviving BAe 748s, 001, is operated by the co-located Presidential Flight, which also has on strength a number of Rockwell Sabreliner 40R/60 executive jets.

II Zona Aérea

II Zona Aérea has three main components which are central to the FAE's defensive and offensive capabilities. The first of these is Ala de Combate 21 and its subordinate Grupo 211, located at the hardened base of Taura, near the main port and largest city, Guayaquil. As with all FAE bases, Taura is situated on the Pacific side of the Andes mountain range that separates the rich fertile plain from the densely forested Amazon basin.

The first component of Grupo 211 is Escuadrón de Combate 2111, equipped with a dwindling force of SEPECAT Jaguar strike/attack aircraft. They were procured during 1974 in a reported US$65 million contract placed with

Above: SATENA operates a large mixed fleet, including this F28, from El Dorado IAP.

Below: The FAC still uses the Cessna T-41D as its basic flying trainer.

Above: Students who graduate from the Escuadrón de Primario go on to fly the T-34As of the Escuadrón Basico. Both are based at Cali.

Below: Colombia's naval air arm maintains a small sea-going aviation capability with its four frigate-based MBB BO 105CBs.

Above: The FAC uses the IAR IS-28B2 sailplane for sport flying and also has a single immaculately maintained 1942-vintage Boeing-Stearman PT-17 Kaydet for the same purpose.

Above: This Piper PA-28 is one of the small selection of general aviation types in service with the navy's single fixed-wing squadron.

The ARC operates several PA-31 Navajo variants, acquired through confiscation. This example has had performance-enhancing winglets added.

This Commander 680 is one of several in use with the ARC's naval air group. The fins of several later-model Commanders are visible in the background.

Above: A single Convair CV580 is now army aviation's flagship.

Above left: This army aviation Cessna U.206G is detached to Apiay.

Left: A pristine Piper PA-34 Seneca is a recent addition to the AJC inventory.

Right: This is an army Rockwell 695A Commander.

139

BAe for 10 single-seat fighters and two twin-seat conversion trainers. The initial cadre of aircrew was trained under the auspices of No. 226 OCU at RAF Lossiemouth between January and October 1977, following which the newly converted pilots ferried their aircraft the 14500 km (9,000 miles) to Ecuador. Since then, the jets have proved popular and reliable, although by 1990 four single-seaters had been lost in accidents. Plans were made for the acquisition of three surplus RAF Jaguar GR.Mk 1s during 1991, but they failed to materialise.

The Dassault Mirage F1JA/JEs of Escuadrón de Caza 2112 are the second component of Grupo 211. The unit received 16 single-seat aircraft (801-816) and a pair of twin-seat trainers (830-831) between December 1978 and November 1980, following the US veto on the sale of 24 J79-engined Israeli Kfir fighters in early 1977. Ecuador perceived a need for them to counter the threat posed by Peru's purchase of 36 Sukhoi Su-20/22-M2 'Fitter-Fs' – a deal that also came about when the US refused the sale of F-5Es, in what proved to be an impossible attempt to prevent the flow of advanced weaponry into South America. The contract also saw the supply of MATRA Super 530 and R.550 missiles. Mirage losses are thought to amount to four aircraft, three F1JAs and a single F1JE.

Incredibly, following the signing of contracts over the sale of these Mirages, the United States in 1979 relaxed its controls on the sale of the General Electric J79 engine, which renewed interest on the part of the FAE in the Kfir offer. This culminated in an order for 12 aircraft and a simulator being placed in mid-1982, with an option for a follow-on batch of another 12. The initial order comprised 10 Kfir C2s (901-910) and two twin-seat Kfir TC2s (930-931) (one of which was lost in an accident early in the type's career), plus a number of Rafael Shafrir missiles. They equipped Escuadrón de Caza 2113, supplanting the Strikemaster Mk 89/89A and last three remaining Canberra B.Mk 6s that had been procured in 1972 and 1954, respectively.

Further attrition has occurred but the FAE seems not to have exercised its original option on the 12 additional aircraft. It is thought that a third Kfir TC2 was received at some point, while during 1996 an order worth an estimated $40 million was placed for four more Kfirs, with an option for another four. It is not clear whether they will be to the older Kfir C2 standard or aircraft upgraded as Kfir C7s with enhanced avionics.

The recent increase in capability by neighbouring Peru when it introduced the MiG-29, and its possible procurement of the Sukhoi Su-25 as a Canberra replacement, has prompted Ecuador to consider similar upgrades to restore the balance of power in the region. One option being considered is the purchase of 12 surplus USN/USMC A-4Ms, and Israel has made it clear that there is no ceiling on the number of Kfir fighters available.

The second of Ecuador's combat wings is Ala de Combate 23 which was formed in 1977 at Base Aérea 'Alfaro' at Manta. This base houses much of the COIN/light-attack aircraft displaced from Taura by the modernisation process. The wing was recently reduced to two operating components following the retirement of the ageing AT-33As of Escuadrón de Combate 2312 during 1996. The venerable 'T-bird' had first been received by Ecuador in 1956, but the last

operational aircraft had been obtained from USAF stocks as late as 1988, partly to off-set other shortages in the COIN role.

The retirement of the AT-33A leaves Grupo 231 with the Strikemaster-equipped Escuadrón de Combate 2313, and Escuadrón de Combate 2311 which has a complement of 10 Cessna A-37Bs. These aircraft had initially equipped Escuadrón 2112 until replaced by the Mirages. Twelve new-build A-37Bs (374-385) were received in 1978 but, because of the demanding environment that its tasking involves, attrition has been relatively high. At least five examples had been lost by 1982 when the Ecuadorian government entered into negotiations to procure a follow-on batch to replace losses and to provide a reserve. Negotiations foundered when the US government concluded that all available stocks of this aircraft were required to fulfil commitments already made.

As a solution, Ecuador turned to nearby Brazil which agreed to supply a number of EMBRAER EMB-326GB Xavantes under a $50 million contract. However, as US Air National Guard units began to upgrade to more modern equipment, during the mid- to late 1980s the United States released a number of A-37Bs for disposal; six, followed by a further three (386-394), were delivered to Ecuador, resulting in the decision not to accept the offer from Brazil.

Surviving Strikemasters

Working alongside the Dragonflys from Manta are the BAe Strikemasters of Escuadrón de Combate 2313. Re-equipment with the BAC Strikemaster, as the type was previously known, occurred in December 1972 when eight Mk 89s were delivered to Escuadrón 2113 at Taura for close air support. They were supplemented by an equal number of Mk 89As in 1977. The squadron relocated to Manta as Escuadrón 2313 on 20 October 1979.

Attrition was quite high, with at least 10 of the original two batches lost by 1981. During 1985 Ecuador expressed an interest in acquiring six more Strikemasters, three being from the embargoed Sudanese order. Built in 1978, these aircraft had been stored unassembled at the BAe Samlesbury facility in expectation of an eventual order; two of the jets were completed to serve as company demonstrators and were registered as G-BIDB and G-BIHZ. Negotiations were completed in 1987 and the first three Strikemaster Mk 90s were accepted in November of the same year, with the final trio following on 21 November 1988. These aircraft now serve in a dual capacity of advanced flying training and close air support.

The last element of II Zona Aérea are the rotary-wing assets of Ala de Combate 22 at Base Aérea 'Simon Bolivar', Guayaquil, which also serves as the administrative headquarters of II Zona Aérea. Ala 22 is perhaps inappropriately named, stemming from a 1985 renaming of the

Ala de Rescate in anticipation of the early arrival of armed helicopters. Consideration of the Agusta A 109K almost led to an order for 24 examples in 1986, while the following year brought a dozen Aérospatiale AS 365 Panthers under discussion. In the event, neither option came to fruition. This left the unit with a title which it, perhaps, had difficulty living up to.

Ala 22 has three assigned squadrons: Escuadrón de Combate 2211, Escuadrón de Rescate 2212 and Escuadrón de Entrenamiento 2213. They share a mix of three SAR-configured SA 315 Lamas, five SA 316 Alouette IIIs and one Bell 212, as well as a DHC-6 and four Cessna 150Ls. The SAR-configured helicopters maintain detachments at both Salinas and Manta, while Taura's needs are provided from Guayaquil.

The former base of 'General Ulpiano Paez', Salinas also houses the Escuela Superior Militar de Aviación and its attendant Escuadrón de Entrenamiento Aéreo. Equipped with two Cessna T-41Ds for use in the liaison role, the squadron also has 17 Beech T-34Cs which it uses in both the primary and basic flying stages. Fourteen of the Turbo-Mentors were acquired under a $5 million contract in 1976 and were supplemented by another nine examples in 1978. They are fitted with four hardpoints under the wings which allow for their use in both tactical training and low-threat COIN operation.

Fuerza Aérea Ecuatoriana

I Zona Aérea – HQ Base Aérea 'Mariscal Sucre', Quito

Ala de Transporte 11, Quito

Escuadrón de Transporte 11	Lockheed C-130B/H, L-100-30, DHC-5D Buffalo, DHC-6 Twin Otter, BAe 748 Srs 2
Escuadrón Presidencial	BAe 748 Srs 2, Rockwell Sabreliner 40R/60

Transportes Aéreos Militares Ecuatorianos (TAME)	Boeing 727-17/134/230/213, Fokker F28 Fellowship 4000, McDonnell Douglas DC-10-30

II Zona Aérea – HQ Base Aérea 'Simon Bolivar', Guayaquil

Ala de Combate 21, Taura

Escuadrón de Combate 2111	SEPECAT Jaguar International E
Escuadrón de Caza 2112	Dassault Mirage F1JA/E
Escuadrón de Caza 2113	Kfir C.2/TC.2

Ala de Combate 22, Guayaquil

Escuadrón de Combate 2211	SA 316 Alouette III, Bell 212
Escuadrón de Rescate 2212	SA 315B Lama, SA 316 Alouette III, DHC-6 Twin Otter
Escuadrón de Entrenamiento 2213	SA 316 Alouette III, Cessna 150L

Ala de Combate 23, Manta

Escuadrón de Combate 2311	Cessna A-37B Dragonfly
Escuadrón de Combate 2313	BAe Strikemaster Mk 89/89A/90

Escuela Superior Militar de Aviación – BA 'General Ulpiano Paez', Salinas

Escuadrón de Entrenamiento Aéreo	Beech T-34C Turbo-Mentor, Cessna T-41D Mescalero

Aviación Naval Ecuatoriana

Formed in 1967 to provide a communications link, the Ecuadorian navy has remained a small operating force with around a dozen aircraft of all types administered through three operational and one training squadron. Aviación Naval Ecuatoriana is located at Base Aérea 'Simon Bolivar', Guayaquil, alongside both air force and army

assets. It undertakes its own pilot training through the Escuadrilla de Entrenamiento with three Beech T-34C Turbo-Mentors procured in 1980. Serialled ANE-223/225, the aircraft are operated in a predominantly white colour scheme with red panels on the nose and tail.

Liaison flying is carried out by 1 Escuadrilla de

Colombia's Cessna 208 Caravans wear FAC markings but have been reported serving with the Policia Nacional.

Right: The Policia Nacional operates a pair of Basler Turbo Dakotas – the force's largest airborne asset.

This Policia Nacional (STOL-modified) Cessna 206 Super Skywagon has a large cargo door fitted to starboard. At least four Model 206s are in use.

A total of seven Bell Model 206L-3 LongRangers was delivered to the Policia; the aircraft serve alongside several larger Bell helicopters.

Colombia's police air arm operates nine twin-engined Bell 212s which complement a smaller number (three) of Bell Model 205s.

Above and left: Ecuador has two front-line air defence squadrons. Esc 2112 is equipped with the Mirage F1 (above) while Esc 2113 flies the Kfir C.2.

Above: Six Jaguar Internationals make up the FAE's third fast jet unit, Esc 2111.

Right: Ecuador is unique in South America in maintaining a squadron of BAC Mk 89 Strikemasters.

Above: T-34C Turbo-Mentors serve with the FAE training unit at Salinas.

Right: The Escuadrón Presidencial operates this BAe 748 Srs 2A.

Above: T-41D basic trainers equip the FAE's Escuadrón de Entrenamiento Aéreo.

Below: The FAE has a single Bell 212 which operates as part of the mixed Ala 22, at Guayaquil.

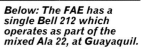

Above: The FAE operates several Rockwell Sabres, including this Sabreliner 40 presidential transport.

Right: The Alouette III serves both as a SAR platform and combat support helicopter.

Above: Escuadrón de Transporte 1111 flies C-130Hs and a single L-100-30 (as seen here) from Quito.

141

Enlace with a single Cessna 500 Citation 1 (ANE-201) and a Cessna 320E Skyknight. The transport tasks fall to 2 Escuadrilla de Transportes with its IPTN-CASA CN.235M-100 (ANE-202) and two Beech Super King Air 200/300s (ANE-231/232).

Rotary-wing support is provided by three Bell 206B JetRangers from a batch of five received in 1986, equipping 3 Escuadrilla de Helicópteros. Plans were believed to exist to add a number of ASW-capable Bell 212s for operation from the navy's corvettes, but funding difficulties appear to have been instrumental in curtailing this proposal.

Aviación Naval Ecuatoriana, Base Aérea 'Simon Bolivar', Guayaquil

1 Escuadrilla de Enlace	Cessna 320E, Cessna Citation 1
2 Escuadrilla de Transportes	Airtech CN.235M-100, Beech Super King Air 200/300
3 Escuadrilla de Helicópteros	Bell 206B Jet Ranger
Escuadrilla de Entrenamiento	Beech T-34C Turbo Mentor

Aérospatiale SA 342K/L armed Gazelle helicopters which it uses for armed reconnaissance and battlefield support. Utility helicopters supporting the various ground units comprise two Aérospatiale SA 330L Pumas, six Eurocopter AS 332B Super Pumas, three Aérospatiale SA 315B Lamas and a single Bell 214B. Two Eurocopter AS 350B Ecureuils are also used for communications flying.

Fixed-wing transport assets are limited but comprise a single DHC-5D Buffalo, an Airtech CN.235M, two Pilatus PC-6/B Turbo-Porters and six IAI Arava 201s. The Instituto Geográfico Militar has a single Gates Learjet 24D, a Beech King Air A100, one of the PC-6/Bs and an SA 315B Lama helicopter.

Servicio Aéreo del Ejército

The flying branch of the Ecuadorian army undertakes a number of taskings, principally observation and communications duties for the ground forces and a limited amount of armed reconnaissance and battlefield support. Equipped with 25-30 helicopters and 15-20 fixed-wing aircraft, the army flying branch is divided into three separate operating functions, two of which are centralised on the 19° Brigada Aérea del Ejército and the third with equal military and government requirements.

The two units under 19° Brigada are split between two primary operating locations. Grupo Aéreo 43 is to be found alongside navy and air force assets at Base Aérea 'Simon Bolivar', Guayaquil, while Grupo Aéreo 45 is located at

Base Aérea 'Mariscal Sucre', Quito, from where the Military Academy and Officers School operate. Both units are believed to also provide other detachments in support of the 11 infantry battalions, 10 independent infantry companies and three artillery regiments of the Ecuadorian army.

Aircraft role is identified by a prefix to the airframe serial. Examples include 'AE' for Artilleria y Escuela, 'E' for Escuela and 'T' for Transporte. Those aircraft with 'IGM' are operated by the Army's Instituto Geográfico Militar, which constitutes the third operating function of the SAE and is in charge of photo survey and weather reconnaissance.

To accomplish these diverse roles, the primary asset of the Ejército flying operation is 13

Servicio Aéreo del Ejército Ecuatoriana

19° Brigada Aérea del Ejército

Grupo Aéreo 43	**Guayaquil**
Aérospatiale SA 342K/L, Aérospatiale SA 330L Puma, Eurocopter AS 332B Super Puma, Aérospatiale SA 315B Lama, Airtech CN.235M, IAI Arava 201, Pilatus PC-6/B	

Grupo Aéreo 45	**Quito**
DHC-5D Buffalo, IAI Arava 201, Eurocopter AS 350B Ecureuil, Eurocopter AS 332B Super Puma, Beech Super King Air 200, Cessna 172G, Bell 214B	

Instituto Geográfico Militar	**Quito**
Gates Learjet 24D, Beech King Air A100, Pilatus PC/6B, Aérospatiale SA 315B Lama	

French Guiana

Still a French *departement* (i.e. one of France's 99 administrative regions), French Guiana has no air force of its own but has hosted a small Armée de l'Air component since 1974. Located on the northeastern edge of the South American continent, sandwiched between Surinam and Brazil, the country has an area of 90000 km² (34,750 sq miles) and a population of approximately 60,000.

The current AA component unit is Escadron d'Hélicoptères Outre-Mer 00/068 'Guyane' (EHOM 00/068), which has its headquarters at Point-à-Pitre-Raizet airfield in Guadeloupe but operates from BA 367 Rochambeau-Matoury,

Cayenne. A detachment is also held on the island of Martinique where it has a base at Fort de France-Lamentin airfield. The unit took over responsibilities for the region from Escadrille de Transport Outre-Mer 58 (ETOM 58) in mid-1992.

EHOM 00/068 is equipped with Fennecs and Pumas and supports the French army's 3ᵉ REI (Foreign Legion) and 9ᵉ BIMᵃ infantry units. Current strength comprises four Aérospatiale SA 330 Pumas (which replaced Alouette IIIs in 1979), and three AS 555AN Fennecs. The Pumas are known as Puma HERONS (Hélicoptère de Reconnaissance, d'Observation et de Navigation

en Solitaire) since they are fitted with extra fuel tanks, weather radar, GPS, NADIR and HF radios to allow long-range autonomous operations over the dense jungle. One of the Fennecs is an 'HL' utility version and two are 20-mm cannon-armed 'HA' variants. They provide security for the Ariane rocket launch complex, are fully NVG-compatible and are tied in to an air defence radar network. The Armée de l'Air exercises in Guiana and has four Mirage F1C-200s assigned, plus one Crotale SAM battery, with C.160NG/Rs or C-130H-30s for rapid deployment.

Guyana

A former British colony which was captured from the Dutch in 1796, Guyana became an independent member of the Commonwealth in 1986. Situated in northeastern South America

between Surinam and Venezuela, it spans an area of 214970 km² (83000 sq miles) with an estimated population of around 890,000. The country became a 'Co-operative Republic' in 1970.

for patrol and transport duties, later to be supplemented by two Short Skyvan Series 3Ms. Rotary-wing assets include two Bell 206B JetRangers and a pair of Bell 212s; the status of three Mil Mi-8s received in 1986 is unclear.

Guyana Defence Force

A Defence Force Air Wing was formed in 1968; later, in 1973, it was renamed Air Command. With its headquarters at Timehri Airport near the capital of Georgetown, the Air Command operates aircraft with civilian registrations

although they carried the inscription 'G.D.F.' on the fuselage sides. The first aircraft received were three Helio H.295 Couriers, which have since been retired. Six Britten-Norman BN-2A Islanders were procured over a five-year period

Guyana Defence Force Air Command

Air Command	BN-2A Islander, Skyvan 3M, Bell 206B, Bell 212, Mil Mi-8

Above: Transportes Aéreos Militares Ecuatorianos (TAME) is Ecuador's military-run domestic airline.

Below: The Ecuadorean navy's JetRanger squadron is based at Guayaquil.

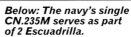

Above: The FAE flies three DHC-6-300s as part of Esc 1111, at Quito.

Below: The navy's single CN.235M serves as part of 2 Escuadrilla.

Above: This (TAME) HS 748 previously wore full military-style camouflage.

Below: Esc 1111 has now taken delivery of surplus USAF C-130s.

Above: The Ecuadorean army air service operates two AS 350Bs.

Right: A single CN.235M was delivered to the Ecuadorean army in 1989.

Above: Still in active service with the army are two Pilatus PC-6B Turbo-Porters, delivered in 1975.

Right: ALAT Pumas based in French Guiana have a significantly improved navigation systems fit.

Far right: Two basic utility model AS 555 Fennecs are based at Cayenne.

Below: The cannon-armed Fennecs detached to French Guiana are an integral part of the security ring around the Ariane launch site there.

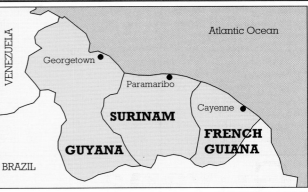

Above and right: Ten single-seat Mirage 2000Ps and two Mirage 2000DPs (right) were delivered to the Fuerza Aérea del Perú in 1986. They now form Escuadrón de Caza-Bombardeo 412 'Hawks', at BA 'Mariano Melgar', La Joya.

Peru

Once the centre of the powerful Inca empire, Peru is strategically located on the South American northwestern seaboard. Containing an area of 1.28 million km² (494,000 sq miles), much of it inhospitable, the country's aviation assets are of prime importance to both its defence and its development.

Although lacking the finance of its wealthy neighbours, the Peruvian forces are backed by the growing Seman Aerospace Industry which is now capable of all depot-level maintenance of the country's aviation assets. Still hampered by a small defence budget, Peru's services in recent times have spread their defence spending in a number of directions including not only traditional ties with bordering Brazil but also France, the United States and the former Soviet Union.

Purchases from this latter source came about following the political changes brought by General Juan Velasco's revolutionary regime of the early to mid-1970s. Influenced by favourable

credit terms, the purchase of a large amount of modern Soviet hardware threatened to shift the balance of power in the region and affect the delicate political situation with neighbouring Ecuador and Chile. Ultimately, reliability of this equipment was found to be wanting, although to some degree this has been redressed by improved maintenance offered by Seman.

Although the more moderate General Francisco Morales Bermúdez became President in August 1975, Peru's stand altered little. Recent years have seen a clamp down on terrorist activities, in particular against the Maoist Shining Path movement, with successes still occurring in early 1997. The December 1996 incident concerning the take-over of the Japanese Embassy in Lima by the Movimiento Revolucionario Tupac Amaru rebels has highlighted that problems still exist. More positively, inflation has largely been tackled by the new civilian government and development of natural mineral resources is being undertaken.

final flying unit of Grupo 8 is Escuadrón de Transporte 843, which is tasked with transport/liaison.

Grupo Aéreo de Transporte 42, better known as Transportes Aéreos Nacionales de la Selva, or TANS 42 for short, is the other main transport unit of the FAP. Equipped with a mixture of DHC-6 Twin Otters, Pilatus PC-6B2/H2 Turbo-Porters and Chinese-built Harbin Y-12s, the unit is based at Antiguo Aeropuerto (Laga Morona Cocha), Iquitos, the city's former main airport situated in the heart of the Amazon. Charged with support of remote areas, TANS 42 maintains detachments at both Piura and Pucallpa with land-based PC-6s and Y-12s, while the float-equipped Turbo-Porters and Twin Otters operate from either the Instalaciones Club de Caza y Pesca or the River Nanay. TANS 42 aircraft are operated in a white colour scheme with red cheat lines, and all have dual military/civilian identities.

All supplies for Iquitos have to be ferried in by either air or river, the bulk of them, including all the aviation fuel, by the latter method. Fuel is concentrated at BA 'Coronel Francisco Secada Vignetta', the Iquitos International Airport, where all aircraft, civil and military, must call for refuelling. An exception is made in the case of the float planes, which are refuelled by hand.

Because of the demanding terrain, attrition has been high, particularly in the case of the float-equipped aircraft. Various reports indicate that over the past 25 years only six of the unit's 18 Twin Otters have survived, while at least one Y-12 has been lost, as have 12 PC-6B2-H2s.

Helicopters

Co-located alongside Grupo 8 at 'Jorge Chavez' IAP/Lima-Callao are the helicopter assets of Grupo Aéreo 3. The unit was formed in October 1972 and inherited two Hiller UH-12Bs that had been funded by the Ministry of Health and were operated by Grupo 8. The unit's major influx of assets occurred under Velasco's revolutionary regime when 48 Mil Mi-8 'Hip-C' and six Mil Mi-6 'Hook' helicopters were received. It is not clear whether the unit received all of the 'Hip-Cs' or whether some were diverted to army charge. Once again, serviceability on these ex-Soviet types was poor and losses have been high.

Today, the operation is much more streamlined and the unit undertakes around 95 per cent of its own maintenance. It still operates a few early-build Mi-8Ts plus a number of the new Mi-8MTV or Mi-17 versions, presumably drawn from the collective buy of 32 from Russia in 1987 or the 12 purchased from El Salvador in 1983. The larger Mi-6s were retired in 1991. Escuadrón de Helicópteros 332 is equipped with the European types, including the Soviet Mi-8/17s, BO 105 and Ecureuil. Its sister unit, Escuadrón de Helicópteros 341, has the Bell 212/UH-1H, 214ST and 412.

This unit also has a major tasking in support of the civilian population and investing companies. To accomplish this, many of its helicopters are painted in pseudo-civilian colour schemes with dual civil/military identities, the latter in the 600

Fuerza Aérea del Peru

Aviation history in Peru dates to 1910, although it was not until January 1919 that the Servicio de Aviación Militar del Ejército was formed. The military and naval air arms merged in May 1929 to form the Cuerpo de Aeronáutica del Peru, the forerunner of the current Fuerza Aérea del Peru. A succession of foreign military missions over the years has helped to shape the structure of the air force, and today it is firmly independent.

The air force, compared to the size of the country, is still relatively small and is administered by the Ministerio de Aeronáutica, Campo de Marte, Lima. The command structure is subdivided into a number of air regions within which are one or more air force groups. Each group is made up of a number of squadrons, for example, Grupo Aéreo 7 located at Piura Air Base has under its command 1,018 personnel assigned to seven squadrons. They are Nos 705 Communications Squadron, 706 Maintenance Squadron, 707 Support Squadron, 708 Anti-aircraft Squadron, 709 Security Squadron, 711 Fighter Training Squadron and 712 Fighter Squadron. All groups are similarly structured although few have more than one flying squadron.

All units within the FAP are charged with three primary taskings. First and foremost, the main task is to support the civilian community. Next is to maintain the defence of the country, and third is interior operations in support of the anti-narcotics and anti-terrorism units. In the latter tasking support is provided by other outside agencies including the US Drug Enforcement Agency (DEA) and US Customs.

Transport

The main transport assets are supplied by Grupo Aéreo de Transporte 8 at Lima-Callao. The Grupo is divided into three flying squadrons as well as parenting the Escuadrilla Presidencial with its newly arrived Boeing 737-300 (PNP-001) and two VIP-configured Douglas DC-8-62CFs

(370 and 371). As with most FAP transport aircraft, the DC-8s are assigned civil registrations (OR-1372 and 1373).

The workhorses of Grupo 8 are the 19 Antonov An-32s purchased in 1987 to replace the ineffective An-26. They have been found ideal for operations in the less developed areas, especially in 'hot and high' conditions and from rough air strips hewn out of either the jungle or mountain areas. A number of accidents have occurred but attrition is thought to have accounted for only two aircraft. Of the An-32s operated by Escuadrón de Transporte 842, four were more recently delivered in December 1995 and operate in a pseudo-civilian guise in support of companies such as Occidental and Texaco, ferrying workers from Lima to the outlying hubs for onward transfer to the oil fields by helicopters. The remainder are operated in a more tactical scheme and have, in the past, been used in COIN operations, during which time they were fitted externally with bomb racks or internally for medical evacuation.

All FAP transport aircraft are serialled in the 300 series. In the case of the An-32, serials are 361-392 for the initial batch and 322-325 for the four newer machines; these aircraft are assigned civilian registrations OV-1379-1393/1640-1943. Communications aircraft are assigned serials in the 700 series but rarely have an equivalent civilian counterpart. Aircraft reassigned to the military-administered Direccion de Aviación Civil at Collique have adopted numbers in the 900 range as well as civilian registrations.

Escuadrón de Transporte 841 is responsible for the operation of the Grupo's Western-sourced Lockheed L-100-20 and C-130As, as well as the former Presidential Fokker F28 (398/OB-1396) and the Boeing 707 (319/OB-1371), which has a dual tanker-transport role. The unit is believed to have eight Hercules on strength, two of which are former USAF C-130As (385 and 393) currently being converted to tanker configuration. The

Above: Peru's Su-22M-2 'Fitter-Js' are operated by Esc 411, which partners the Mirage 2000s at BA 'Jorge Chavez'.

Left: FAP A-37B Dragonflys are flown by Esc 711 from Piura.

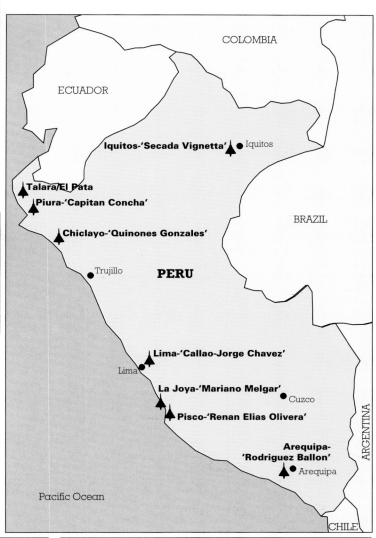

Above: This A-37B is seen at its home base of BA 'Capitan Concha', for a practice bombing mission.

Left: Peru's Mi-25 'Hind-Ds' were acquired in 1983, via El Salvador, and 10 are operated by Escuadrón Aéreo 211 from Arequipa – 14 are also in use with Peru's army aviation.

Above and left: The FAP's remaining dozen or so Canberras are flown by Escuadrón de Bombardeo 921, at Pisco. Seen here are a T.Mk 4 trainer (left) and a B(I).Mk 68 bomber.

Above and above left: FAP Tucanos have an important combat/drug-interdiction role.

Left: Mi-17s have been in FAP service since 1984.

Right: MB-339APs serve as trainers with Esc 513.

145

series. It is possible to identify eight Bell 212s, two Bell 214STs, six BO 105s, three Mi-8Ts and four Mi-17s from the Peruvian civil register, although there may be more helicopters than this on charge, the residue having a purely military role. This premise is supported by a number of helicopters seen during 1996 operating in a tactical scheme and lacking any clear national insignia.

In the desert region near Arequipa is the Grupo de Fuerzas Especiales at Base Aérea 'Rodrigues Ballon', Vitor. It is here that the FAP's 10 or so Mi-25 'Hind-D' helicopter gunships are based. Acquired in 1983 from El Salvador, they have been used exclusively by the air force in spite of repeated reports that the army has similar aircraft.

FAP training

Within the Lima area can be found the Academia del Aire (Air Force Academy), located at Las Palmas, which also houses the Seman Aerospace facility. Flying training is undertaken by Grupo Aéreo 51 which has under its control four flying squadrons. Primary training is conducted by Escuadrón de Entrenamiento on the Cessna T-41D (400 to 415), from where students progress to the EMBRAER T-27 Tucano of Escuadrón de Entrenamiento 512 for the basic flying stage. Peru purchased 20 of these Brazilian aircraft in 1984, with a reported follow-on order of 10 in 1990; most are configured as AT-27s and camouflaged accordingly. Attrition is known to have accounted for at least two examples. The air force has also recently purchased a number of microlight aircraft for cadet flying. All training aircraft have an assigned range of serials in the 400 series but lack any particular sequence.

Some examples of the Tucano are used for basic training only and sport the appropriate orange/white training scheme similar to that adopted by the FAB. The remainder can be found either in a tactical green/brown disruptive pattern or all-over matt black for COIN and anti-narcotics operations. The latter aircraft double in the training role but operationally are used by Escuadrón 514, whose crews are drawn from instructor pilots of the other three squadrons assigned to Grupo 51.

The final flying element of Grupo 51 is that of Escuadrón de Entrenamiento 513 with its 13 Macchi MB-339APs, survivors of 16 delivered in 1981. Flying training on the Macchis is conducted as a fighter lead-in phase of training. This part of the course lasts in the region of 80 hours, spread over a period of three to four months.

The three attrition MB-339s were all lost during 1985. It had been planned to begin licence-production of the type, with an ultimate target of 66 examples. They were to be built over a three-year period from 1983 in a new Indaer-Peru factory that was to be constructed with Macchi assistance. Once again, funding problems caused this programme to be abandoned.

Photogrammetry

Also located at Las Palmas is the autonomous Servicio Aerofotográfico Nacional and its Escuadrón 331. The unit is equipped with a pair of Learjet 25Bs (522-523/OB-1429-30) and a single Dassault Mystère 20F (300/OB-1493) for survey work, much of which is conducted alongside operations by the DEA. The unit also uses two Learjet 36As (524-525/OB-1431-32) for airfield calibration duties.

Front-line strength begins with the Canberra bombers of Grupo Aéreo 9 located at Base Aérea 'Renan Elias Olivera', Pisco. The Canberra first arrived in May 1956 and since that time 36 examples have been received, either new-build or from surplus RAF stocks. The last 11 Canberra B(I).Mk 68s arriving following refurbishment by Marshall Engineering at Teversham during 1975. The new-build aircraft initially were allocated serials in the 400 range but, following the reorganisation in 1960, were subsequently assigned serials in the 200 range, some of them being reused from the retiring Douglas B-26B Invaders.

Attrition and fatigue have had major influences on the Canberra fleet but – once again – with only limited funding available the aircraft are destined to be retained until their hours expire. To help maintain a credible force, six surviving former South African Air Force examples were purchased following their retirement in 1991; the five B(I).Mk 12s (200-204) and a single T.Mk 4 (205) all retain their former SAAF blue colour scheme. By late 1995 only 12 aircraft of all versions were still on strength, and since then one has been lost in a crash at La Joya on 22 October 1996. A planned retirement date of late 1997 is envisaged, their replacement probably taking the form of 14 ex-Belarus Sukhoi Su-25s.

Combat assets

The remaining fighter assets all have a dual intercept/attack commitment. In 1968 10 Dassault Mirage 5Ps (182-192) and two 5DP two-seaters (196-197) were delivered under a contract known as Martello 1. They were followed by four Mirage 5Ps (192-195). In 1974 a third 5DP (197) was delivered as an attrition replacement, assuming the serial of the missing aircraft. A single 5P (188) arrived in March 1976, followed by a further delivery of seven Mirage 5P3s (108-114) and one 5DP3 (199) in 1980. By this time the type had relocated from its initial operating base at Piura to its current home under Grupo de Caza 6 at Base Aérea 'Capitan José Abelardo Quinones Gonzales', Chiclayo.

Just after the end of the Falklands War in June 1982, 10 Mirage 5Ps were transferred to Argentina to cover FAA Dagger attrition, taking up the serials of those aircraft lost in combat. Peru then received additional examples from Dassault in four small contracts, bringing the total to 40 different aircraft to see service with the FAP. These later deliveries were of the 5P3/5P4 standard with fixed refuelling probes, new RWR, HF radio and laser rangefinder. Survivors of the earlier batches were subsequently upgraded to this standard by Seman Aerospace, a programme still ongoing in 1995.

Dragonfly operations

In the mid-1970s a number of upgrade programmes for the FAP come to fruition, allowing the retirement of the Hawker Hunters and F-86 Sabres. During 1975 the United States began delivery of the first of 36 Cessna A-37B COIN/attack aircraft, from two batches funded in the US's 1974 and 1975 fiscal years and supplied under MAP. They appear to have received FAP serials running sequentially between 115 and 156. By late 1995 only 20 of the jets were thought to remain in service.

The A-37s originally saw service with Grupos 13 and 21 but are now assigned to Grupo 7 at Base Aérea 'Capitan Concha', Piura, a location they took over from the Dassault Mirage 5Ps when those aircraft transferred to Chiclayo. At least nine are known to have been lost in accidents, including 124 which was shot down on 10 February 1995 by an Ecuadorian Kfir during the border clashes. A number of other airframes appear to have been withdrawn, which has resulted in Escuadrón de Caza 712 being temporarily inactivated, leaving Escuadrón 711 to undertake the dual responsibility of training and operations.

The A-37B is being widely used in the anti-narcotics field and, with its greater speed compared to the Tucano and more effective armament, has achieved a number of successes. During 1995 alone, when working with AWACS control, the unit is reported to have destroyed six aircraft involved in drug-running while operating from the detachments at both Pucallpa and Iquitos.

'Fitter' and Mirage force

Following the US-built A-37Bs into the FAP inventory were the Soviet-supplied Sukhoi designs. The exact details of these deliveries are difficult to establish. Initially it was said that the air force was to receive 32 Su-20 'Fitter-Fs' and four Su-22UM3 'Fitter-G' twin-seat trainers of this variable-geometry design at the low cost of $250 million. Deliveries began during 1978 to re-equip Grupo de Caza 12 at Limatambo, replacing the unit's obsolete Hawker Hunters.

They were followed by an additional order in 1980 for 16 aircraft, which appear to have been the more capable Su-22M2K 'Fitter-J' version. It is thought that this second batch of aircraft was assigned to Escuadrón de Caza-Bombardeo 411 'Eagles' at Base Aérea 'Mariano Melgar', La Joya, 80 km (50 miles) southeast of Arequipa. The arrival of these Su-22M2s necessitated the relocation of one squadron of Cessna A-37Bs to Piura to join the other squadron transferred from Chiclayo to make the current wing structure.

Due to continued border tensions, the Su-20s of Escuadrón de Caza-Bombardeo 111 have now relocated on a more or less permanent basis to Base Aérea 'Capitan Montes', Talara (El Pata) on Peru's northern border with Ecuador, where they are joined periodically by their sister unit from La Joya. The aircraft are operated in a mix of schemes; those initially assigned to Escuadrón 411 received a desert camouflage, while current operations call for a tactical green scheme more in keeping with the border regions. Serialling of these aircraft has not been restricted to the normal 100 series assigned to fighter aircraft but is incorporated in the 001-099 range, presumably due to insufficient slots being available.

Attrition is believed to have been quite high and serviceability was very poor initially. This has seen Escuadrón 411 forced into operating a mix of Su-20/Su-22 airframes. Today, however, with the advent of Seman Aerospace, significant improvements have been made, including the TBO on the Su-22's Tumanskii R-29B engines increasing by 50 per cent. The arrival of the MiG-29 was scheduled to see retirement of the early Su-20s although the current problems with service support may see this postponed.

The jewel in the crown for the Fuerza Aérea del Peru is its Dassault Mirage 2000Ps. Acquired in 1986, the 10 single-seat Mirage 2000P and two Mirage 2000DP are assigned to Escuadrón de Caza-Bombardeo 412 'Hawks' as part of Grupo

Above and below: A mix of BO 105CBS/LS utility helicopters serves with Escuadrón de Helicópteros 332, at Lima. Aircraft wearing a civilian-style colour scheme, such as the one below, are used for oil field support missions.

Right: Harbin Y-12-IIs are in service with Transportes Aéreos Nacionales de la Selva (TANS), the FAP's 'airline'.

Above right: The VIP scheme on this Bell 212 belies its 'part-time' gunship role with Escuadrón de Helicópteros 341.

Above: This L-100-20 Hercules is one of five allocated to Esc 841 at Lima-Callao, but which operate in civilian colours.

Right: Five Pilatus PC-6B/B2s Turbo-Porters are also allocated to the TANS airline service – as is the bulk of the FAP's transport fleet.

Above: The FAP exchanged its earlier Antonov An-26s for An-32s which boast far better 'hot-and-high' performance.

Right: In 1971 six DHC-6-300s were delivered to the FAP. This ski-equipped example is now in TANS service.

The FAP's single Boeing 707-323C has been converted to operate as a tanker-transport and currently serves with Escuadrón de Transporte 841 at BA 'Jorge Chavez' IAP, Lima-Callao.

Long-range VIP transport duties are now the sole responsibility of the FAP's Douglas DC-8-62CF. It is flown by the Escuadrilla Presidencial, part of Grupo Aéreo de Transporte 8, at Lima.

In addition to two Bell 412HPs and one recently delivered Boeing 737-528 (and a DC-8), the Escuadrilla Presidencial also operates this Fokker F28-1000.

Aéreo 4 at Base Aérea 'Mariano Melgar', La Joya. The remote base lies in the desert region 800 miles (1290 km) south of Lima, with the nearest major town of Arequipa 80 km (50 miles) away. Arequipa's airport is often used as a diversion point, along with Juliaca. Grupo 4, although maintaining a constant alert state with two aircraft, often deploys to Madre de Dios, Ucayali, Huallaga, Iquitos and Lima itself. Extensive modernisation was carried out at La Joya prior to the arrival of the Mirages, including improvements to the 4,000-ft (1220-m) wide main runway and the building of a HAS complex. The base has a purpose-built engine test facility and radar calibration complex. Defences include a number of AAA systems plus SA-2 and SA-7 missiles.

Combat with Ecuador

Once again a restricted defence budget had reduced the planned 1982 purchase of this big Mirage from 26 (with an option of 10 more) to the eventual 12. The aircraft's extensive capability has been reduced by the lack of a BVR system, the unit relying on the close-range MATRA Magic AAM for interceptions. During the 1995 skirmish with Ecuador, the Mirages were committed but, although managing to 'paint' a number of potential targets, without the BVR ability they could achieve no results.

Problems with Ecuador have intensified in recent years. Skirmishes between ground forces over border disputes erupted in 1981 and heightened in early 1995 when the air forces of both countries met in combat, with Peru coming out worse. This resulted in the loss of two Su-22s and a Cessna A-37B to Kfir fighters of the FAE.

MiG acquisition

Although peace has once again returned to the region, tension remains high and the inferiority of the ageing Soviet design has led to a call for the introduction of more up to date equipment. The US, not wanting to escalate matters further, has steadfastly refused the sale of third- or fourth-generation equipment, while financial concerns have prevented Peru from looking to other Western manufacturers. It has been reported that a deal was struck with Belarus over the sale of a squadron of surplus 1987/89-vintage Mikoyan MiG-29 'Fulcrum-A' fighters. Deliveries reportedly began in November 1996 with the arrival of the first four aircraft, but ceased when both the Russian state-owned export company, Rosvoorouzhenie, and MIG MAPO refused to supply the requested technical support.

It transpires that MIG MAPO had offered to sell the Fuerza Aérea del Peru the new export version of the MiG-29V for $24 million each, along with a number of upgraded former Russian air force examples. However, financially constrained Peru felt that the cut-price $11-14 million per copy deal with Belarus was more appealing, a decision that may ultimately backfire.

Other reports suggest that a requirement for an equal number of Sukhoi Su-25 attack aircraft may also come to fruition. Fourteen aircraft are allegedly on offer from the same Belarus source.

Although such upgrading of its capabilities could alter any return to hostilities in Peru's favour, the country has no belligerent designs on Ecuador and is only interested in maintaining its rights to territory awarded following the signing of the Rio de Janeiro Protocol in 1942.

Fuerza Aérea del Peru

Grupo Aéreo n° 3
Base Aérea 'Jorge Chavez' IAP, Lima-Callao
Escuadrón de Helicópteros 332	Mil Mi-8T/Mi-17, BO 105CBS/LS, Eurocopter AS 350B Ecureuil
Escuadrón de Helicópteros 341	Bell UH-1H, Bell 212/214ST, Bell 206

Grupo Aéreo n° 4
Base Aérea 'Mariano Melgar', La Joya
Escuadrón de Caza-Bombardeo 411 'Eagles'	Sukhoi Su-20/ Sukhoi Su-22M-2/UM-3
Escuadrón de Caza-Bombardeo 412 'Hawks'	Mirage 2000P/DP

Grupo Aéreo n° 6
Base Aérea 'Capitan José Abelardo Quinones Gonzales', Chiclayo
Escuadrón de Caza 611	Dassault Mirage 5P/DP

Grupo Aéreo n° 7 – Base Aérea 'Capitan Concha', Piura
Escuadrón de Caza-Bombardeo 711	Cessna A-37B Dragonfly

Grupo Aéreo de Transporte n° 8
Base Aérea 'Jorge Chavez' IAP, Lima-Callao
Escuadrón de Transporte 841	Lockheed C-130A/L-100 Hercules, Boeing 707-323C, Fokker F28
Escuadrón de Transporte 842	Antonov An-32
Escuadrón de Transporte 843	Cessna 421, Beech Queen Air A80
Escuadrilla Presidencial	Boeing 737-528, Bell 412HP, Douglas DC-8 Srs 62CF, Fokker F28-1000

Grupo Aéreo n° 9
Base Aérea 'Renan Elias Olivera', Pisco
Escuadrón de Bombardeo 921	Canberra B(I).Mk 12/68, T.Mk 54, B.Mk 52/56

Grupo Aéreo n° 11
Base Aérea 'Capitan Montes', Talara (El Pata)
Escuadrón de Caza-Bombardeo 111	Sukhoi Su-20/22UM-3

Grupo Aéreo de Transporte n° 42
Base Aérea 'Coronel Francisco Secada Vignetta', Iquitos
Transporte Aéreo Nacionales de Selva	Harbin Y-12-II, Pilatus PC-6/B2, DHC-6 Twin Otter 300

Grupo de Fuerzas Especiales
Base Aérea 'Rodriguez Ballon', Vitor, Arequipa
Escuadrón Aéreo 211	Mil Mi-8T/Mi-17, Mi-25

Academia del Aire

Grupo Aéreo Entrenamiento n° 51
Base Aérea 'Las Palmas', Lima
Escuadrón de Instrucción Primaria 511	Cessna T-41D, Beech Queen Air 80
Escuadrón de Instrucción Basica 512	EMBRAER T-27A Tucano
Escuadrón de Instrucción Avanzada 513	Macchi MB-339AP
Escuadrón Aéreo Táctico 514	EMBRAER AT-27A Tucano

Servicio Aerofotográfico Nacional
Base Aérea 'Las Palmas', Lima
Escuadrón de Aerofotográfico 331	Gates Learjet 25B/36A, Dassault Falcon 20F

Servicio Aeronaval de la Marina

Although the original naval air service had amalgamated with the army in 1929 to form the Cuerpo de Aeronáutica del Peru, it was re-established as an autonomous flying service in 1950. Relocating its headquarters and flying facilities from Ancon, 20 miles (32 km) north of Lima, to the 'Jorge Chavez' IAP at Callao, the service was renamed Servicio Aeronaval de la Marina Peruana. Its aircraft have or currently wear the differing titles 'NAVAL', 'ARMADA' or 'GUARDA COSTA'.

The main operating location is at Lima-Callao. The navy is charged with anti-terrorist duties at Pucallpa where it has a garrison, which has a helipad within its complex to also support police helicopter activities. The Pucallpa airport provides facilities for fixed-wing operation. The only other known navy operation is at Iquitos, where it maintains a pair of float-equipped DHC-6.

Shipborne assets rely heavily on five Agusta-Bell 212AS helicopters and six Agusta-Sikorsky AS 61D/ASH-3D Sea Kings with both an anti-submarine capability and anti-surface ability. With their Aérospatiale AM39 Exocet and OTO-Melara OTOMAT missiles they deploy aboard a number of Peruvian navy ships. The rotary-wing squadron also has three Mil Mi-8Ts acquired from unsold new-build examples that were stored at the Tokol factory in Hungary during 1993. They are utilised for transport and training, and although to date they still defy identification each helicopter has different markings. A pair of Aérospatiale SA 319B Alouette IIIs was also on charge for communications but may no longer be current.

In 1978 the navy purchased six Beech T-34C Turbo-Mentors for training, which were operated in a standard red/white scheme. More recently, a few have received a two-tone green tactical scheme for use in support of naval forces involved in anti-terrorist operations.

Transport support is currently provided by a pair of Antonov An-32s, a type that has found much favour within Peru. They were received during 1994 in place of a pair of surplus ex-USAF Lockheed C-130As (AT-530/531) assigned in 1988 but apparently not delivered, and of the last of a number of Douglas C-47s. Three Beech Super King B200CTs supply communications. An additional two are assigned to maritime patrol alongside a number of Fokker F27-200s believed to have replaced the surviving Grumman S-2E/G Trackers. Three EMBRAER EMB-110 Bandeirante and a single EMB-120 Brasilia are thought to be on order.

Most of the shipborne helicopters are operated in a white/grey scheme, while of the three drab grey Mil Mi-8Ts two appear not to sport any navy markings and the third displays only the word 'NAVAL'. The maritime patrol aircraft - including the two Twin Otters at Iquitos - wear an all-over grey scheme.

Serialling of the naval aircraft is in the 400 series for helicopters, pre-fixed by HA, B, C or E depending on role. In a similar fashion, the fixed-wing aircraft run in the 500 series pre-fixed by the letters AA, B, E, I or T.

Servicio Aeronaval de la Marina Peruana

Escuadrón Antisubmarino 12	Fokker F27-200 Friendship, Beech Super King Air 200T
Escuadrón de Transporte	Antonov An-32, Beech Super King Air 200CT
Escuadrón de Helicópteros	Agusta-Bell 212AS, Agusta-Sikorsky AS 61D/ASH-3H Sea King, Mil Mi-8T 'Hip-C'
Escuadrón de Instrucción	Beech T-34C Turbo-Mentor
Escuadrón de Amazonos, Iquitos	DHC-6 Twin Otter
Escuadrón de Amazonos, Pucallpa	T-34C, Mil Mi-8T 'Hip-C'

Above: This Cessna 421 Golden Eagle is on strength with Escuadrón de Transporte 843, at Lima-Callao.

Above: Twelve Cessna T-41D basic trainers serve with Esc 511, at Lima.

Below: In 1991 12 Agusta A 109K2s were delivered to Peruvian army aviation in 1991.

Above: Army aviation has approximately 40 Mil Mi-8/17 'Hips' in service.

Below: Escuadrón 200 of Peru's police air wing flies the MBB BO 105SA-3.

Above: Peru's veteran S-2E Trackers have been replaced, in the naval air service, by 12 maritime patrol-configured Fokker F27-200s.

Below: Peruvian coast guard aircraft, like this DHC-6, come under the aegis of the Servicio Aeronaval de la Marina Peruana.

Above: Aviación del Ejército Peruana maintains a substantial helicopter and fixed-wing force from its chief base at Lima-Callao. Visible here, from left to right, are examples of the Bell 412, SA 315B Lama, Enstrom F28F Falcon and Piper PA-34-200T Seneca.

Above: The PNP's two BK 117B-1s have been upgraded to the more powerful BK 117B-2 standard.

Right: The irregular colour scheme worn by this PNP UH-1H, of the Pucallpa detachment, points to it being an ex-FAP aircraft.

Aviación del Ejército Peruana

Separate army aviation in Peru was established in 1971 when it acquired on loan five air force Helio Super Couriers, followed by the transfer of eight Bell 47G helicopters from the same source. The service has since expanded considerably. Expansion came in earnest during the Communist-inspired government of General Velasco, when a number of Soviet advisors were attached to the embryo aviation brigade.

Army air elements appear to be assigned in small flights in support of regional garrisons. The main operating, training and maintenance facility is located at Lima's 'Jorges Chavez' international airport, where the fixed-wing support to army headquarters is also located. Many of these assorted types have been acquired following confiscation from narcotics traffickers. The mainstay of army aviation logistics are three An-32s received in 1994. Detachments are also at Arequipa and with special forces units at Pisco, Piura and Talara.

The bulk of the tasking assigned to the army seems to be to units operating in and around the Amazon, in support of troops protecting the borders and those working against both the narcotics traders and the resurgent terrorist groups. Helicopter assets seem to be used in the roles of transport, communications, supply and assault but appear to have no offensive capability, this being supplied by air force units.

A purchase of large numbers of Mil Mi-8 'Hip-Cs' for both the air force and the army occurred in the mid-1970s. The army is believed to have received the bulk of the aircraft, with a figure of 42 being quoted by a number of sources. Tasked primarily with support of its ground forces, these assault helicopters have proved ideal for the needs of the army. As with those assigned to the FAP, poor serviceability and a number of losses have seen numbers reduced dramatically. The helicopter was well liked, and serviceability has increased with improvements in maintenance procedures. This led to a further purchase of the newer Mi-17 derivative, which continues to serve in significant numbers and today comprises the bulk of the army's tactical helicopter force.

A number of Aérospatiale SA 315B Lamas are still used for training alongside nine Enstrom F28F Falcons received in 1992. Also used are a few Agusta A 109K2s and Bell 412s. The latest acquisition has been three Mil Mi-26 'Halos'.

Most army aircraft are operated in an all-over matt black scheme with white markings. A number of the Mi-17s sport red/white or blue/white pseudo-civilian colours with full Ejército titles. US and western European helicopters have adopted serials in the 300 range, with the exception of the Enstroms which are EP901 to 909. Former Soviet designs are allocated numbers in the 500, 600 or 700 series, and all current fixed-wing aircraft are in the 800 range.

Policia Nacional Peruana

The police air wing, PNP, was formed in 1983 with Bell 47Gs, Bell 212s and a single Hughes 369D. Since then this paramilitary organisation has grown to two full squadrons, with the main operating, training and maintenance facility being at 'Jorge Chavez' airport. The PNP has divided into two operating units: Escuadrón 200 has responsibility for all rotary-wing operation and Escuadrón 500 for all fixed-wing.

Helicopter assets include 16 UH-1Hs recently donated by the US to assist in the struggle against both the narcotics trade and terrorist activities. They are assigned to the Pucallpa region and operate from the Peruvian navy complex in that town. Ten recently acquired Mil Mi-17s are locally deployed in a number of areas, including both Pucallpa and Iquitos. Four MBB-Bolkow BO 105LSA-3s and two BK 117B-1s are used for training and missions around Lima. The two BK 117B-1s, delivered in 1989, are being brought up to BK 117B-2 standard and the surviving Hughes 369D is currently under a major rebuild.

Fixed-wing assets are predominantly drawn from aircraft confiscated from narcotics traffickers. The exceptions are three An-32s received in 1994 and two surviving Harbin Y-12. All except the Bell UH-1Hs are operated in a green and white scheme. The Iroquois have received an all-over gloss grey scheme and wear the inscription 'DOS AIR WING'.

Policia Nacional Peruana, Lima-Callao

Escuadrón 200	Mil Mi-17, Bolkow BO 105SA-3, Eurocopter/Kawasaki BK 117B-1, Hughes 369D
Escuadrón 500	Antonov An-32, Harbin Y-12, Rockwell Commander 680, Piper PA-31, PA-34, Beech King Air E90
Detachment Pucallpa	Bell UH-1H Iroquois, Mil Mi-17, BN-2A Islander
Detachment Iquitos	Mi-17, Harbin Y-12

Surinam

A British colony from 1650 to 1667, after which it passed into Dutch control and was known as Dutch Guyana, Surinam achieved self-government in 1954 and full independence in 1975. Situated on the northeastern coast of South America between Guyana and French Guiana, the country has an area of 163265 km² (63,040 sq miles) and a population of around 405,000.

In 1982 a small air arm was formed within the Surinam Defence Force, equipped with four PBN BN-2A Defenders. Later, a Cessna 172 and 310 were added to the inventory. All aircraft undertake border patrols and search and rescue missions from the main base at Paramaribo-Zanderij, and are occasionally detached to both Zorg en Hoop and Moengo. Anti-government guerrilla activity, in 1986, prompted the air element to receive a pair of Aérospatiale SA 316B Alouette IIIs and then two Pilatus PC-7s for COIN missions, but one of the helicopters was later lost in a crash and one of the PC-7s was returned to Switzerland.

Surinam Defence Force

Air Element, Paramaribo-Zanderij
Pilatus PC-7 Turbo Trainer, Pilatus BN-2A Defender, Cessna 172, Cessna 310, Aérospatiale SA 316B Alouette III

Venezuela

With a total area of some 912050 km² (352,163 sq miles), oil-rich Venezuela is the seventh largest South American country. It borders Colombia to the west, Guyana to the east and, well into its extensive Amazon rain forest, Brazil to the south.

Fuerza Aérea Venezolana

Military aviation was inaugurated in December 1920 with the creation of an Academia Aeronáutica at Maracay, following a Presidential decree on 17 April 1920. France provided the initial influence, to be followed by the Italians and then the United States which, in 1939, was looking to expand its interests in Latin America. During the war years there was very little in the way of material help, but Venezuela benefited post-war from vast amounts of surplus hardware, as did most other Latin American countries.

In 1949 the air service became an autonomous organisation, independent of army control. By the time the Fuerza Aérea Venezolana was formed, much had been achieved. The need to modernise the air force led to successive orders throughout the 1950s to both the United States and United Kingdom. As Venezuela's oil-based economy improved so did the FAV's expansion; plans continued right up until the 1980s, when

Above: Peru's national police can call on substantial airborne support, including several Antonov An-32s.

Right: The 10 Mi-17s delivered to the PNP (sometimes reported as army aircraft) are used for anti-narcotics operations.

Above: Like many South American air arms the PNP has amassed a variety of types, largely through confiscation. This is one of its two PA-34s.

Other PNP airborne assets include Hughes 369A helicopters, BN-2A, Commander 680 and Y-12 twins along with Beech E90 King Airs (left) and Piper PA-31s (above).

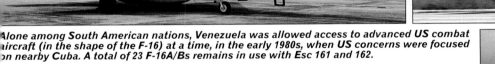

Alone among South American nations, Venezuela was allowed access to advanced US combat aircraft (in the shape of the F-16) at a time, in the early 1980s, when US concerns were focused on nearby Cuba. A total of 23 F-16A/Bs remains in use with Esc 161 and 162.

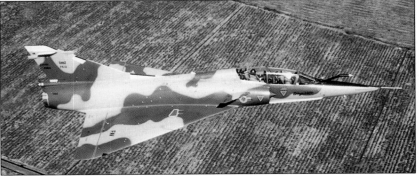

Venezuela's Mirage 50EVs serve with Escuadrón 33, at Palo Negro, alongside the two-seat Mirage 50DVs. Delivered in 1972, the Mirages have now undergone an upgrade programme with Dassault that adds canards, a new radar, RWR, chaff/flare dispensers, HUD and other avionics.

the economy came near to collapse and the air force, along with everything else, had to take stock.

Recent civil turmoil

The economic situation then facing Venezuela led to a number of internal problems over the coming decade, resulting in two *coup* attempts, with the air force at the centre of both. The first occurred on 4 February 1992 when paratroopers of Grupo de Paracaidistas 'Argua' led by Lieutenant Colonel H. Chavaz made an abortive *coup* attempt. This was quickly quelled but feelings still ran high, and at dawn on 27 November 1992 another attempt was made by elements of the FAV, led by Brigadier General Visconti, the Air Force Logistic Service Inspector. Under cover of the Air Force Day preparations, Visconti had contrived to move assets sympathetic to Chavaz to El Libertador Air Base, which, together with the units stationed at the base, gave him a very commanding situation. This attempt ultimately was quashed, but it entailed the loss of equipment and life, with FAV aircraft in combat with one another: an F-16 of Grupo 16, one of the few units to remain loyal to the government, shot down two North American OV-10A Broncos and an AT-27 Tucano.

More recently, stability has returned to the region and a number of modernisation plans are beginning to come to fruition. The air force today is one of the most advanced in South America, although its operational capacity is still restrained by severe budgetary considerations. This situation continues to improve.

The FAV's headquarters are at La Carlota, Caracas. The air force is heavily weighted on the tactical side, enabling it to respond quickly in support of the other services. With six main operating locations, the FAV is divided into three major commands responsible for 10 wings (Grupos), comprising three fighter, two close support, three transport and two training. Each Grupo is then sub-divided into a number of operating squadrons, two of which will generally be flying units and the remainder support squadrons.

Unlike most Latin American countries, the aircraft of the FAV are not given a type or role prefix under its serialling system. The system – if in fact there is one – is obscure, with individual airframes being assigned a four-digit serial at random in the range 0001 to 9999. Duplications do not exist, although serials are reused when they become vacant. The tactical orientation of the air force is reflected through the adoption of a disruptive green/brown scheme on the upper surfaces and light grey undersides, which is applied to all aircraft, irrespective of type.

Comando Aéreo de Combate

Venezuela is unique in South America, becoming the first and, to date, the only Latin American country to operate the Lockheed Martin F-16A/B Fighting Falcon. Twenty-four aircraft – 18 single-seat F-16As and six twin-seat F-16Bs – were purchased from 1982 to 1984 for use by Grupo Aéreo de Caza. Sixteen are stationed at Base Aérea 'El Libertador', Maracay, the FAV's main air force base, as part of Comando Aéreo de Combate. Type conversion for the crews began with an initial cadre of FAV pilots undergoing tuition with the then 58th Tactical Fighter Training Wing at Luke AFB, Arizona.

The first aircraft deliveries to 'El Libertador' occurred on 16 November 1983, for use by Escuadrón 161 which was declared operational barely a month later, on 10 December. Final delivery occurred in 1985, by which time the second squadron, Escuadrón 162, had also stood up with the type. The aircraft are operated on a pool basis.

In 1991 the FAV had been the first South American air force to be invited to participate in a Red Flag exercise at Nellis AFB. In Red Flag '92-4, five F-16As from Grupo 16 undertook the three-week detachment, during which they flew with BDU-33 practice bomb dispensers, an AIS pod and a Sidewinder acquisition round. Later, live Mk 82 bombs were carried.

In 13 years of F-16 operation, attrition has been light, with only three losses. The first was in April 1994, of which no details are available; the second was in August 1995 when an F-16A crashed on approach to 'El Libertador' following a bird strike. The third incident occurred three months later, on 16 November 1995, and involved an F-16B which crashed while rehearsing a display routine at 'El Libertador' for the annual Air Day.

Mirage 50 force

Operating alongside the Fighting Falcons at 'El Libertador' are the Dassault Mirage 50EVs of Grupo Aéreo de Caza 11, once part of Grupo de Caza nº 12 at Base Aérea 'Teniente Vicente Landaeta', Barquisimeto. The aircraft are operated by Escuadrón 33 in the air defence role. The unit was to have received 18 of this upgraded version of the Mirage III. Under a deal signed in March 1988, the surviving Mirage IIIEVs, 5Vs and 5DVs were returned to Dassault at Bordeaux for modernisation with new avionics, the uprated SNECMA ATAR 9K-50 engine and canards. The package also included the purchase of a number of new airframes, six new-build and three former Armée de l'Air machines. A phased withdrawal saw the surviving Mirage 5V/DVs (including 1297, 2473, 5706 and 7512) return to France in 1989, leaving the unit to soldier on for the next 18 months considerably under strength with just three Mirage IIIEVs (0624, 4058 and 6732). They were to enter the modernisation programme as 'new' aircraft and be returned to Venezuela. Aircraft 0624 was lost in an accident early in 1992, reducing the eventual total to 17. The first Mirage 50EV to be received by the FAV was 0160, handed over on 30 October 1990, which was presumably a new-build machine. This was followed by the return of former Mirage 5V 2473 on 22 November 1990, with deliveries of the remainder scheduled for completion by the end of 1993. With the total thought to have already been reduced to 17 examples, it was unfortunate that early in the work-up phase Mirage 50EV 2056, another 'new' aircraft, was lost in an accident on 5 April 1993, reducing the total yet again to 16.

Escuadrón 33's sister unit, Escuadrón 34, also operates the Dassault Mirage 50EV/DV although it is tasked with the air-to-ground role. The unit also has on charge three Dassault Falcon 20DC jets which it utilises in the communications/ECM training role. Coincidentally, this unit was also temporarily stood down from operations during the same period as Escuadrón 33 while 0442, 5761 and 5840 awaited funding for

overhaul. The lack of such investment in the early 1990s seriously undermined the FAV and was a contributory factor to the unrest that brought about the two *coup* attempts.

F-5 overhaul programme

Grupo de Caza nº 12 at Barquisimeto and its attendant Escuadrónes 35 and 36 have on strength the Rockwell T-2D Buckeye and Canadair VF-5 Freedom Fighter. The latter were originally operated by Escuadrónes de Caza 34 and 35 but today only equip Escuadrón 36. In the late 1980s/early 1990s this squadron had been another to suffer from a long period of limited funding, and by May 1990 had been effectively grounded due to fatigue problems on its surviving one VF-5D and 13 VF-5A/R Freedom Fighters. These 14 airframes were placed in open storage pending funding to return them to flying condition.

When it came, that programme had two stages. The first involved the signing of a contract with Singapore Aerospace in June 1990 to refurbish and upgrade two pattern aircraft, VF-5A 9124 and VF-5D 5681. They were despatched to Singapore in May 1991 and had a scheduled return-to-service date of May 1993. The second phase saw the purchase of seven ex-Dutch KLu Canadair-built NF-5s, one -5A and six -5Bs. The first of these, 1711 (formerly K-4018), flew in its refurbished state during February 1992 and had been delivered to the unit by November 1992 along with NF-5A 6324 (formerly K-3057) and NF-5B 1721 (formerly K-4002).

Following completion of the two aircraft despatched to Singapore, funding was then provided to refurbish and upgrade seven more airframes, VF-5A/R 3274, 3318, 5276, 6018, 9348, 9456 and 9538; the work was carried out in Venezuela with the assistance of Singapore Aerospace technicians. At that time a decision on the remaining five aircraft was awaited, but events of October 1992's attempted *coup* meant that three of the five aircraft which were stored at Barquisimeto, drawn from 6719, 7200, 8707, 8792 and 9215, were destroyed by strafing Mirage 50s and OV-10 Broncos.

South American Buckeyes

During the period of grounding of the VF-5 Freedom Fighters, Escuadrón 35 was temporarily re-equipped with the Rockwell T-2D Buckeye relocated from the Escuela de Aviación Militar. The FAV had received two batches of the carrierborne training aircraft in the mid-1970s. The first 12 were received and subsequently operated in a standard US Navy red/white colour scheme, and the second 12 were in the standard tactical green/brown disruptive camouflage. They were fitted with hardpoints for the conveyance of weapons and, in addition to their utilisation in the advanced training stage, also had a tactical application. It is believed that following the completion of the VF-5 upgrade programme most of the surviving 19 T-2Ds, if not all, returned to Comando Aéreo de Instrucción at BA 'Mariscal Sucre', Boco del Rio-Maracay.

The final unit assigned to the Comando Aéreo de Combate is that of Grupo Aéreo de Operaciónes Especiales nº 15 at BA 'General Urdaneta', Maracaibo. Under Grupo 15, Escuadrónes 151 and 152 were both utilised in the COIN role with a semi-permanent detachment of three aircraft to Base Aérea 'Mayor Buenaventura

Above: Venezuela's T-2D Buckeyes remain in service with Escuadrón 35.

Right: The FAV has acquired additional F-5s to allow its depleted force to be modernised.

Above: Esc 41, the FAV's VIP unit based at Caracas, operates this Learjet 24D and another Learjet 35A.

Below: Three Bell 214STs serve with Escuadrón 42, at BA 'Generalisimo Francisco de Miranda', Caracas.

Above: Two squadrons (Esc 151 and 152) of OV-10A/E Broncos operate from Palo Negro on COIN taskings.

Right: This Gulfstream III partners a Gulfstream II at Escuadrón 41.

Below: Escuadrón T1, of Grupo Aéreo de Transporte 6, is responsible for the FAV's Boeing 707-346C tanker/transport.

Right: This Boeing 737-2N1 serves with the 'El Libertador' detachment of Esc 41, at Palo Negro.

Above: Esc 51 is part of Grupo Aéreo de Transporte 5, based at La Carlota, in Caracas. It operates this Beech 200 Super King Air alongside the Cessna Citation and Dassault Falcon executive jets of sister unit Escuadrón 52.

Vivas', Santo Domingo, where they work in association with other agencies, including the DEA, and with neighbouring Colombia in the anti-narcotics task. Other detachments occur to Puerto Ayncucho in January, Puerto Ordaz in February, Maracay in March and November to work with Grupo de Paracaidistas 'Argua', and Barquisimeto in July.

COIN assets

The current North American-Rockwell OV-10A/E Broncos were originally assigned to Escuadrón de Bombardeo 40 as part of Grupo 13 at Barquisimeto. The unit relocated to Maracaibo in 1975, becoming part of Grupo 2 before it was renumbered a few months later. The Broncos were assigned to Escuadrón 151, and upon the arrival of the EMB-312 AT-27 Tucano in 1987 they formed Escuadrón 152, both operating in a COIN role. The AT-27s were reassigned in April 1991 to Escuadrón 131 under Grupo 13 at Base Aérea 'Teniente Luis del Villa Garcia', Barcelona, a location without an active unit following the retirement of the last Canberra bombers a year earlier.

This move coincided with the acquisition of 18 surplus USAF OV-10A Broncos in April 1991. These additional aircraft were delivered to Grupo 15 and pooled with the survivors of the 16 OV-10Es that were delivered as part of the 1971 modernisation programme. It would appear that most of the survivors, thought to number nine or 10, have now been retired, leaving the wing to continue to operate the higher-houred but upgraded ex-USAF OV-10As until funding for a suitable replacement can be found.

Comando Aéreo Logístico

The FAV's heavy lift transport capacity and other transport assets come under the purview of Comando Aéreo Logístico, the bulk of which is also based at 'El Libertador'. Grupo de Transporte n° 6 exercises this responsibility through Escuadrón de Transporte n° 1, which operates the five surviving Lockheed C-130H Hercules and two Boeing 707-346C transport/tanker aircraft. Escuadrón de Transporte n° 2, its sister unit, has not only a transport tasking but also is responsible for multi-engine conversion. Formed originally in 1958, the unit initially operated the Fairchild C-123B Provider and became part of Grupo 6 on 27 July 1961. The Alenia G222 was acquired as a replacement in 1986, the unit receiving a total of six aircraft. It has subsequently taken on strength two similar machines originally assigned to the Servicio Aéreo del Ejército.

Grupo Aéreo de Operaciónes Especiales n° 10 controls most FAV helicopters. Escuadrón 101's lineage dates to 12 March 1948, making it one of the oldest squadrons in the FAV today. It is assigned the US types of Bell 212, 412 and UH-1H Iroquois. The unit has operated Bell UH-1B/D and H models in variable quantities, the actual numbers being undefined although thought to be four UH-1Bs and 24 UH-1Ds, the survivors of which were upgraded to UH-1H standards in 1975. The earlier versions are now all out of service and the unit is believed to operate eight surviving H models alongside a pair of Bell 212s and two 412SPs that were acquired in 1981.

Escuadrón 102 is assigned the European helicopters from Aérospatiale. At least 21 Alouette IIIs were delivered to the FAV in 1968 and it is thought that approximately six remain in operational use today. Joining the squadron in 1990 were eight Eurocopter AS 332B-2/M-1 Cougar medium lift helicopters. Both squadrons maintain out-based detachments in support of forces in the interior.

The last of Comando Aéreo Logístico's assets are to be found at Base Area 'Generalisimo Francisco de Miranda', La Carlota, in downtown Caracas. Once the main international airport and transport base, the encroachment of the city and subsequent restriction of airport expansion pushed much of the traffic to other locations. The base still serves as headquarters of the Fuerza Aérea Venezolana and as a consequence retains some of the communications and liaison aircraft. Grupo Aéreo de Transporte n° 4 and its attendant Escuadrón 41 serve in the VIP role, utilising a number of government-owned civil-registered Beech Super King Air 200s, three military Gulfstream II/III/IV derivatives and a pair of Learjet 24D/35As. The unit also parents the Presidential Boeing 737-2N1 which generally operates from Base Aérea 'El Libertador', relocating to Maiquetia/Simon Bolivar International Airport when necessary. The sister unit, Escuadrón 42, has on charge three Bell 214ST helicopters which it also uses in the VIP role.

More general communication duties fall to Grupo de Transporte n° 5. Its two associated squadrons, Escuadrónes 51 and 52, are equipped with several more military-registered Beech Super King Air 200s, and two Cessna Citation 500/550 series executive jets.

Comando Aéreo de Instrucción

The final major command is Comando Aéreo de Instrucción, which is responsible for all training with Grupo de Entrenamiento n° 14, under which is the Escuela de Aviación Militar. The two subordinate units are known as both Escuadrón 141/Escuadrón de Vuelo Primario and Escuadrón 142/Escuadrón de Vuelo Basico. Primary training is undertaken on the Beech T-34A Mentor, of which around 14 remain in service out of a total of 34 originally delivered in 1959 to both the air force and Escuela de Aviación Civil. Basic training is being conducted on the EMBRAER EMB-312 T-27 Tucano. The FAV procured 30 of these versatile trainers in 1985, with deliveries occurring over the following two years. Eighteen Tucanos were assigned to the school, the remaining 12 being tasked in the advanced flying training stage, including weapons conversion. They are on the strength of Grupo Aéreo de Instrucción Táctico n° 13 at Base Aérea 'Teniente Luis de Valle Garcia', Barcelona. Losses during 1987 have accounted for two aircraft, although they were later replaced.

The Escuadrón 142 Tucanos are operated in natural metal scheme with red training bands, a scheme which is also applied to the pristine Beech T-34A Mentors. The tactical AT-27s of Grupo Aéreo de Instrucción Táctico have received the standard FAV camouflage scheme as applied to other aircraft.

Fuerza Aérea Venezolana

Comando Aéreo de Combate

Grupo Aéreo de Caza n° 11,
Base Aérea 'El Libertador', Palo Negro

Escuadrón 33 'Halcónes'	Dassault Mirage 50EV/DV
Escuadrón 34 'Caciques'	Dassault Mirage 50EV/DV, Dassault Falcon 20DC

Grupo Aéreo de Caza n° 12,
Base Aérea 'Teniente Vicente Landaeta', Barquisimeto

Escuadrón 35	Rockwell T-2D Buckeye
Escuadrón 36	Canadair CF/NF-5A/B/D Freedom Fighter

Grupo Aéreo de Operaciónes Especiales n° 15,
Base Aérea 'General Urdaneta', Maracaibo

Escuadrón 151 'Los Linces'	North American OV-10A/E Bronco
Escuadrón 152 'Zorros'	North American OV-10A/E Bronco

Grupo Aéreo de Caza n° 16,
Base Aérea 'El Libertador', Palo Negro

Escuadrón 161 'Caribes'	Lockheed Martin F-16A/B Fighting Falcon
Escuadrón 162 'Gavilanes'	Lockheed Martin F-16A/B Fighting Falcon

Comando Aéreo Logístico

Grupo Aéreo de Transporte n° 4,
Base Aérea 'Generalisimo Francisco de Miranda',
La Carlota, Caracas

Escuadrón 41	Gulfstream II/II/IV, Gates Learjet 24D/35A, Beech Super King Air 200
Detachment 'El Libertador'	Boeing 737-2N1
Escuadrón 42	Bell 214ST

Grupo Aéreo de Transporte n° 5,
Base Aérea 'Generalisimo Francisco de Miranda',
La Carlota, Caracas

Escuadrón 51	Beech Super King Air 200
Escuadrón 52	Cessna Citation 500/550, Dassault Falcon 20F

Grupo Aéreo de Transporte n° 6,
Base Aérea 'El Libertador', Palo Negro

Escuadrón T1	Boeing 707-346C, Lockheed C-130H Hercules
Escuadrón T2	Alenia G222

Grupo Aéreo de Operaciónes Especiales n° 10,
Base Aérea 'El Libertador', Palo Negro

Escuadrón 101 'Guerreros'	Bell 212/412, UH-1D/H Iroquois
Escuadrón 102 'Piaros'	Aérospatiale SA 316 Alouette III, Eurocopter AS 332B2/M1 Cougar

Comando Aéreo de Instrucción

Grupo Aéreo de Instrucción n° 13,
Base Aérea 'Teniente Luis de Valle Garcia', Barcelona

Escuadrón 131 'Los Aviopones'	EMBRAER EMB-312 AT-27 Tucano

Grupo Aéreo de Entrenamiento n° 14,
Base Area 'Mariscal Sucre', Maracay

Escuadrón 141	Beech T-34A Mentor
Escuadrón 142	EMBRAER EMB-312 T-27 Tucano

Aviación de la Marina Venezolana

The Venezuelan naval air service formed in the mid-1970s as an organisation in its own right, although it can trace its ancestry back to 1922 when, as Centro de Aviación Naval, it was controlled by the army. Today, it is still a very small organisation tasked primarily with shipborne and shore-based ASV, supported by a mix of light transport and communications aircraft. With its headquarters in Caracas, Armade Venezolana has two principal operating locations.

The main base is located at Puerto Cabello 60 miles (96 km) north of Caracas on the Caribbean coast. Here Escuadrón Aéreo de Helicópteros Antisubmarinos 3 (EAdHA 3) has its shore base

Cessna 550 Citation II (above) and Dassault Falcon 20D (below) of Esc 52 are seen in the hanger at Caracas.

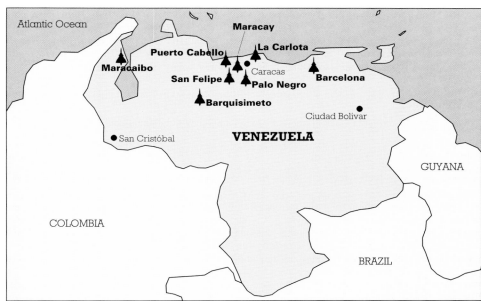

Above: Venezuela acquired eight G222s in 1984, which today serve with Escuadrón 2 at Palo Negro.

Above right: Operating alongside the G222s are the C-130Hs of Escuadrón T1, which also flies a Boeing 707.

Above: This brightly-painted Pitts S-2B Special belongs to the FAV's Escuadrón de Vuelo Acrobático.

Below: The FAV still flies 10 SA 316B Alouette IIIs, delivered in 1968, as part of Escuadrón 102.

Above: FAV training is undertaken at BA 'Mariscal Sucre', at Maracay, by Grupo Aéreo de Entrenamiento 14. Basic flying training is undertaken by the T-34A Mentors of Escuadrón 141.

Right: Eight Aérospatiale AS 532UL Cougars have been delivered to the FAV and serve alongside the Alouette III in Escuadrón 102.

for its 12 Agusta-Bell 212AS anti-submarine helicopters acquired in 1980. When embarked, the squadron is assigned to Venezuela's 'Sucre'-class frigates and carries the Marte anti-ship missile (in its secondary anti-shipping) role. The AB 212s can also provide mid-course guidance for the frigate's OTO-Melara Otomat anti-ship missiles. For the anti-submarine role, the AB 212AS is equipped with a Bendix ASQ-18A dipping sonar and the helicopters can carry a pair of either Mk 46 or A244/S torpedoes. The navy has German-built 209 class (type 1300) diesel-electric submarines against which the aviation arm can practise its ASW tactics.

The Venezuelan navy's six 'Sucre'-class frigates are based on the Italian modified 'Lupo'-class frigate design, and are the cornerstone of the navy's surface fleet. The vessels were all laid down between 1976 and 1979 and commissioned between 1980 and 1982. Like Peru's four modified 'Lupo'-class vessels, the Venezuelan frigates are armed with eight OTO-Melara/MATRA Otomat Teseo II high-speed (Mach 0.9) sea-skimming missiles, which have a maximum effective range of 190 km (99.4 miles).

In June 1992 Israel Aircraft Industries was awarded a contract to upgrade the first two of

EAdHA 3's AB 212ASs with new avionics and electronic warfare equipment. Each AB 212AS was already equipped with a chin-mounted Selenia MM/APS-705 search radar and limited ESM sensors.

The shore-based ASW and maritime patrol capability is provided by three CASA C.212-200ASW aircraft of Escuadrón Aéreo de Patrulla 4 (EAdP 4), which have now assumed the role from the eight Grumman S-2E Trackers of the inactivated Esc AS-01 (all of the Trackers were retired in 1987). The CASA C.212s (delivered from 1982) also replaced the navy's even more elderly Grumman HU-16A Albatrosses, four of which survived into the early 1980s. The CASA C.212-200ASWs each are equipped with APS-128 search radar.

Base Aérea 'Generalisimo Francisco de Miranda', La Carlota, provides the AMV with its second operating base. Here, adjoining the other three services, is the home of Escuadrón Aéreo de Transporte 2 (EAdT 2). This unit is charged with VIP transport and communications and has a variety of fixed-wing twins, including two more CASA C.212-200s, a single de Havilland Canada DHC-7 (which previously served as a maritime patrol aircraft), Cessna 310R/402Cs, a Piper

PA-23 Aztec, a Rockwell Commander 695 and a Beech King Air 90/200. Some of these aircraft will be detached to Puerto Cabello.

Aviación de la Marina Venezolana

Base Aeronaval La Carlota, Caracas

Escuadrón Aéreo de Transporte 2
CASA C.212-200, DHC-7, Cessna 310R, Cessna 402C, PA-23 Aztec, Beech King Air 90/200, Commander 695

Base Aeronaval Puerto Cabello

Escuadrón Aéreo de Helicópteros Antisubmarinos 3 AB 212AS
Escuadrón Aéreo de Patrulla 4 CASA C.212-200ASW

Destacamento Aéreo, Caracas
Arava 201, Beech King Air 90/200, Beech Queen Air B80, Baron 55, Cessna 337, Cessna U206G, Eurocopter AS 355F-2 Ecureuil, Bell 206B/L, 214ST, Agusta A 109

Detachment No. 3, Maracaibo
Arava 201, Beech King Air 90, Cessna 402C, Eurocopter AS 355F

Detachment No. 4, Barquisimeto Bell 206B/L

Servicio Aéreo del Ejército Venezolana

The Servicio Aéreo is a small but highly mobile unit of the Venezuelan army. Formed with 81° Regimiento de Caballeria Aérea, the command currently appears to have three operating squadrons. Tasked with reconnaissance, liaison and casevac duties, the regiment is autonomous in its structure although it relies on the FAV for any heavy-lift capacity since it transferred its two Alenia G222s (which had been built for a cancelled Somali order) to the air force in 1989.

The original air department of the army was formed in 1970 with a communications flight of a single Beech Queen Air and King Air. This fleet did not expand until 1977 when Bell UH-1Hs and Bell 206s were acquired. Today, there are three permanent operating locations. The primary base is to be found at Base Aérea 'Generalisimo Francisco de Miranda', La Carlota, Caracas, where the Ejército Venezolana operates alongside the other three services. The unit here, 811 Grupo a Aéreo de Logística (811 GaAdL), has the bulk of the regiment's aviation assets assigned although many of these are to be found detached to remote sites in support of ground troops. The unit has on charge two Arava 201 transports

(delivered in 1980), Beech King Air 90/200, Queen Air B80 and all of the rotary-wing assets.

Helicopters comprise the survivors of 10 Agusta A 109A/A-2s received in 1983 and 1989 which are currently used for communication and liaison duties. Utility services are provided by four Agusta-Sikorsky AS 61D Sea Kings (HH-3F Pelicans) received in 1984, four Bell UH-1H Iroquois, two Bell 205A-1s and a pair of Bell 412s. Most are operated in the standard Ejército scheme of wrap-round olive green/brown, although at least one of the AB 205A-1s retains a VIP scheme of white and green. The fixed-wing aircraft are painted in a brown and white scheme. Serialling is a simple system, with an 'EV' prefix (for Ejército Venezolana) followed by the year of acquisition and then two digits in sequential order.

Most of the remaining aircraft assigned to the regiment are with 812 Grupo de Transporte (812 GdT) at Aeropuerto del Centro, Caracas. Here the unit has the remaining three Arava 201/202s, a Beech Queen Air B80, a Britten Norman BN-2A-6 Islander and a number of single-engined Cessnas.

Finally, the army is responsible for its own

aircrew training, which it carries out under the auspices of 817 Centro de Instrucción (817 CdI) at San Felipe. The unit is believed to have a few Cessna 182Ns on strength for primary training and a single Bell 206B for rotary-wing transition.

Servicio Aéreo del Ejército Venezolana

**81 Regimiento de Caballeria Aérea,
BA 'Generalisimo Francisco de Miranda', La Carlota, Caracas**

*811 Grupo a Aéreo de Logística,
BA 'Generalisimo Francisco de Miranda', La Carlota*
Beech King Air E90/200, Arava 201, Bell 205A-1, UH-1H Iroquois, Bell 206L, Bell 412, Agusta A 109A/A-2, Agusta-Sikorsky AS 61D Sea King

812 Grupo de Transporte del Centro, Caracas
Beech Queen Air B80, Arava 201/202, Pilatus/Britten-Norman BN-2A-6, Cessna 172L, 182N, TU.206G, Cessna T.207A

*817 Centro de Instrucción,
Base 'General Juan Gomez', San Felipe*
Cessna 182N, Bell 206B

Fuerza Armadas de Cooperación (Civil Guard)

This paramilitary organisation comprises land, sea and air assets controlled by the Ministry of Defence but responsible for civilian matters including internal security, anti-terrorism, forestry patrols and customs duties. The air assets belong to the Destacamento Aéreo (Air Detachment), with the prime operating and maintenance facility at Base Aérea 'Generalisimo Francisco de Miranda', La Carlota, Caracas, alongside units of the other three services. The Guardia Nacional, as the organisation is more

commonly known, has a number of detachments including Barquisimeto and Maracaibo.

The aviation assets incorporate a number of medium-sized fixed-wing twins including six IAI Arava 201s used for transportation and five Beech Queen Air/King Air variants, a Beech 55 Baron, two Cessna 337s, a Cessna 402C and a Cessna U206G for communications. The remainder of the force, which is thought to number around 30 of all types, comprises helicopters including five Agusta A 109As, 11 Eurocopter AS 355-F2

Ecureuils, the survivors of 15 Bell 206B/Ls procured between 1972 and 1979, and a single Bell 214ST.

The aircraft are operated in a predominantly white colour scheme with red/yellow/blue cheat lines and normal military national insignia. The serialling system is similar to that adopted by the Ejército, with each number prefixed by 'GN' (for Guardia Nacional) then date of build rather than acquisition, and finally a two-digit sequential number. **Peter R. Foster**

Left: FAV student pilots graduate from the T-34A to Escuadrón 142's EMBRAER EMB-312 (T-27) Tucanos, 30 of which were delivered in the mid-1980s.

Above: Venezuela's army air service is headquartered at La Carlota, Caracas, where this Agusta A 109A is based.

Above: This CASA 212-200 transport serves with the navy's EAdT 2.

Above right: This is one of five IAI 201/202 Aravas delivered to the Venezuelan army from 1980.

Right: The civil guard's large fleet of small transport aircraft includes this A 109A.

Above: This camouflaged Servicio Aéreo del Ejército Venezolano Arava 201 is one of those operated by 811° Grupo a Aéreo de Logística.

Below: Venezuela's army air service acquired four AS 61Ds in 1984 and they serve with the army's lead aviation unit, 811° GaAdL.

Above: Venezuela's civil guard is also an IAI Arava operator.

Below: The civil guard maintains this Beech Super King Air along with a King Air E90 and Queen Air.

INDEX

INDEX

Picture acknowledgments

Front cover: Katsuhiko Tokunaga/DACT Inc. **4:** Terry Senior, Graham Robson. **5:** Kevin Wills, Jaroslav Spacek, Stephan J. Brennan/Eagle Aviation Photos. **6:** Steven Zaloga (two), Matthias Becker. **7:** Tim Senior, Chris Lofting, Lindsay Peacock. **8:** Emiel Sloot/STAS. **9:** Eddie de Kruyff (four). **10:** McDonnell Douglas, Sikorsky. **11:** Salvador Mafé Huertas, Nigel Pittaway (two), Craig P. Justo/Aero Aspects. **12:** via Simon Watson (two). **13:** via Simon Watson (two), Embraer/Ericsson. **14:** McDonnell Douglas, via Robert F.Dorr. **15:** Jack Callaway via Robert F.Dorr (two), Stephan J. Brennan/Eagle Aviation Photos. **16:** Henry Ham, via Robert F.Dorr. **17:** Robert Hewson (two), Lockheed Martin. **18-19:** via Simon Watson. **20-21:** Yves Debay. **22-24:** Frank Rozendaal (twelve)/Tieme Festner. **25-26:** David Cibley. **27-28:** Zoltán Buza. **29:** Tim Ripley. **30:** Ted Carlson/Fotodynamics, Rick Llinares/Dash 2. **31:** Chuck Lloyd/Dash 2. **32:** Mark Munzel (two), Randy Jolly. **33:** Chuck Lloyd/Dash 2, Randy Jolly. **35:** Randy Jolly, Chuck Lloyd/Dash 2, Ted Carlson/ Fotodynamics. **36:** via Robert F.Dorr (two), Ian C. Anderson. **37:** Randy Jolly (two), Ted Carlson/ Fotodynamics (four). **38:** David F. Brown. **40:** Rick Llinares/Dash 2, M. Ottagali & V. Marchetti/G.R.S.A., Tieme Festner. **41:** Luigino Caliaro, Ted Carlson/Fotodynamics. **42:** Tim Ripley, Jeremy Flack/Aviation Photographs International. **43:** Matt Olafsen/Fox 1, Jeremy Flack/Aviation Photographs International, Randy Jolly. **44:** Ted Carlson/Fotodynamics, Luigino Caliaro, Hans Nijhuis. **45:** Randy Jolly, Luigino Caliaro. **46-49:** Peter Steinemann. **50:** Sergei Skrynnikov. **51:** Robert Hewson. **52:** Sukhoi Design Bureau via Yefim Gordon, Emiel Sloot/STAS. **53:** Heinz Berger, Yefim Gordon (three), Sukhoi Design Bureau via Yefim Gordon, Yefim Gordon archive (two). **55:** Martin Baumann, Yefim Gordon archive. **56:** Sukhoi Design Bureau via Yefim Gordon (three). **57:** Yefim Gordon (two), Martin Salajka. **58:** Yefim Gordon, Alan Key/Key Aviation Photography, Yefim Gordon archive. **59:** Sukhoi Design Bureau via Yefim Gordon, Yefim Gordon archive (two). **60:** Chris Ryan, Yefim Gordon. **61:** Peter R. March. **62:** Yefim Gordon, Werner Greppmeir. **63:** Katsuhiko Tokunaga/DACT Inc. **64:** Yefim Gordon (three). **65:** Heinz Berger, Yefim Gordon, Robert Sant. **66:** Yefim Gordon archive, Yefim Gordon (two). **67:** Katsuhiko Tokunaga/DACT Inc, Robert Hewson. **68:** Yefim Gordon, Chris Ryan (two), Jon Lake, William Turner, Gábor Szekeres, Stefan Petersen, René van Woezik. **69:** René van Woezik. **70:** Georg Mader, Tieme Festner, Stefan Petersen. **76:** Martin Salajka, René van Woezik, Gert Kromhout. **77:** Hans Nijhuis (seven), Martin Salajka, Tieme Festner. **78:** Jan Jørgensen, Alan Key/Key Aviation Photography. **79:** Katsuhiko Tokunaga/DACT Inc, Tieme Festner. **80:** Yefim Gordon archive, Simon Watson (five). **81:** Martin Baumann, René van Woezik. **82:** Chris Ryan, Hans Nijhuis. **83:** Chris Lofting, Peter R. Foster. **84:** Hans Nijhuis, Paul van Oers, Martin Baumann. **85:** Peter R. Foster, Marcus Fülber. **86:** Chris Ryan, Tieme Festner. **87:** Jeroen M. Brinkman, Bulgarian AF via Robin Poldermann, Alexander Mladenov. **88:** Alexander Mladenov(two). **89:** Alexander Mladenov(two). **90:** Hans Nijhuis, Alan Key/Key Aviation Photography, Peter R. March. **91:** Hans Nijhuis, Heinz Berger. **92:** Robert Hewson, US DoD. **93:** Martin Baumann, Yefim Gordon. **94:** Roman Kondrat'yev via Yefim Gordon, William Turner, Marc Brouyere, Frank G. Rozendaal. **95:** Yefim Gordon archive, Yefim Gordon. **96:** Alexander Mladenov (three), C.F. Foss via Steven J. Zaloga. **97:** Hans Nijhuis, Claudio Toselli, Mike Fisher, Gábor Szekeres (two), M.A.Herbert. **98:** Stefan Petersen, Peter R.Foster. **99:** David Donald, R.Mancini & C.de Napoli. **100:** D. Ireland, Frederic Lert. **101:** Stefan Petersen, M.Knight. **102:** Stefan Petersen. **103:** Frederic Lert, Stefan Petersen, BAe. **104:** BAe, Daimler Benz via Jim Winchester. **105:** David Donald, Sgt Rick Brewell/MoD, M. Knight. **106:** MBB, BAe(two), Paul Van Oers. **107:** Aeritalia, MBB (two), MoD.**108:** Aeritalia, BAe. **109:** RDD/Aerospace, Stefan Petersen. **110:** Frederic Lert, A.B.Ward (two). **111:** Max Waldron, David Donald (two). **112:** Timm Ziegenthaler, BAe. **113:** via Simon Watson, Derek Bowers, BAe, Peter R. Foster. **114:** Chris Ryan, Geoff Lee/BAe, Peter R. March, A.B. Ward. **115:** BAe, Peter R. Foster, Tieme Festner. **116:** D. Sorochan, Geoff Lee/BAe. **117:** M. Knight, Geoff Lee/BAe. **118:** T.Gibbons, MBB, Gert Kromhout, Frederic Lert. **119:** Martin Herbert, Alenia, Derek Bower. **120:** BAe, Terry Senior. **121:** Kevin Wills, Timm Ziegenthaler, Frederic Lert, Rockwell. **122-128:** Katsuhiko Tokunaga/DACT Inc. **129:** Katsuhiko Tokunaga/DACT Inc, Ryuta Amamiya/Koku Fan. **133:** Frederic Lert, Chris Knott/Air Photographic International (two). **135:** Peter R. Foster (three), Chris Knott/Air Photographic International (six). **137:** Chris Knott/Air Photographic International (eight), Peter R. Foster (four), R Choufer, Alan Key/Key Aviation Photography. **139:** Gerry Manning, Chris Knott/Air Photographic International (two), Peter R. Foster (three), Angelo Siani (four). **141:** Alan Key/Key Aviation Photography, Gerry Manning (five), Peter R. Foster, Peter Steinemann (eleven). **145:** Patrick Laureau (two), Peter R. Foster, Peter Steinemann (three), Peter R. Foster, J.J. Petit. **147:** Peter R. Foster (nine), Baldur Sveinsson. **149:** Peter R. Foster (eleven). **151:** Peter R. Foster (ten), Carl Richards. **153:** Peter R. Foster (nine). **155:** Peter R. Foster, Gerry Manning. **157:** Peter R. Foster (four),Gerry Manning (three), Aldo Ciarini (two).